THE WORLD'S GREAT TANKS

FROM 1916 TO THE PRESENT DAY

THE WORLD'S GREAT
TANKS
FROM 1916 TO THE PRESENT DAY

ROGER FORD

ISBN: 1-897884-29-X

Printed in Hong Kong

Conceived and produced by Brown Packaging Books Ltd
255-257 Liverpool Road
London N1 1LX

Picture credits
TRH Pictures: 6, 9 (top right), 11 (bottom right), 12, 15 (top left), 16 (top left),
  19 (bottom right), 20–21, 25 (bottom right), 26, 29, 31, 34 (top left),
  37 (top and bottom), 38 (top right), 39 (bottom left), 42–43, 44, 45, 47 (top right),
  48, 49 (top right), 50, 52, 53 (top right), 56 (top left), 57 (top right), 58 (top right),
  63 (top left), 65 (top right), 66 (top left), 67 (bottom left), 68 (top left), 69 (top left),
  72 (top left), 76 (bottom right), 79 (top right), 81 (top left), 82, 83 (bottom left), 86,
  89 (top left), 90 (top right), 91 (top right), 92 (top right), 94–95, 96 (top left)
  98 (top left), 99, 101 (bottom right), 104 (top right), 107, 109, 111, 112, 114, 117, 119,
  120 (top left), 123, 124, 129, 130 (bottom left) 132–133, 134–135, 136, 138, 141, 142,
  145, 147, 149, 150, 152, 155, 157 (top right), 158, 161, 162 (top left), 165, 166, 167,
  169, 170, 173, 174

Artwork credits
Aerospace Publishing: 8–9, 10–11, 13 (bottom right), 14 (top left), 17 (top right),
  18 (top left), 22, 23, 24, 26, 28, 30, 32, 33, 35, 36, 38, 40, 41, 45 (top right), 46, 48, 50,
  53, 57, 59, 62, 62–63, 67, 71, 74, 75, 77, 78, 80, 83, 86, 87, 88, 89, 92–93, 93, 98–99,
  100–101, 102–103, 104–105, 106–107, 108–109, 112–113, 115, 116, 118, 120–121,
  122–123, 124–125, 126–127, 128, 130–131, 134–135, 137, 140, 142–143, 144, 148,
  151, 152–153, 159, 162–163, 164–165
De Agostini: 110–111, 138–139, 146–147, 168, 171, 172
Ray Hutchins: 54–55, 60–61, 84–85, 97
Peter Sarson: 64

CONTENTS

CHAPTER 1
A DIFFICULT BIRTH

In September of 1916, as the first British tanks lurched ponderously towards the German trenches, a new chapter in the history of warfare was opened. Few could have imagined the impact these ungainly machines were destined to have on twentieth-century warfare.

There seemed no way to break the deadlock. The terrain between the opposing armies facing one another across the battlefields of eastern and northern France was often virtually impassable, even to men on foot; and even before the rusting thickets of barbed wire and the defensive fire from machine guns were taken into consideration. Unprotected men tried to cross this desolate no-man's-land, stopped, stuck and died. No vehicle stood a chance of crossing, even if by some miracle it could be made immune to the machine gun rounds and the howitzer shells that turned mudbaths into charnel houses. And still World War I ground on. . .

When war broke out in August 1914, there was very little in the way of mechanical transport to be found on either side. Draught horses, in huge numbers, provided most of the motive power, all the way from the rear echelons almost to the fighting fronts themselves – and horses stood even less chance in no-man's-land than men did. But there were motorised tractors, both with internal combustion engines and with steam engines, to pull very heavy loads, such as the biggest artillery pieces. Some of the former type were fitted with continuous tracks in place of wheels. They didn't often come within 10 miles of the actual

■ **LEFT: The British 'Tank' developed rapidly after its introduction. The Mk IV version became available in October 1916, with significant improvements in armour, traction, and crew safety. This example was donated to the British Government by the Malay States.**

fighting, but the presence of these tractors in the rear echelons, where conditions underfoot were often little better than at the front, set some people thinking.

SWINTON'S VEHICLES
In 1912, an Australian engineer and professional inventor named Lancelot de Mole had sent a design for an armoured tracked vehicle to the British War Office. He was ignored. Now, with the world at war, a serving British officer, Lieutenant-Colonel Ernest Swinton, put forward something similar. Instead of a design starting from scratch, though, Swinton suggested utilising the Holt caterpillar tractor, then just coming into service as a prime mover with the artillery. Suitably armoured and armed with guns, such a vehicle could act as a mobile machine gun destroyer. Swinton – at the time Deputy Secretary of the Committee of Imperial Defence – had seen at first hand what armoured fighting vehicles (AFVs) could do. He had been briefly with Commander Charles Samson's Royal Naval Air Service (RNAS) squadron in France in the role of 'official eyewitness', the only form of war correspondent then permitted to visit the war zone. Samson's squadron rescued downed airmen and carried out ground reconnaissance missions, at first using touring cars they had armoured themselves, and later in vehicles armed and armoured by the Admiralty. Swinton had also worked alongside Sir Ian Hamilton on the official report on the Russo-Japanese War and thus had seen exactly what machine guns could achieve against massed infantry.

Tank Mk V Male

Armament: two 6pdr guns, four .303in machine guns
Crew: eight
Length: 8.04m (26.4ft)
Width: 4.12m (13.5ft)
Height: 2.64m (8.66ft)
Armour: 8-16mm (.32-.63in)
Engine: 150bhp petrol
Range: 73km (45 miles)
Speed: 7.4km/h (4.6mph)
Country of origin: United Kingdom

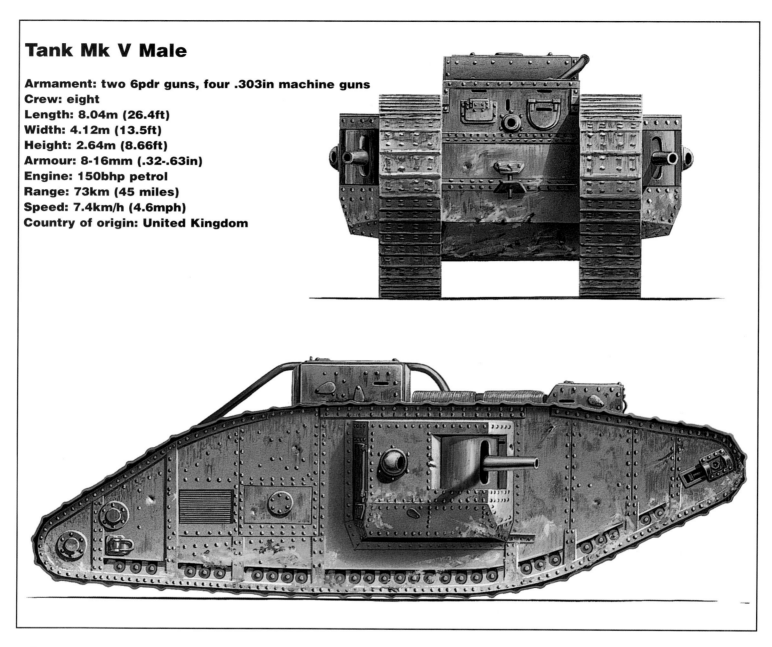

Swinton made his suggestion in the form of a memorandum to Lieutenant-Colonel Maurice Hankey, the committee's secretary. Hankey passed it up to the Imperial General Staff and to its unenthusiastic chief, Lord Kitchener. There, for the moment at least, the suggestion stalled. Hankey, however, had been convinced. He next wrote a long memorandum to Winston Churchill, who as First Lord of the Admiralty had been in favour of sending armoured cars to France and Belgium and had been impressed by the vehicles' success. Churchill responded by convincing Prime Minister Asquith to put heavy pressure on the War Office to reconsider. The War Office decided to give the Holt tractor a trial before senior officials over a prepared obstacle course on the artillery ranges at Shoeburyness. The day of the

trial – 17 February 1915 – it was raining heavily and the ground was sodden. It was a fair test, in fact, except that the unarmoured and unarmed Holt tractor was called upon to negotiate the course towing a truck laden with 2.5 tonnes of sandbags. The load was supposed to represent the weight the vehicle would have to carry when armed and armoured, and the tractor found it impossible to pull this burden over trenches. There is a great deal of difference between a load aboard a vehicle and one being towed behind, especially under such conditions, but that counted for nothing. In the opinion of the War Office committee, the vehicle had failed the trial and the idea was impractical and worthy of no further consideration.

The committee counted without Churchill's determination, however. So

much the better if the Army was not interested – he would make sure that the Navy retained the initiative. Churchill convened what he called the Admiralty 'Landships Committee' to look once again at mechanisation on the battlefield. Chairmanship of the committee was given to an undeniable expert of his own, Sir Eustace Tennyson d'Eyncourt, Director of Naval Construction. The committee's secretary was to be an enthusiastic amateur, a City banker named Albert Stern.

THE LINCOLN MACHINE
After a series of false starts and unsuccessful attempts to employ commercially available tracked vehicles, a small design team was formed. It was placed under the leadership of the managing director of traction engine

manufacturers Fowler's of Lincoln, Sir William Tritton, with naval engineer turned car maker Walter Wilson as his deputy. At the same time, sensible new performance criteria, developed by Swinton and based realistically on conditions at the fighting front, were adopted. Any new vehicle would now have to prove itself capable of climbing a 1.5m (5ft) parapet with a 45-degree slope and crossing a 2.5m (8ft) trench.

Construction of the No 1 Lincoln Machine – or the Tritton Machine, as it was sometimes called – commenced on 11 August 1915, and the vehicle was first tested on 10 September. This was no mean engineering feat, but it soon became clear that the track system used, from a Bullock tractor imported from the United States, was entirely inadequate, in terms of both endurance and performance, for a vehicle of this size and weight. The designers went back to the drawing board, and it was Tritton who came up with the answer. He suggested a system of articulated metal shoes riveted to links that had an internal lip to engage runners in the track frame. This arrangement would prevent the tracks dropping away from the guide rollers when unsupported, as they were when crossing a trench. The system was fitted to a rebuilt No 1 Lincoln Machine known as 'Little Willie', which could then span a 1.5m (5ft) trench and scale a 1.4m (4ft 6in) parapet.

THE TRITTON-WILSON

But this improved version was already obsolescent, for Wilson had had an inspiration even before the original vehicle was finished. At the September trial, he had produced a wooden mock-up of a new concept that he believed would come much closer to meeting Swinton's criteria. Swinton himself agreed. It was clear that big wheels scaled parapets better than tracks did. However, Wilson realised that he could improve the tracked vehicle's climbing ability if he could increase the vertical distance between the forward and rearward track runs and project the upper track run forwards. By doing this, Wilson ensured that the track at the front of the vehicle ran in an arc much greater in diameter than that of any wheel ever contemplated. In fact, the effective arc described by the track of his prototype was equivalent to that of a wheel some 18m (60ft) in diameter. The distinctive lozenge, or rhomboidal, shape of the

second Tritton-Wilson vehicle, with its tracks running around the full height of the hull, has come to typify the armoured vehicles of World War I, although it was by no means the only layout employed.

The specification for a new prototype embodying Wilson's improved scheme was accepted at a meeting of the Landships Committee held on 29 September 1915, and detailed design work began immediately. The vehicle – variously called 'Big Willie', the 'Centipede', the 'Wilson Machine' and eventually 'Mother' – emerged from Foster's workshops on 26 January 1916. The new machine was 9.9m (32ft 6in) long, including its rear-mounted steering/stabilising wheels, 2.4m (8ft) high, 4.25m (14ft) wide, including the detachable sponsons, and weighed in at more than 28 tonnes. The main armament was two Hotchkiss L/40 six-pounder guns in side sponsons. The machine had armour 10mm (.4in) thick on the front face and 8mm (.375in) thick on the sides and boasted a top speed of just over 5.5km/h (3.5mph). It had a range on the road of 40km (24 miles) on a full 227-litre (60 US gallon) tank, could climb a 25 per cent gradient, surmount a vertical obstacle 1.4m (4ft 6in) high and cross a 3.3m (11ft) trench. Steering was effected by preventing one track or the other from turning by means of a gearbox between each transverse drive shaft and the chain that connected it with the drive wheels at the very rear. To turn the vehicle, the gearbox in question was put into neutral. When the manoeuvre had been accomplished, the gearbox was put back into gear again. All this took the coordinated actions of four men – the

ABOVE: This is the first official picture of a tank going into action (distinguished as a Mk I 'Female' by the twin machine guns in the side sponsons), at the Battle of Flers-Courcelette on 15 September 1916.

commander and the driver in the forward cupola and the two gearmen. Since the interior of the tank was far too noisy to permit speech to be heard (the engine was unsilenced), the commander's instructions to the gearmen in the rear could be passed only by hand signal or by banging on the engine cover with a hammer in a predetermined code. Small course changes could be made by use of the exposed rear wheels in ideal conditions, although their real purpose was to improve stability and enhance the vehicle's trench-crossing performance. Not surprisingly, the rear wheels proved to be very vulnerable in battle and were removed from November 1916 onwards. At a pinch, the tank commander could to some extent steer through the brakes, which he controlled, although the effort required was almost superhuman. Even though the vehicle was proceeding only at walking pace, it was no easy job to keep the vehicle pointing in the right direction, even under the best conditions. In battle it was to prove to be next to impossible.

KITCHENER'S DOUBTS

After successful trials in early 1916, an official order was placed for just 40 units. While prepared to agree, albeit reluctantly, that the vehicle under test performed adequately, Kitchener was still far from convinced that armoured

Tank Mk IV Male

Armament: two 6pdr guns, four .303in machine guns
Crew: eight
Length: 8.04m (26.4ft)
Width: 4.12m (13.5ft)
Height: 2.49m (8.2ft)
Armour: 8-16mm (.32-.63in)
Engine: 105bhp
Range: 55km (34 miles)
Speed: 6.0km/h (3.7mph)
Country of origin: United Kingdom

vehicles ('pretty mechanical toys', he called them) had any real tactical merit whatsoever. Minister of Munitions David Lloyd-George, on the other hand, saw the armoured vehicle as a way of breaking the machine gun's stranglehold on the battlefield, and was prepared to give it the benefit of the doubt. By dint of considerable political acumen, Lloyd-George managed to get the Landships Committee absorbed into his ministry. In fact, at Swinton's suggestion, the Landships Committee had become the Tank Supply Committee, in an attempt to keep the very existence of the new weapon secret. The official story was that mobile water containers were being built for use in the deserts of Mesopotamia (in what is now Iraq). The name stuck, and heavy, tracked armoured vehicles have been known, in English, as tanks ever since. Within just a few days of the committee's absorption into Lloyd-George's ministry, the order for what was now officially known as the Tank Mark I (Mk I) was increased to 100, and subsequently to 150. The first tanks came off the production lines in the last week of June.

With the technical problems if not

solved, then at least addressed, Swinton turned his thoughts to exactly how the tanks should operate on the battlefield. In March 1916, he had been named as head of the unit which was to operate the machines – the Armoured Car Section, Motor Machine Gun Service.

MACHINE-GUN CARRIERS
Swinton's original concept of the tank as a machine gun destroyer still stood, but now he began to question its ability to defend itself. Would the four less-than-perfect clip-fed Hotchkiss machine guns originally specified as defensive armament be enough to drive off counterattacking infantry, or would determined enemy troops be able to press home an assault, disable the tank and destroy it at leisure? Indeed, two of these machine guns were to be manned only in extreme circumstances, by the second members of the six-pounders' crews. Swinton knew he could not take the chance, and in April 1916 he requested that half the tanks should be equipped with paired .303in Vickers Class C belt-fed, water-cooled machine guns, arguably the best of their kind in the world at the time. The Vickers machine guns were to

replace the six-pounder guns in slightly modified sponsons, and the 'female' tanks that resulted were earmarked to accompany the six-pounder-armed 'males' into battle and defend them against infantry assault. His terms stuck, and until after World War I, British tanks were divided into male and female types according to their armament. In 1918, they were joined by so-called 'hermaphrodites', tanks with one male and one female sponson.

FRENCH DEVELOPMENTS
With Germany having examined and rejected the concept of armoured fighting vehicles in 1914, the only nation besides Britain looking to develop such machines early in the war was France. In May 1915, Schneider, France's main heavy arms manufacturer, ordered two Holt tractors from the United States and began experimenting with them. In mid-December 1915, Schneider invited the political head of France's Department of Inventions, Jules-Louis Breton, to a demonstration of a Baby Holt 45 horsepower (hp) tractor fitted with a box-like armoured body. The machine was the work of Schneider's chief engineer,

an angled girder to cut or force down wire entanglements. As in the case of the first British prototype, however, the performance and endurance of the French vehicles' tracks – designed for a much lighter vehicle – proved to be very poor. But unlike the British, the French did nothing about that deficiency, and for that reason above all others the first-generation French vehicles proved unbattleworthy. The Schneider chars d'assaut were well-enough armed, with a short-barrelled version of the justly famous 75mm quick-firing gun, but the weapon was mounted in an embrasure to the right of the driving position. This placement gave it a very limited field of fire – from dead ahead through about 60 degrees to the right-hand side only.

CA-1 ARMAMENT

Defensive fire was provided by two 8mm Hotchkiss machine guns like those fitted to the British tanks. The char d'assaut was particularly vulnerable to catching fire, thanks to its petrol container being mounted high enough to feed the engine's carburettor by gravity, and the vehicle earned the nickname 'mobile crematorium' as a result. Two more powerful versions, the CA-2 and CA-3, reached the design stage, and the CA-2, with its embrasure gun replaced by a 47mm cannon in a rotating roof turret, actually appeared in prototype form. The CA-1 first saw action at Berry-au-Bac on 16 April 1917. Of 132 tanks, 57 were

work of Schneider's chief engineer, Eugène Brillié, and although it was very clearly underpowered, Breton came away convinced that it had some merit and wrote a favourable report to staff officers at Grand Quartier Général (GQG).

Within a few days, news of a guardedly favourable response to Breton's report came back from the commander-in-chief, General Joseph Joffre. On 20 December, Brillié started work on what was to become the Schneider char d'assaut (CA). His collaborator on the project was Jean-Baptiste Estienne, who was in charge of experimental work on armoured vehicles. Designing the vehicle took the pair six days, and on 21 February 1916 an armed and armoured prototype using the existing Holt track system was demonstrated in front of the French commander-in-chief. Four days after that, a contract was signed for the production of 400 vehicles. However, it was to be well over a year before

■ RIGHT: In order to prevent enemy infantry hurling grenades onto the hull in battle, the British Mk I 'Male' had a triangular wood and wire frame attached to the roof.

Schneider CA-1s, as they were designated, had been delivered in sufficient numbers for them to be ready and able to go into battle. The Schneider chars had pointed, boat-like bows, with

■ ABOVE: Despite some successes, most notably at Cambrai in October 1917, the tank did not play a major role in the Great War. Mechanical problems plagued the crews, and the susceptibility of the heavy machines to bog down on the battlefield and thus be incapacitated was rapidly exploited by the enemy.

destroyed, largely as a result of their armour being vulnerable to the German K-Patrone rifle round.

THE ST CHAMOND

Even before it went into production, the Schneider char d'assaut had a rival – the St Chamond. This was a heavier, though similarly armed, vehicle, named after the town in which it was produced by the Compagnie des Forges et Acieries de la Marine et Homecourt (FAMH). Designed by Colonel Rimailho of the French Army's vehicle procurement section, the Service Technique Automobile (STA), the St Chamond, too, employed the inadequate Holt track system, but with a very important difference. The St Chamond's tracks were driven by individual electric motors, and since the power to each track could be controlled by a rheostat, steering was much simplified. In this respect, the St Chamond was a long way ahead of its time. Had the electric motors been powerful enough to overcome the handicap of the vehicle's huge weight, the St Chamond might well have been more successful. As it was, the vehicle was

badly underpowered, and this, plus the design of its 22-tonne body, which had excessive overhangs at both front and rear, almost guaranteed that the St Chamond would bog down at the first obstacle. When it did, the driver would promptly burn out the electric motors in a futile attempt to extricate his tank. As in the case of the Schneider char, it was more than a year before significant deliveries of the St Chamond were made because of the heavy demands already being made on France's depleted industry. The St Chamond was soon eclipsed by the two-man FT-17, a light tank produced by Renault in 1917. Of the 16 St Chamonds that first went into battle, at Moule de Laffaux on 5 May 1917, all but one ditched in the first line of German trenches and were lost. No more St Chamonds were produced, and by early 1918, the few that remained had been relegated to training duties, much to the relief of the men who crewed them.

THE SOMME, 15 SEPTEMBER 1916

The first British tanks – designated as His Majesty's Landships – left the Bristol Channel port of Avonmouth for Le Havre in mid-August 1916, just after the second anniversary of the start of the war. By then, the death toll on the Western Front, with the attrition battles of the Somme and Verdun well advanced, already stood at well over a million men. By the end of the month, there were 50 operational vehicles at Yvrench, where the camp to

receive them had been set up. As early as February 1916, when the tank was still a completely unknown force, the British commander in France, Sir Douglas Haig, had voiced his approval of proposals for tactical deployment that Swinton had put forward in a memorandum. In this document, Swinton advocated that tanks should be kept out of the line of battle until a sufficient number had been assembled for a massed assault. By mid-summer, with plans for a huge attack on the Somme at an advanced stage, Haig revised his opinion, and orders began to emanate from his headquarters calling for tanks to be included in the order of battle as they became available. They were to be moved into the combat zone itself in an attempt to change the course of an offensive battle that had bogged down in the face of defensive positions a year and more in the making.

Some 49 tanks reached the 15km-wide (nine-mile) sector between Thiepval and Combles in time to join in the third phase of the Somme offensive scheduled to begin on 15 September. Here, as one of the British corps commanders, Sir Henry Rawlinson, noted at the time, 'The Chief [Haig] is anxious to have a gamble with all the available troops . . . with the objective of breaking down the German line and getting through to Bapaume.' The tanks were not to operate all together, but were immediately distributed piecemeal across the battle line. During the nights of 13 and 14

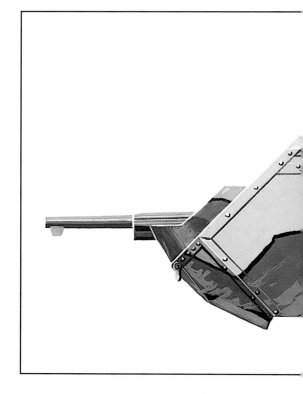

September, the vehicles were moved up to their jumping-off points under conditions of great secrecy and even greater difficulty. Driving at night was a hazardous business at best; under the prevailing conditions it was a nightmare.

In total, just 36 of the available 49 tanks were in position by 5 a.m. on 15 September. One tank, D1, under the command of Captain H.W. Mortimer and with two companies from the 6th Battalion, the King's Own Yorkshire Light Infantry, in support, was soon despatched to deal with a particularly troublesome fortified machine gun nest near Delville Wood. D1 achieved its objective handsomely – and became the first tracked armoured vehicle ever to go into action – but was almost immediately disabled by an artillery shell and took no further part in the action. Most of the remaining tanks waited in their allotted positions for an hour and 20 minutes, until the moment designated as H-Hour arrived. As the preparatory barrage lifted, and the infantrymen launched themselves 'over the top' of their defensive parapets and began their straggling death march across no-man's-land, a new noise came to the battlefield – the rumble of tracks and the roar of engines. The sound was deafening at close quarters but often got lost from further away in the general cacophony. Because of this, the first most infantrymen on either side knew of the new weapons was their sudden

appearance, trundling out of the smoke and mist like monsters, rearing to cross obstacles, crashing down on barbed wire and men alike and weaving dangerously from side to side as the crews battled to maintain a course across the uneven ground. Slowly but inexorably the tanks ground forward, leading the serried lines of infantrymen, while small arms fire bounced off their toughened skins, and their own machine guns and six-pounders spat out in retribution. Tanks were not invincible, perhaps, but certainly a decisive step in the right direction – a means, at last, of destroying the hated, deadly machine gun nests.

CREW CONDITIONS

Inside the vehicles, the crews had a rather different perspective. The interior of a Tank Mk I was crowded and confused. Crammed into the confined space were eight men and their personal kit, rudimentary protective clothing (including plate armour and chain-mail face masks) and rations, the engine and gearbox, together with the 227-litre (60 US gallon) fuel tank. There were also the weapons and ammunition – 336 six-pounder rounds and 6272 rounds of 8mm machine gun ammunition in the case of the male tanks; some 33,000 rounds of machine gun ammunition in 8mm and .303in calibres in the case of the females. Each tank also carried drums of lubricating oil and grease, about 90 litres (24 US gallons) of drinking water, a

basket of carrier pigeons, signalling lamps and flags, a crude field telephone and a drum carrying several hundred metres of telephone cable, as well as spares for the guns and for the engine. Nothing was lashed down, and the awkward, arhythmic movement ('like a torpedo-boat in a storm', as one ex-naval crewman described it) set it all in confused motion and threatened the crewmen with broken bones and cracked heads. Working conditions were truly appalling. There was no silencing of the machinery, nor any meaningful form of ventilation or cooling. Within 10 minutes of starting off, the temperature inside a Mk I was up to over 40 degrees Celsius, even in a north European winter, while the noise from engine and transmission left each man isolated in a cocoon of total deafness. At the same time, the lurching, unpredictable motion spilled crewmen about the interior of the vehicle like twigs in a millrace, and the exhaust fumes from the engine and the waste gases from the machine gun and artillery ammunition expended in the ill-ventilated interior soon made breathing itself difficult.

FIRST SUCCESSES

Almost against the odds, and at considerable cost, the early tanks proved themselves to be effective in the limited tactical role allotted to them. Many a German infantryman broke and ran from the frontline defences at the sight of them, and many more were shot down or

St Chamond

Armament: 75mm gun,
 four 7.5mm machine guns
Crew: nine
Length: (hull) 8.08m (26.5ft)

Width: 2.72m (8.9ft)
Height: 2.39m (7.84ft)
Armour: 11.5mm (.45in)
Engine: 90hp

Range: 55km (34 miles)
Speed: 8.5km/h (5.3mph)
Country of origin: France

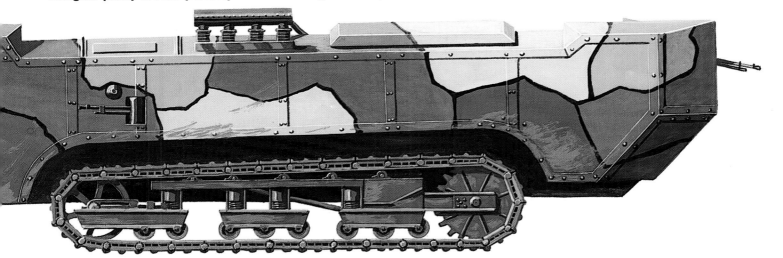

Renault FT-17 (1917)

**Armament: one 8mm machine gun or
  one 37mm gun**
Crew: two
Length: (with tail) 5.0m (16.4ft)
Width: 1.74m (5.7ft)
Height: 2.29m (7.5ft)
Armour: 6–16mm (.24–.63in)
Engine: 35bhp petrol
Range: 55km (34 miles)
Speed: 7.7km/h (4.8mph)
Country of origin: France

German infantryman broke and ran from the frontline defences at the sight of them, and many more were shot down or crushed, while the hitherto impregnable hardened defensive positions proved vulnerable to the combination of armoured vehicles and infantryman in close support. Of the seven tanks that left the start line together in the centre of XV Corps's sector (the largest number of tanks deployed together on 15 September) four were knocked out, but the three survivors pushed on to the objective – the village of Flers, almost 2km (one mile) behind what had been the German front line. There they chalked up the first important success for the new weapon with the battle just two and a half hours old. In all, the 'push' of 15 September saw the British line thrust forward by almost 2km (1.2 miles) across a front more than 9km (six miles) wide. The day's achievements included the

capture of three villages that had been very strongly fortified indeed – a greater gain than any made in a single day during the entire Somme offensive up to that time.

Still the real worth of the new weapon was by no means clear. The tank's detractors could always effectively argue that the gains made between Albert and Bapaume would have been made anyway, whether the armoured vehicles had taken part in the battle or not. The tank's supporters, on the other hand, could not point to any single significant incident to gainsay them. Haig, however, was by now a definite enthusiast and requested the construction of a further 1000 tanks. One hundred and fifty were completed as Mk Is; 50 more were built as Mk IIs (basically this was the original design with an enlarged roof hatch with a raised coaming, and improved traction); and a similar number were constructed as

Mk IIIs (with their armour improved to the standard of the Mk IVs). The bulk of the order, though, was made up of Mk IVs.

THE BRITISH MK IV
The Mk IV tanks differed from the Mk Is chiefly in their armour and armament. The powerplant was unchanged, although the petrol tank that fed it was enlarged and moved outside the vehicle to an armoured position between the rear 'horns'. Male tanks retained their six-pounder Hotchkiss quick-firing guns, but the handier short-barrelled L/23 version was substituted for the L/40. Their Hotchkiss machine guns were exchanged for Lewis guns in .303in calibre, and two more machine guns were added in the rear portion of each sponson. The female tanks' Vickers Class C machine guns were also exchanged for Lewis guns. The Lewis guns were soon found to be

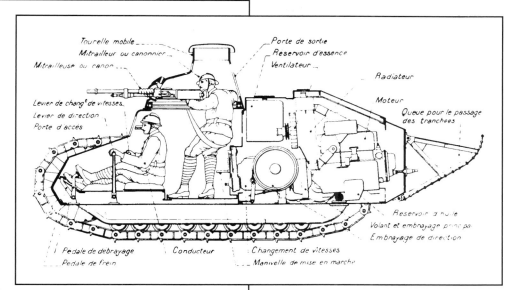

■LEFT: A cutaway of the Renault FT-17 showing the position of the engine and crew compartment. Crew comfort was never high on the list of early tank designers or manufacturers.

unsuitable, however, since the male tanks' gun slits had to be much larger than before. The guns' cooling system also drew petrol fumes into the tank, polluting the atmosphere even more than ever. The Lewis guns were replaced by modified Hotchkisses. In female tanks this allowed smaller sponsons to be fitted, with escape hatches incorporated below them. The design of the male sponsons was improved, too, in an attempt to limit their tendency to dig their corners into uneven ground.

THE MK IV'S ARMOUR

The Mk IV's armour was upgraded to a thickness of 16mm (.625in) at the front, while elsewhere it was either 12.5mm (.5in) or 8mm (.375in) thick. The upgrade was necessary to protect the vehicles against the German tungsten-cored K-Patrone 7.92mm rifle ammunition, which was capable of penetrating the skin of a

Mk I or Mk II tank. The other significant feature of the new tank (although it was not added until after the attack on Messines on 7 June 1917) was the set of paired upper rails that ran from front to rear and supported the unditching beam. This was a stout timber baulk that could be chained to the tracks and used to help the vehicle climb out of deep mud. In all, some 1200 Mk IVs were to be produced, in the ratio of three female versions to two males, and they started to arrive in France in April 1917.

THE SIEGFRIED LINE

Meanwhile, however, in March, the German High Command – much to the surprise of the British and French – had pulled its troops back to the Siegfried Line from the positions they had held since the 'Race to the Sea' of August 1914. The Siegfried Line (which the British called the Hindenburg Line) was a series of in-depth defensive positions that made those on the Somme front look puny. Haig determined to launch an offensive to test the new defensive line and in early April attacked near Arras, at the point where the old line joined the new. All the tanks available – 34 Mk Is and 26 Mk IIs – were pressed into action. Once again they were distributed piecemeal and sent in after a prolonged artillery barrage.

Some tanks managed to make significant contributions to the offensive. On Day 1, tanks helped capture the fortified villages of Neuville-Vitasse and Tilloy, for example, and on Day 2, three tanks took the hitherto impregnable strongpoint of Manchy-le-Preux. In general, though, it was the Somme all

over again. Most tanks were immobilised, either becoming bogged down in shell-torn trenches or knocked out by close-range artillery fire. On Day 3, the 4th Australian Division was sent into the assault near Bullecourt, supported by 11 of its 12 allotted tanks. The German field artillery was waiting for them in depth, and during the night of 10 April, a thick covering of snow had fallen. As the tanks moved out into the emptiness of no-man's-land, they stuck out like training targets against the whiteness. Nine of the 11 succumbed to artillery fire as they ground their slow way towards their first-line objectives, and the remaining two were later captured. The Australian infantry they were to support lost huge numbers of officers and men – 2250 out of 3000 in one brigade alone. Although it succeeded in breaking into the Siegfried Line, the offensive was unable to consolidate and was soon driven out again. And there was worse to come . . .

As spring turned to summer, the British General Staff turned its attention northwards to the countryside around Ypres – already the scene of two clashes of epic proportions and now set to be the site of another. The battle began on 7 June 1917 at Messines and continued through August, September, October and the first 10 days of November to the east and north of Ypres. The attack at Messines, where Mk IV tanks went into action for the first time, was a success, thanks largely to the string of 19 huge mines, months in the digging and packed with over 400 tonnes of explosive, which were detonated under the German lines just before H-Hour. The tanks gave valuable support to the assaulting infantry, particularly in Messines village itself. Of the 40 that started the battle, 25 reached the limit of their objective. At Ypres, though, it was another matter. More than 200 Mk IV tanks were committed to the third battle of Ypres – or Passchendaele, as it is often called. One after another, they sank into the morass of mud churned up by shellfire and were destroyed, battered into oblivion by artillery. Alongside them, tens upon tens of thousands of infantrymen met the same fate. Eventually, after 14

weeks of fighting, the offensive petered out, with a bare 6.5km (four miles) of muddy ground won at a cost of over 400,000 casualties.

CRITICS OF THE TANK
The tank's disastrous performance at Ypres seemed to lend undeniable weight to the words of one senior Army commander, who said: 'One, tanks are unable to negotiate bad ground; two, the ground on a battlefield will always be bad; three, therefore tanks are no good on a battlefield.' Senior tank officers, on the other hand, while knowing, perhaps better than anyone, the tank's limitations, also knew that properly used, and under favourable conditions, armour was a battlewinner. They were to be given their chance that winter at Cambrai.

CAMBRAI, 20 NOVEMBER 1917
On 13 October 1917, Haig gave the go-ahead for the preliminary planning stages of what was to be known as Operation GY – the assault at Cambrai. Within a week the date of the attack had been fixed for 20 November, and the massive task of planning logistics and assembling supplies got under way. The plan called for the commitment of every available up-to-date tank then in existence. As well as 376 fighting tanks, the British tank force of three brigades mustered 18 supply and gun-carrying tanks and three wireless tanks. A further 32 tanks were equipped with towing gear

ABOVE: The Whippet was a light, fast tank designed to take advantage of the gaps created in enemy defences by the heavy tank sections. Peace in 1918 curtailed any further development of the model 'A' pictured here.

and grapnels to clear paths through the wire for the cavalry units that were to follow them into battle. Two more tanks carried bridging materials, and one carried a drum of telephone cable. This amounted to a grand total of 474 armoured vehicles.

Before the assault could go ahead, a means needed to be thought of to get the tanks across the trenches of the Siegfried Line, which were wider than a Mk IV could normally span. First of all, modifications to the basic Mk IV design were suggested, but they proved unworkable. Eventually a really quite simple method was devised. Each tank would go into battle carrying a bundle of brushwood on its deck. At around 2 tonnes each, these bundles – or 'fascines', as they were properly known – were actually extremely substantial, being composed of the trunks of saplings and small trees up to about 10cm (4in) in diameter. Each finished fascine measured 1.4m (4ft 6in) in diameter and more than 3m (10ft) long and could bear the weight of a fully laden tank. The bundles were loaded onto the upper deck rails of the frontline tanks, from which they could be released by a catch from inside the vehicle to roll down the front face of the

tank and into the trench.
Since there was no question of recovering and redeploying the fascines afterwards, considerable care went into planning exactly where and how they would be placed for the greatest effect.

EARLY TANK TACTICS
It was decided the tanks were to work in groups of three. The first tank was to advance to the enemy frontline trench, turn to the left and run parallel with it, suppressing any defensive activity with its machine guns. The two following tanks would then have a clear run to a predetermined position on the trench, where the second tank would dump its fascine and cross, followed by its fellow, and make for the second defensive line. It would then turn left in turn and work down the trench, while the third tank crossed and continued on towards the third defensive line. Here it would provide suppressive fire for the first tank, which would by then have come up from behind to dump its fascine and cross in its turn. This arrangement, simple though it sounds, was more complex than

the battle tactics of the day normally called for, especially considering the presence of supporting infantry in addition to the tanks. In the event, though, the plan went well, except in the 51st (Highland) Division, whose commander, Major-General G.M. Harper, insisted that the 70 frontline tanks supporting his division would turn right, not left, during the trench-crossing manoeuvres, and that they would be deployed in groups of four, not three. A further instruction – that his infantrymen were to deploy in line abreast by company, some 100m (330ft) behind the tanks, rather than by platoon in single file immediately behind each vehicle – resulted not only in the unnecessary deaths of many of Harper's own men, but also caused problems across the entire battlefield.

Compared with those of an infantry corps, the tank force's needs for what was to have been a short battle were quite meagre. They required 775,500 litres (205,000 US gallons) of petrol, 34 tonnes of grease, 500,000 rounds of six-pounder ammunition and five million rounds of

machine gun ammunition, plus the men's rations. Bringing all this material and the 474 vehicles themselves quickly, smoothly and in conditions of great secrecy up to the narrow, 10km-wide (six miles) sector of the front from which they were to operate was not easy. Much of the railway system in the rear echelon was still in operation, and it was by using this that the tanks and their supplies were moved up from the dispersal and training areas near the coast. The move was accomplished on time, and the build-up continued in secret on the night of 18 November. At 6.20 a.m. on 20 November, the attack was launched as planned.

GERMANY'S TANKS

The first German tank saw the light of day in prototype form in April 1917 and was accepted for production on 14 May as the Sturmpanzerwagen A7V. Further testing went on throughout the summer and showed the vehicle's design to be deeply flawed. In particular, the track system had insufficient rise at the front, and the twin 100hp Daimler engines were hard pushed to perform in a vehicle

with an all-up weight of 33 tonnes, which included a crew of 18 men, fuel and supplies, and ammunition for a single 57mm gun and six machine guns. The first fully armoured A7V was delivered on 1 October, and despite its shortcomings, an order for 100 was placed with Daimler on 1 December, delivery to take place by the following spring in time for the planned offensive. In all, however, 35 at most had been delivered to the Wehrmacht by the following November, plus a further 30 with mild steel bodies and no armament, for use as supply vehicles. The A7V tank went into action for the first time at St Quentin on 21 March 1918 and proved largely useless, except in bolstering German morale. About a month later, on 24 April, near Villers Bretonneux, the first tank-versus-tank engagement saw one A7V drive off two British female Mk IVs before it was knocked out by a male, which then engaged two more A7Vs, knocking out one of them and driving off the other.

It was clear that no amount of modification would turn the A7V into a successful fighting machine, and the

Medium tank Mark A 'Whippet'

Armament: three or four .303mm machine guns
Crew: three or four
Length: 6.1 m (20ft)
Width: 2.6m (8.5ft)
Height: 2.9m (9.5ft)
Armour: 5–14mm (.19–.55in)
Engine: 2 x 45bhp petrol
Range: 130km (81 miles)
Speed: 13.25km/h (8.23mph)
Country of origin: United Kingdom

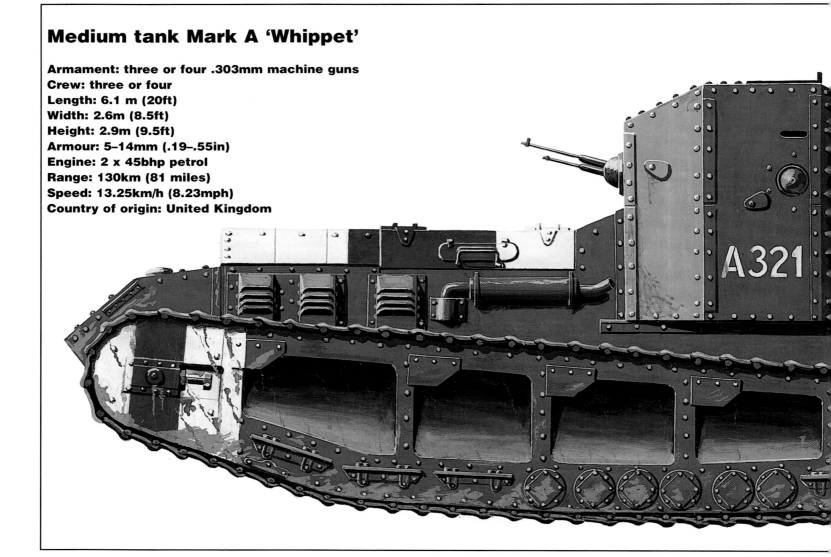

design team turned instead to producing plans for a vehicle very similar indeed to the British tanks. This vehicle was the A7V/U, with an overall length of 8.5m (almost 28 ft) and a fighting weight of 40 tonnes. A prototype was produced, but too late to go into production. Like the original A7V tank, the A7V/U was rather more heavily armoured than its British counterparts, with plate between 10 and 30mm (.4 and 1.2in) thick. There is said to have been considerable variation in the quality of German tank armour at this time, and certainly, the earlier vehicles were constructed of such plates of armour as were available, some small, some large. Those built up out of small plate sections, which naturally needed vast numbers of rivets to hold them together, suffered badly from 'splash', as the sprawling effect of effective fire was known. Germany was also responsible for planning one of the biggest, heaviest tanks ever proposed – the giant Grosskampfwagen or K-Wagen, which

would perhaps have exceeded 150 tonnes all-up weight in fighting order. Crewed by 22 men, and armed with four 77mm guns and seven machine guns, the K-Wagen was to have run on four roller-type tracks powered by two 650hp Daimler-Benz aero engines. Work had begun on two prototypes before the war ended, but neither was anything like complete at the armistice, and both were subsequently broken up for scrap.

THE HEAVY TANK

As it developed during World War I, the heavy tank changed the character of the conflict more and more. The heavy tank can fairly be said to have been the decisive factor on land, and certainly, had a wide range of interlinked events not brought Germany to its knees when it did, it would have been on huge numbers of heavy tanks that the Allies' progress through the German positions would have depended, as plans for the aborted 1919 offensive show. But the steel

monsters still had their critics. And their criticisms – of the tanks' poor manoeuvrability and sluggishness, above all – had both foundation and validity. If, thanks to the tank, the days of static warfare were done, and mobility was to become of paramount importance once more, then there had to be a modern substitute for the cavalry of old, whose role had been expunged by the invention of the machine gun. In this way was born the concept of the cavalry, or 'exploitation', tank. It was tracked to allow it mobility over terrain that would defeat wheeled vehicles, but it was smaller, lighter and above all faster than the heavy tank and able to develop a breakthrough more rapidly than the defending infantry could retire or regroup.

CAVALRY TANKS

As early as 1916, William Tritton designed a light tank that he called the Chaser, which he envisaged being used in the cavalry support and liaison roles. The

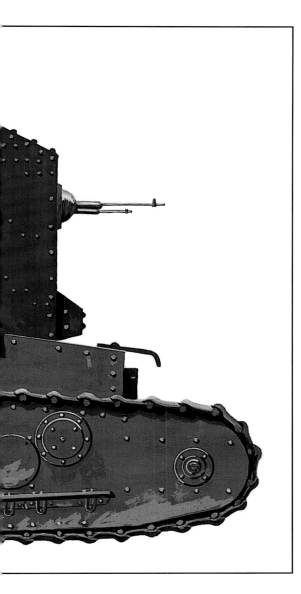

Chaser first ran in February 1917, and its trials were generally successful. In June, an order was placed for 200 Mk A Medium Tanks, deliveries commencing four months later. The Chaser's design was quite different from that of the heavy tanks. To start with, the tracks were unsprung and low slung, with a comparatively small rise, although they were long enough to allow the tank to cross a 2.1m (7ft) trench. Between the tracks, forward, were placed two 45hp Taylor four-cylinder engines, each with its own clutch and gearbox and each driving one track. The steering wheel was linked directly to the throttles – turning it increased the power to one engine and reduced it to the other. This solution to the problems of differential control was simple, but made the tank devilishly difficult to drive, even at slow speeds. To the rear was the crew compartment, for three or four men, with a raised, fixed barbette mounting three or four machine guns. The tank's armour was riveted steel plate, 5–12.5mm (.2–5in) in thickness, and in fighting order, with 5400 rounds of ammunition and 318 litres (84 US gallons) of fuel aboard, the vehicle weighed slightly more than 14 tonnes. Nonetheless, it could manage 13.5km/h (8.5mph) on the road, and by contemporary standards, that was fast indeed. However, with no form of suspension at all, the ride at that speed must have been rough to say the least.

The Mk A tank developed from the Chaser, and widely known as the Whippet, it went into action for the first time at Colincamps on 26 March 1918. But it was 8 August, at Amiens, before the Whippet first showed its potential,

when a force of 96 Mk As of the 3rd Tank Brigade was deployed in support of the (still horseborne) Cavalry Corps. Thanks to the still-prevalent tendency to employ tanks piecemeal, the results were inconclusive, but there were sufficient grounds to believe that had the tanks been employed en masse, a major breakthrough would have been possible. As it was, where the light tanks did penetrate, they were effective.

FRANCE, AGAIN

In France, Jean-Baptiste Estienne, in conjunction with Renault, came up with what became known as the FT17. It weighed just under 7 tonnes, had a two-man crew and was armed with either a single Hotchkiss machine gun (the char mitrailleuse version) or a short-barrelled Puteaux 37mm cannon (the char canon version) in a turret with 360-degree traverse. The tank's weight was kept down by doing away with a conventional chassis and attaching the major components to the 6–16mm (.25–.6in) armoured body instead, using the monocoque construction principle later used for virtually all passenger cars and light vehicles. The FT17's tracks had an exaggerated idler wheel at the front to increase the track rise and improve the tank's climbing ability. Being only 5m (16ft 6in) long, the FT17 was unable to cross a trench more than 1.8m (6ft) wide. Its 35hp Renault petrol engine gave it a top speed of under 8km/h (5mph), and its range, on 100 litres (26 US gallons), was only 35km (22 miles).

The Renault FT influenced two of its foreign users – Italy and the USA – enough for them both to produce tanks of their own based on the same basic concept. Italy's version was the Tipo 3000, which, although it did not come into service until 1923, certainly had its origins in World War I. The Tipo 3000 was an advanced design, well suited to Italy's requirements. It succeeded the FIAT Tipo 2000, an absolute giant of a heavy tank, with a crew of 10 and armed with one 65mm short-barrelled gun, one 14mm machine gun and no fewer than seven 6.5mm machine guns. The Tipo 2000's best feature was probably its top-mounted turret, with 360-degree traverse and elevation between −10 and 75 degrees. The tank's 15–20mm (.6–.8in) armour gave it an all-up weight of 40 tonnes, which meant that even with a 240hp FIAT aero engine, it could attain no more than 6km/h (4mph).

■ BELOW: Renault FT-17 light tanks, in service with the 326th Battalion of the US Tank Corps, approaching the front line near Boureullies, France, in September 1918.

CHAPTER 2
THE TANK BETWEEN THE TWO WORLD WARS

Although tank development continued apace in Europe and the USA in the aftermath of World War I, only the German High Command embraced the concept of armoured warfare. Elsewhere the tank was seen primarily as an infantry support weapon.

Primitive though the tanks of 1918 were by later standards, the advances in performance that armoured fighting vehicles had made in the first three years of their existence were considerable. Nevertheless, with World War I over, the future of the tank was far from certain. It had proved outrageously expensive to develop, produce and operate, and it still had enemies in high places. Would it – could it – survive?

INTERWAR UNCERTAINTY

By 1919, the armoured corps of Britain and France were facing the threat of disbandment. Traditionalists maintained that their own particular arm, be it infantry, artillery or even cavalry, was still the most important, had clearly won the war just ended and therefore had to be nurtured at the expense of all others. Indeed, the following year, the US Army's armoured corps actually was disbanded. The problem was that the 'tankers' had few men of real influence in their ranks, and as a result they were excluded as a class from the highest levels of decision-making and policy-setting. There was another factor, too. Against the widespread horror at what had happened

■**LEFT: A sergeant of the newly formed Royal Tank Regiment directs the novice driver of a Medium Mk II tank during trials on Salisbury Plain in 1932.**

in World War I, there was little hope of raising the sort of budget necessary to develop new 'engines of war' such as tanks. In this climate, the only way for the tank's adherents to keep the pot simmering was to work with such material as already existed. The US Army followed this course, assembling Mk VIII 'Liberty' tanks from components manufactured before the original programme was cancelled at the end of the war and using them as the basis for a medium tank force. The French, for their part, persevered with their Renault FTs, even though they were technically obsolescent. The FTs pointed the way forward in one respect. Their armament was mounted in a turret that could rotate through 360 degrees and was set above the return run of the tracks, making the gunner entirely independent of the driver at last. Although there have been tanks with hull-mounted main guns produced since, the flexibility of action provided by a rotating turret became widely accepted as essential.

BRITAIN'S LIGHT TANK MK I

The first British Army tank with a rotating turret to go into production was the Vickers Medium. Officially designated the Light Tank Mk I when it was delivered in 1924, the Medium was also the first British tank with sprung suspension and the first with an air-

Light Tank Mk VII Tetrarch

Armament: one 2pdr gun, one 7.92mm machine gun
Crew: three
Length: (gun forward) 4.3m (14.1ft)
Width: 2.3m (7.5ft)
Height: 2.1m (6.9ft)
Armour: 4–16mm (.15–.62in)
Engine: 165bhp petrol
Range: 225km (140 miles)
Speed: 65km/h (40mph)
Country of origin: United Kingdom

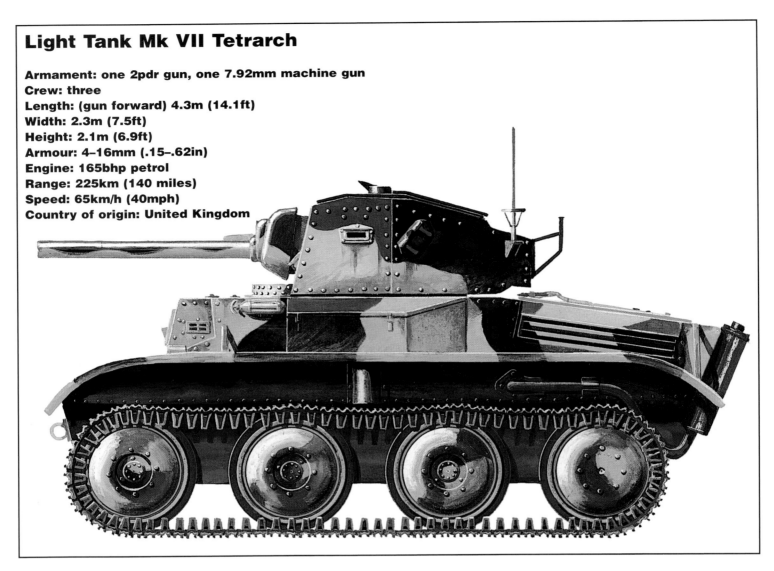

cooled engine. Derivatives of the design continued to be the British Army's mainstay for the next two decades. Weighing in at under 12 tonnes, thanks to its 7mm (.25in) armour, the Medium had a crew of five and was armed with a 47mm three-pounder QF gun plus four Hotchkiss and two water-cooled Vickers Class C machine guns. The vehicle's 90hp Armstrong-Siddeley engine gave it a road speed of 24km/h (15mph), although it is said that unofficial engine modifications in later versions boosted that to 40km/h (25mph). A 327-litre (86 US gallon) fuel tank gave the Medium a range of 195km (120 miles). Only 27 of the original Mk Is were ever built. Later models – Mk IAs, Mk IIs and Mk IIAs – had progressively upgraded armour and an improved version of the QF gun, which gave slightly greater muzzle velocity and therefore slightly better penetration of enemy armour. In all, around 160 Mediums, in their various guises, were built, and they stayed in frontline service with the Royal Tank Corps until the late

1930s. Vickers sold a small number of Mk IIAs to the fledgling Soviet Union as the 'English Workman'. Perhaps the most significant feature incorporated during the Medium's development was the co-axial machine gun mount, incapable of movement independent of the main gun, which was to become an established feature of virtually every tank that came after it.

BIGGER AND BETTER
While the first Medium Mk IIs were rolling out of the Vickers factory in 1925, the company was turning its attention to a much bigger tank, designed to be able to operate without support and known as the 'Independent'. The Independent – or A1E1, as it was later designated – was comparable in size and weight with the Mk V heavy tanks still in service. It was 7.75m (25.4ft) long and weighed over 32 tonnes, combat-ready, largely thanks to its 13–29mm (.5–1.14in) armour. It had a crew of eight, a turret-mounted three-pounder gun and four Vickers C machine

guns in stubby, cylindrical subsidiary turrets at each corner of the main turret mount. The tank's air-cooled Armstrong-Siddeley 350hp V-12 engine gave it a top speed of 32km/h (20mph). However, in the course of an evaluation programme that lasted some nine years, the A1E1 covered just 1015km (630 miles) on its tracks, for a total cost in excess of £150,000. And in the end, the Army did not buy it.

The A1E1 was followed by the A6 and A7 prototypes, neither of which reached production because of the length of time it took to correct basic design faults. By the time they were perfected, it had become clear that quite different types of tank from the general-purpose medium were needed to fill different roles. Light, fast 'cruiser' tanks were required for mobile operations, and more heavily armoured infantry tanks, not as fast but with better obstacle-crossing capabilities, were needed for use in the original close support role. The first British cruiser tank, the Cruiser Tank Mk I, was designed by Sir John Carden of Vickers-

Armstrong in 1934. With its crew of six, a full ammunition load and 327 litres (86 US gallons) of fuel for the 9.6-litre, 150hp AEC petrol engine, the tank's all-up weight was around 13 tonnes. It went into production in 1937, and a total of 125 were built in two basic types. There was the cavalry tank, with a 40mm two-pounder main gun, which had greater penetrating power than the earlier three-pounder, and a close support tank, with a 3.7in howitzer. Both variants also carried three Vickers machine guns, one mounted co-axially with the main gun and elevating and traversing with it, the other two in subsidiary cylindrical turrets flanking the driver's 'cab' and capable of traversing through 120 degrees to each side from the ahead position. The subsidiary turrets produced dangerous shot-traps between themselves and the rest of the tank's superstructure, reducing the chances of incoming rounds bouncing off. The new tank had a number of interesting features. The most ingenious was what became known as Carden's 'Bright Idea' suspension. The two bogies per side were made up of one larger-diameter roller, at front or back, and two smaller-diameter rollers, all of them rubber-covered, on coil-spring suspension. The Cruiser Mk I also had a hydraulically powered turret traverse.

VICKERS' HEAVY

In parallel with the A9 tank, as the Cruiser Mk I was designated, Vickers also took on the development of a heavier version, to the A10 specification, which called for 30mm (1.2in) of armour. The Cruiser Mk II was essentially the same tank as the Mk I, with the same main armament of either two-pounder gun or 3.7in howitzer, but with plates of additional armour attached to the hull, the first time appliqué armour had been used on a British tank. Even with the removal of the two subsidiary turrets, the all-up weight increased to 14 tonnes, and with the same AEC Type 179 engine, this had the effect of cutting the tank's top speed to 26km/h (16mph) and its endurance by a third. Uparmoured as it was, by the time the A10 appeared in 1938 it was clear that it did not have adequate protection for the close infantry support role, where it could be expected to encounter anti-tank guns at short range. Its operational description was therefore changed to that of 'heavy cruiser', even though no such classification had actually existed until then and there was absolutely no tactical requirement for such a vehicle. The entire cruiser concept called for a tank fast enough and agile enough to run away from anything it could not handle, and that the Cruiser Mk II could not do.

THE CRUISER MK III

In 1936, with Cruiser Mk I production just about to start, the General Staff issued another specification, A13, for a similarly armoured cruiser tank to be fitted with a suspension system developed by Walter Christie in the United States. A prototype of what was to become the Cruiser Mk III was completed the following year. From the outset, it was clear that this tank had impressive performance, both on and off the road, thanks both to the revolutionary suspension system and to its 350hp engine, the long-lived Liberty in a modified form. Despite being 1.5 tonnes heavier than the Mk I, the Mk III's power-to-weight ratio was more than twice as great, and it was capable of 48km/h (30mph), although with reduced range. It mounted the same turret as the

Renault Schneider B1-bis

Armament: one 75mm gun, one 47mm gun, two 7.5mm machine guns
Crew: four
Length: 6.52m (21.4ft)
Width: 2.5m (8.2ft)
Height: 2.8m (9.2ft)
Armour: 20-60mm (0.8in-2.4in)
Engine: 250bhp petrol
Range: 140km (85 miles)
Speed: 27.7km/h (17.2mph)
Country of origin: France

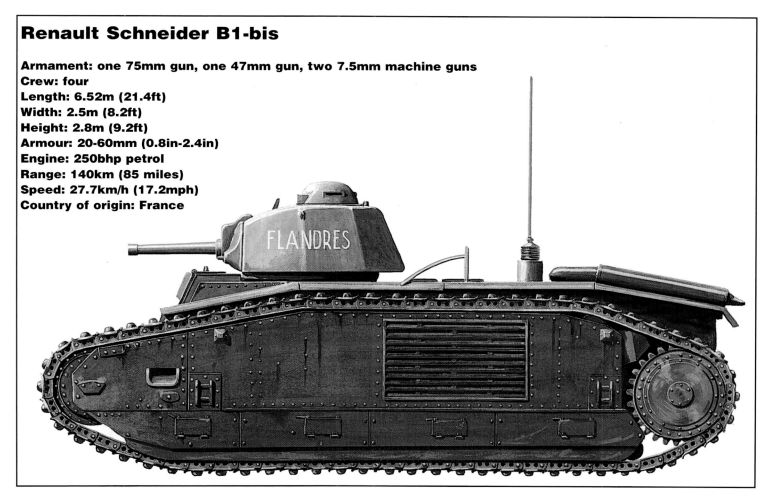

two earlier cruiser designs, but dispensed with the hull-mounted machine gun, thus bringing down the crewing level to four men. However, its 14mm (.5in) armour proved woefully inadequate in combat in France and North Africa in 1940 and 1941, as German armoured formations smashed their way west.

Just as the A10 tank was basically an uparmoured A9, so the next heavy cruiser, the A13 Mk III Cruiser Tank Mk V 'Covenanter', was essentially a Cruiser Mk III with extra armour bolted on, although it did have a more modern powerplant, a 300hp flat 12 unit specially designed by Meadows. To give it its due, the Covenanter was a stop-gap measure, commissioned when the A14 and A16 prototypes proved unworkable and had to be abandoned. It was ordered 'off the drawing board', without a prototype having been built and tested first. Nonetheless, no Covenanter ever saw combat. The tank's enduring problem was

its engine, which always overheated, no matter how many modifications were made to it. Another major defect lay in its complicated, difficult-to-maintain compressed-air assistance for steering and gear-changing. Even so, almost 1800 Covenanters were completed, and the majority of British and Empire World War II tank crews did their basic training in them.

THE TANKETTE CONCEPT
Besides medium tanks, the British Army also had small, light tanks, conceived very much on the Renault FT model, and even so-called 'tankettes', smaller still and more properly regarded as machine gun carriers. The tankette concept owed a good deal to Jean-Baptiste Estienne's work in developing the Renault FTs in the latter part of World War I, but was probably the brainchild of Colonel Henry Karslake. He saw the little cars both as reconnaissance vehicles and as the

mechanised equivalent of the old cavalry screen, protecting medium tanks as they manoeuvred. He discussed his notion with Lieutenant-Colonel Giffard Martel, who saw greater possibilities in the tankette – a machine-gun-armed armoured vehicle small enough and cheap enough to be used in large numbers during the infantry assault phase to give close supporting fire to the men as they advanced. Martel built a prototype vehicle himself and offered it to the War Office for evaluation. With the assistance of Philip Johnson, with whom he had served in France, he completed a half-track, steered by a pair of wheels at the rear, and with the driver/operator seated roughly amidships, behind the engine, in what would eventually be an armoured, open-top box. He handed it over to the Tank and Tracked Transport Experimental Establishment (TTTEE) and awaited results. The War Office guardedly approved Martel's light vehicle

Char-Leger (Hotchkiss) H-39

Armament: one 37mm gun, one 7.5mm machine gun
Crew: two
Length: 4.25m (14ft)
Width: 1.85m (6ft)
Height: 2.14m (7ft)
Armour: 12-40mm
(.47-1.57in)
Engine: 120bhp petrol
Range: 140km (85 miles)
Speed: 36km/h (22mph)
Country of origin: France

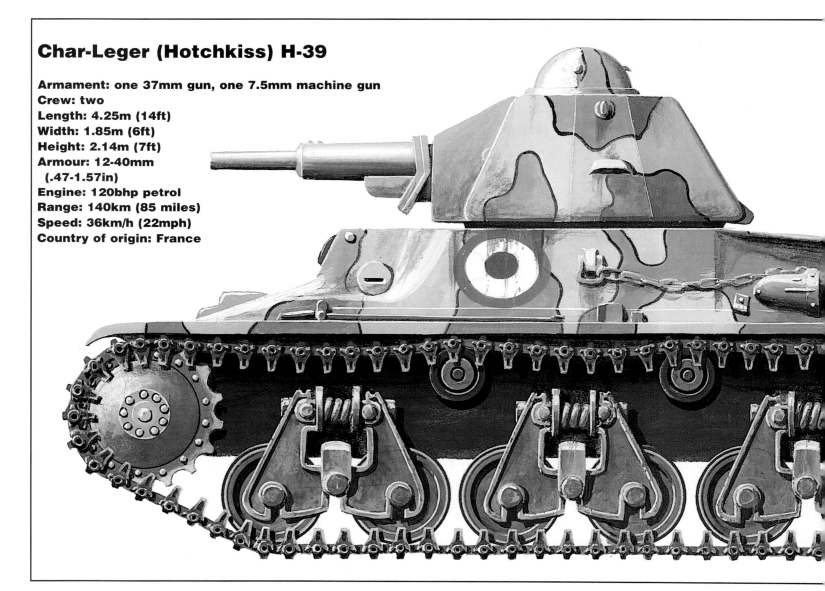

and eventually placed orders with Morris Motors for eight Morris-Martel machines in both one- and two-man versions. The tankette concept was on its way.

TEETHING PROBLEMS

The Morris-Martel received quite a lot of publicity, which brought it to the attention of John (later Sir John) Carden. Carden had already produced and sold both a light car and a light aircraft, the excellent Flying Flea, and by 1925 was involved with another ex-Army Service Corps officer, Vivian Loyd, in a garage business in west London. Carden, too, had turned his attentions to the design of a very small tank, and in March 1926 delivered a prototype tracked vehicle to TTTEE for evaluation. After modification, the Carden-Loyd carrier was accepted and evolved into the Universal Carrier (better known as the Bren Gun Carrier). It formed the basis, at least conceptually, for a family of light tanks, starting with

the prototype A3E1, built at the Royal Ordnance Factory in 1926. The A3E1 used a standard bus engine from AEC, a four-speed gearbox, the by-now standard Rackham steering clutches, and simple, cast-steel track shoes. It weighed a little over 6 tonnes with its 12.7mm (.5in) armour plate and could manage 26km/h (16mph). Its three-man crew consisted of a driver and two machine gunners, who communicated by means of a device called the Laryngaphone – a form of throat microphone – which was designed to exclude extraneous noise but which also translated the human voice into a flat croak that was barely comprehensible. Thus, there was no way the crew could act in concert, and the driver was hampered by having poor vision to the front and to his right and none at all to his left, the driving position being alongside the forward turret. In the circumstances, it is hardly surprising that nothing further was heard of the A3E1 after it arrived at TTTEE for trials in the spring of 1926.

It was two years before the next faltering step was taken, in the shape of the Carden-Loyd Mk VII Carrier, or the A4E1. The vehicle put up for trials showed considerable promise, although Carden had gone too far in trying to give it an ultra-low profile – it was barely 1.2m (4ft) in height – and had cramped both the driving position and the turret in the process. Both the driver and gunner (the only crew members) found the A4E1 almost impossible. When the

■ **BELOW: On manoeuvres. A detachment of British armour, made up of Mk VI Light tanks and Mk II Medium tanks, crosses Salisbury Plain in southern England in late 1939.**

design was translated into a preproduction version, the fighting compartment was considerably deepened, which eased both men's positions considerably. Late in 1928, the War Office placed orders for four Light Tank Mk Is, and distributed them to Royal Tank Corps units for evaluation. They never entered service, but they were sufficiently well received for more orders to be placed with Vickers-Armstrong, which had by now acquired Carden-Loyd.

BRITISH LIGHT TANKS

Orders for 16 Light Tanks Mk IA were placed at the end of 1930, and these vehicles reached operational units the following year as Light Tank Mk IIs. The addition of the crewmen's personal gear and radio sets, and the batteries to power them, increased the vehicle's weight to well above the 3.5 tonnes originally specified. Happily, the tank's appearance coincided with the development of a new type of armour plate that was some 20 per cent lighter than the old homogenous armour for the same degree of protection. This Cemented Tank Armour (CMT) was immediately specified for all further British light tanks up to the Vickers Mk VI, which entered service in 1936.

The light tanks in the series Mk I–III were a progression, and the last was recognisably a development of the first. The Mk IV was a shorter vehicle overall, but in technical terms its most significant feature was its monocoque construction. The Mk V introduced a two-man turret, with room for both commander and a machine gunner, armed with a Vickers .5in gun to supplement the single .303in Mk 4B fitted to the earlier vehicles. By the time the Mk VI was put into production, in 1936, the entire light tank

Char-Leger R-35 (Renault ZM)

Armament: one 37mm gun, one 7.5mm machine gun
Crew: two
Length: 4.3m (14.1ft)
Width: 2m (6.6ft)
Height: 2.25m (7.3ft)
Armour: 40mm (1.57in)
Engine: 82bhp petrol
Range: 140km (85 miles)
Speed: 20km/h (12.5mph)
Country of origin: France

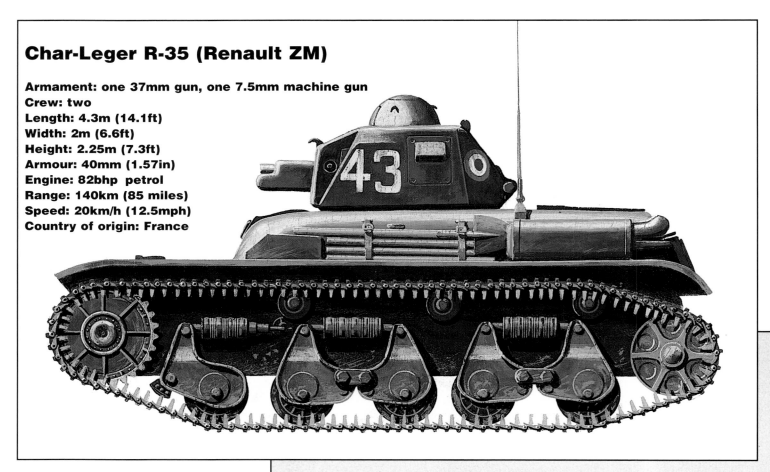

■RIGHT: British Mk II Light Tanks patrolling the Egyptian desert during the late 1930s. The Vickers Light Tank was first introduced in 1931, and served the British Army in a variety of guises until 1940.

concept had come of age, and by the beginning of World War II, in September 1939, the British Army had a light tank force some 1000 vehicles strong. Unfortunately, by that time developments elsewhere had rendered these little 4.5-tonne tanks, with their 15mm (.6in) of armour and their light armament, completely obsolescent, and wherever they saw action over the next few years, in Europe, North Africa and the Middle East, they suffered heavy losses. There were two more British light tanks, the Mk VII 'Tetrarch' and the Mark VIII 'Harry Hopkins', the former produced in 1938, the latter in 1941. Neither was produced in large numbers or saw much operational use. Their tracks could be flexed to negotiate gentle curves, while sharper turns were accomplished by the standard declutch/brake-and-skid manoeuvre. In as much as they were considerably better armed than earlier light tanks, having the same two-pounder gun found in the medium tanks of the

day, the Mk VII and Mk VIII were something of an improvement. Nonetheless, they were still so hopelessly underarmoured as to be vulnerable to even second-string anti-tank (AT) weapons such as the German Panzerbusche anti-tank rifles.

INFANTRY TANKS
Vickers-Armstrong produced for export two other light tanks based on the original Carden-Loyd designs. The more

successful design of the two was the Six-Ton Tank Mk E, which was available in two forms. One had paired, side-by-side turrets, each containing a machine gun; the other had a single turret mounting a 47mm three-pounder QF gun and a co-axial machine gun. The Six-Ton sold to a dozen countries and was to influence light tank design in Poland, the USA and the USSR, where derivatives – the 7TP, the T1 and the T-26, respectively – were developed and manufactured partly under licence. The second of the export tanks was a derivative of the British Mk IV, and between 1933 and 1936 it attracted orders from many overseas nations.

Before his untimely death in an air crash in December 1935, John Carden also played a part in the development of the infantry tank, even if his contribution was, ultimately, to be largely set aside. In 1934, General Sir Hugh Elles, the former commanding officer of the Tank Corps and now Master General of the Ordnance, issued a directive for a new breed of tank designed to offer close support to assaulting infantry. Primarily, the tank would have to be invulnerable to the best and most effective AT weapons then available and have good rough-

ground performance. By the time Carden was approached in October 1935 to undertake the actual design of the vehicle to the A11 specification, it had been decided that the tank would be a heavily armoured small vehicle, armed only with machine guns and produced in large numbers. Carden was briefed accordingly, and the project was developed under the code name 'Matilda'. The name stuck, not just for the project, but for the tank that resulted – and then

got transferred to its successor. The Infantry Tank Mk I was clearly designed to a fixed price, and showed it. It met Elles's basic criteria well enough, and with 60mm (2.36in) of frontal armour was impervious to absolutely anything, except perhaps a heavy artillery shell at close range. But the severe restriction on the cost of the finished article meant that it rolled out of the Vickers factory as a two-man tank capable of about 11km/h (7mph), with a track and suspension system that was absolutely inadequate, and carrying one .303in Vickers machine gun in its turret. From the outset, those in the know questioned the tank's ultimate effectiveness and began a campaign to get the new vehicle replaced even before it entered service. Eventually, it was decided to limit production of the Infantry Tank Mk I to just 139 units, and specification A12 was issued to the Vulcan Foundry Co for what had by then become known as Matilda Senior. The result was as much a success as the original Matilda had been a failure. It was probably the best tank of its kind in the world at the time.

THE MATILDA

Specification A12 leaned heavily on the lessons learned in the A7 project. Indeed the tank in question had the same powerplant – twin 87hp AEC diesels – and running gear, along with the same main armament and a very similar turret to that found in the A7E3. In order to protect its four-man crew from anti-tank guns at close range, the A12's frontal armour was 78mm (3in) thick, diminishing to 13mm (.5in) in less vulnerable areas. As a result, the tank's all-up weight was almost 27 tonnes, making it the heaviest armoured vehicle contemplated in Britain since the aborted Mk VIII. In all, almost 3000 Infantry Tank Mk II Matildas were completed, in a variety of different forms and types, including a mine clearance variant. New types of diesel engines improved the power-to-weight ratio somewhat, but even in its final form, with paired 95hp Leyland engines, the Mk II Matilda could still manage no more than 24km/h (15mph) on the road, although its range was a respectable 260km (160 miles).

France, having shared with Britain the distinction of bringing armoured vehicles to the battlefield, faced similar problems to its ally in determining a direction for the development of the new weapon after the war was over. In 1921, a

development programme calling for two types of tank – a char de rupture (breakthrough tank) and a char de bataille (battle tank) – was formulated under the guidance of Jean-Baptiste Estienne, now a general. The ancestry of the breakthrough tank that ensued, the Char FCM 2C, can be traced back to 1916, by which time it was already clear that the Schneider and St Chamond tanks then going into production would not be up to the task demanded of them. Forges et Chantier de la Mediterranée (FCM) of Toulon was commissioned to produce a char lourd (heavy tank), and produced two prototypes of the 40-tonne Char 1A, built to a rhomboidal design, one with mechanical and one with electro-mechanical transmission. FCM also built a similar Char 1B, with a 105mm gun in place of the lighter 75mm weapon, the main armament being located in a top-mounted turret with 270-degree traverse. Neither version ever came to production, but the Jammy and Sabatier design formed the basis for the electro-mechanical 2C, which was a monster by any stretch of the imagination. It was the biggest, heaviest tank ever built, weighing in at 70 tonnes and measuring almost 10.5m (34ft) long and 4m (13ft) high. It carried a crew of 12 or 13 men, yet it was armed with just one 75mm gun and four 8mm machine guns, although with frontal armour 45mm (1.75in) thick, tapering off to 13mm (.5in) elsewhere, it was proof against anything it was likely to encounter on a battlefield besides a direct hit from heavy artillery firing armour-piercing rounds. Of 300 2Cs projected for the planned 1919 offensive, only 10 had been started – and just one delivered – by the time of the armistice, whereupon the order for further units was cancelled. The last of the 10 tanks started was delivered in 1922, and the type stayed in service right up until June 1940, when the six surviving operational 2Cs were knocked out while still on their railcars when Germany invaded.

THE CHAR B1

In the case of battle tanks, five proposals eventually came out of the 1921 programme, but it was 1927 before the prototypes were ordered – from FAMH, FCM and Renault/Schneider – of what was to become the Char B1. The specification called for a 15-tonne tank with a crew of four, to be armed with a hull-mounted 47mm or 75mm gun. When

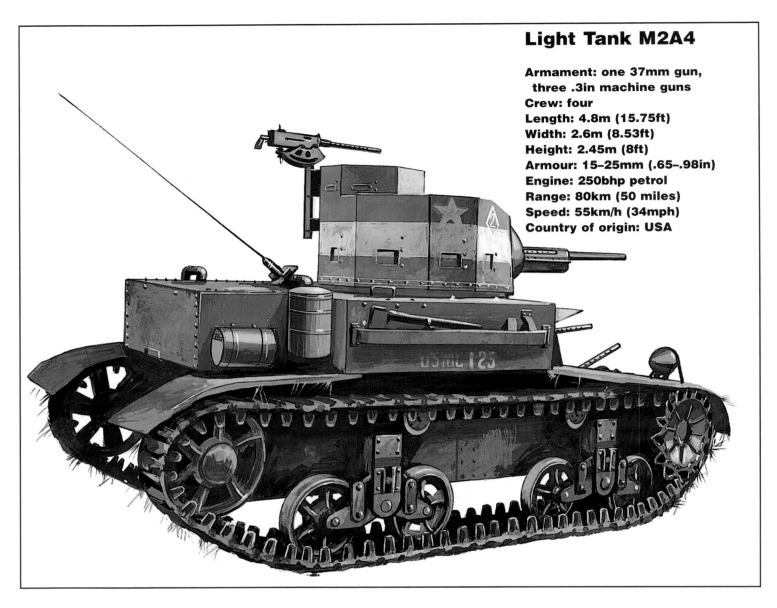

Light Tank M2A4

**Armament: one 37mm gun,
  three .3in machine guns
Crew: four
Length: 4.8m (15.75ft)
Width: 2.6m (8.53ft)
Height: 2.45m (8ft)
Armour: 15–25mm (.65–.98in)
Engine: 250bhp petrol
Range: 80km (50 miles)
Speed: 55km/h (34mph)
Country of origin: USA**

the prototypes appeared, between 1929 and 1931, they weighed around 25 tonnes. This was found to be acceptable, though, and after exhaustive trials, the tank was ordered into production with its armament supplemented by a 37mm gun in a turret with all-round traverse. Just 36 B1s were completed before a revised specification was issued for what was to be called the B1-bis, with armour up to 40mm (1.57in), a 47mm gun in its turret, and a 250hp engine to replace the original 180hp unit. A total of 365 had been produced when France was overrun in June 1940, by which time a yet more potent version, the B1-ter, had begun to appear. This model had armour up to a maximum thickness of 70mm (2.75in) and a 310hp engine to compensate for the extra weight.

By 1926, a replacement for the long-obsolete Renault FT was urgently needed in the light tank category. Money was tight, and the result was not a new

vehicle, but an updating of the FT into the Char NC1/NC27 and Char NC2/NC31. Neither was adopted by the French Army, although some were sold abroad. Then, in 1931, orders for a category of light tanks known as chars légers were placed with FCM, Hotchkiss and Renault, for what were to be the FCM-36, the H-38 and the R-35, respectively. The first to appear, the Renault, was a 10-tonne tank with a two-man crew, armed with a short-barrelled 37mm gun and a machine gun in its turret, powered by an 82hp petrol engine and armoured up to 45mm (1.75in). The main gun was never satisfactory and was replaced by a longer L/33 version. In all, some 300 of these tanks were produced for the French Army, and export orders were secured from Poland, Romania, Turkey and Yugoslavia. The R-35's main drawback was its relative slowness. A maximum speed of just 20km/h (12.5mph) was hardly what was expected

of a tank designed to exploit a breakthrough and support the cavalry. The FCM-36, when it appeared the following year, was essentially similar, but had a Ricardo-designed, Berliet-built diesel engine. This tank had a considerably greater range than the petrol-driven Renault – 320km (200 miles) against 140km (85 miles) – and a 25 per cent higher top speed. Nonetheless, the FCM-36 always took a back seat to the R-35/R-40, largely because only about 100 were ever produced. And it never received the more powerful SA 38 gun to replace its original SA 18.

THE HOTCHKISS H-38

The Hotchkiss H-35 also shared the same main armament as the R-35, but had considerably lighter armour. Before long, a revised specification, calling for armour of the same thickness as that found on the other two comparable vehicles, was

■LEFT: At the start of World War II the French Hotchkiss H-38 was the standard light tank of the French Army. Many were captured and pressed into service with German units following the fall of France, particularly after the huge losses on the Eastern Front.

At the same time that the AM programme was coming to fruition, the French Army also began to take delivery of yet another class of armoured vehicles. These were the chars moyens, which came between the chars lourds and the chars légers. Two vehicles fell into the char moyen category – the Char Renault D1 and the Char SOMUA S-35. They were distinctly different from one another in character. The former was classified as an infantry tank, whereas the latter, although it was 50 per cent heavier and better protected, was designated a cavalry tank. The Renault D1 first made an appearance in 1931. Mechanically it was a simple derivative of the NC1/NC27 light tank, fitted with a two-man cast-steel turret mounting a 37mm main gun and a co-axial machine gun. Armoured skirt plates protected its suspension. A 65hp engine combined with a combat weight of 12 tonnes, thanks to its 12–30mm (.5–1.18in) of armour, made the D1 a somewhat ponderous vehicle, with a top speed of just 18km/h (11mph). Satisfactory though the design was, it had never been intended as more than a first step, and was soon superseded by the upgunned and upengined D1B. In all, 160 D1s were produced between 1932 and 1935, by which time they were looking rather inadequate. In 1934 a new, improved version, the D2, went into production, with a more powerful 150hp engine and 20mm (.8in) of secondary armour, together with a 47mm gun. It had been envisaged that a total of 100 D2s would be produced, but it soon became obvious that the tank was decidedly inferior to the SOMUA S-35, and the order was halved.

THE SUPERIOR SOMUA S-35

From the outset, the SOMUA S-35 was clearly a very superior tank indeed. Principally, it was the first ever tank to have a cast-steel hull, rather than one fabricated from plates. The three individual castings, which varied in thickness from 20 to 56mm (.8 to 2.2in), were the lower hull, a rear upper casing and a front upper casing. These three huge components were bolted together.

issued, and was realised as the H-38. The H-38's 120hp petrol engine gave it a better top speed than either of the other two – 36km/h (23mph). Over the next two years, the H-38 was further uparmoured, and it also received the longer-barrelled SA 38 gun. It is widely accepted that these three tanks were the equal of their German counterparts in 1940. Their downfall came mainly as a result of the small number that were available and the way they were deployed – in small packets, rather than in strength.

To the British, the classification of the above tanks as 'light' was a little odd, but the French also had armoured vehicles which came closer to the British notion of what constituted a light tank. These were the auto-mitrailleuses (AMs), which translates as self-propelled machine guns. Tracked AMs came in two classes – auto-mitrailleuses de reconnaissance (AMR) and auto-mitrailleuses de combat (AMC). The four models of AM that entered service between 1933 and 1935 were all designed and produced (at least initially) by Renault. The company's Types VM and ZT were accepted as the AMR 33R and the AMR 35R respectively, and the heavier Types YR and ACG1 became the AMC 34R and AMC 35R.

HEAVIER AND HEAVIER

The Type VM was a 5-tonne vehicle with armour to a maximum of 13mm (.5in) and an 82hp petrol engine that gave it a road speed of 60km/h (38mph). It had a crew of two, and one 7.5mm machine gun

in a turret. The rather more sophisticated Type ZT was a little heavier at 6.5 tonnes, and although it had a slightly more powerful 85hp engine, it was somewhat slower as a result. The real improvement the ZT brought over the earlier vehicle was in its suspension system, which was sturdy enough to support even heavier vehicles and was used in later light and medium tanks. The ZT had heavier armament, too, and could mount the Hotchkiss 25mm anti-tank gun, a 13.2mm heavy machine gun or a 7.5mm machine gun. Some 200 ZTs were produced in all to complement the 125 AMR 33Rs then in service.

FRENCH CAVALRY TANKS

The automitrailleuses de combat were intended for hit-and-run cavalry operations, so they were designed primarily as fighting vehicles and not as reconnaissance vehicles with defensive armament. The AMC 34R was a simple adaptation of the AMR 33R, with a two-man turret mounting a 25mm gun and a co-axial 7.5mm machine gun. Despite its combat weight of almost 11 tonnes, the AMC 34R's 120hp engine gave it a respectable top speed of 40km/h (25 mph). The successor AMC 35R was a variant of the AMR 35R, uparmoured to a maximum of 25mm (1in) and armed with a 47mm main gun and a co-axial machine gun. The 180hp engine was enough to give a 40km/h (25mph) top speed, even though the all-up weight had increased to 14.5 tonnes.

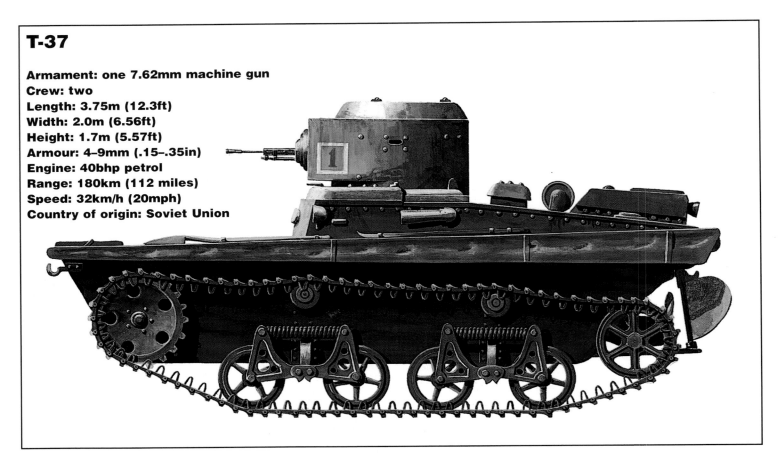

T-37

Armament: one 7.62mm machine gun
Crew: two
Length: 3.75m (12.3ft)
Width: 2.0m (6.56ft)
Height: 1.7m (5.57ft)
Armour: 4–9mm (.15–.35in)
Engine: 40bhp petrol
Range: 180km (112 miles)
Speed: 32km/h (20mph)
Country of origin: Soviet Union

The S-35's suspension was distinctly different from the coil-sprung bellcranks employed by Renault and Hotchkiss and employed nine roadwheels per side, four pairs and a single, covered by an armoured skirt plate. The cast turret was electrically powered and mounted the 47mm SA 35 gun and a co-axial machine gun with a small degree of independence of movement. If the tank had a major fault, beyond the weak points where it was bolted together, it was that it could carry just 18 rounds of main gun ammunition. Despite an all-up weight of over 20 tonnes, the S-35 could achieve 40km/h (25mph), thanks to its 190hp petrol engine; and its 410 litres (110 US gallons) of fuel gave it a very useful 260km (160-mile) range. The vehicle's success can be gauged from the fact that more than 500 were produced in four years. In 1940, an improved version, with modified suspension and a 220hp engine, started to come off the production lines, but very few S-40s, as they were designated, ever made it to frontline units.

THE UNITED STATES OF AMERICA

By the closing months of 1918, the US Army was poised to throw itself wholeheartedly into a European war that it had been slow to enter. One result of

US involvement in the war was huge orders for tanks. And then came the armistice, and with it the cancellation of all tank projects and the demobilisation of millions of men. The US Army found itself back at peacetime establishment in very short order, and in 1920, its tank corps ceased to exist altogether. Responsibility for such armoured operations as there were passed to the infantry. There was a great danger of armoured vehicle development coming to a complete halt, but this was averted by the formation, in 1922, of the Tank Board, charged with both developing strategic and tactical policy and specifying vehicles capable of carrying it out. The board opted for a combination of light and medium tanks. The former were to be armed with machine guns only, weigh in at 5 tonnes, and be transportable over long distances by road on trucks. The latter were to mount a 37mm gun and a machine gun, be limited in weight to the 15 tonnes capacity of contemporary bridging equipment and be capable of 20km/h (12mph).

The US Army had successfully operated Renault FTs during the war and had ordered almost 4500 from American manufacturers just before the armistice. It therefore comes as no real surprise to find that the design specification for the

light tank bore a considerable resemblance to the French vehicle, although the design was modified considerably to make the tank easier to produce. As its name suggests, the Six-Ton Tank, or M1917, was a little over the weight limit, but otherwise it met its specification fairly well. Its 42hp Buda engine was never quite powerful enough, however, and was being replaced in new vehicles with a 100hp air-cooled Franklin power unit when in 1929 a radical rethink halted the development programme in favour of a wholly new vehicle.

ROCK ISLAND'S TANKS

The first prototype of the M1917's replacement, designated T1E1, was a two-man tank, almost 7 tonnes in weight and armed with a 37mm gun and a .30-calibre machine gun. Its 105hp engine gave it a top speed of 32km/h (20mph), but with armour only 9.5mm (.37in) thick at most, the tank would have been very vulnerable indeed, even to light AT fire. The final version, the T1E6, was a better proposition, having been uparmoured and upengined. In 1933, the Rock Island Arsenal took over the project, rolling out the T2E1 and T2E2 prototypes the following year. They had Vickers-Armstrong-pattern suspension and were armed with a .5in and a .3in machine gun in a cylindrical, slope-top turret. Power came from a modified Continental radial aircraft engine that developed 250hp. Small production orders were placed for what came to be the M2A1 and M2A2 light tanks, 8.5-tonne vehicles capable of 72km/h (45mph). The M2A2 went through a considerable development programme and was tried out with a variety of engines, heavier armour and different turret designs. In 1938 a modified version on a longer wheelbase, designated the M2A3, was put into production, and the following year its twin turrets gave way to a single unit mounting a 37mm gun and a pair of machine guns in side sponsons. The frontal armour of what was now the M2A4 was thickened to 25mm (1in), which increased the tank's all-up weight to about 10.5 tonnes. Nonetheless, the original 250hp engine still bowled it along at a respectable 55km/h (35mph). In all, some 375 M2A4s were produced, and they were to be most valuable as training tools in 1940 and 1941, even though they were technically obsolete by then. Some even saw action against the Japanese at the very outbreak of war in the Pacific theatre. The same basic design of tank was adopted for the US Cavalry as part of the wholesale mechanisation programme put in train by then Chief of Staff General Douglas MacArthur in 1932. It was originally designated the Combat Car M1 but in 1940 became the Light Tank M1A2.

AMERICAN MEDIUMS

Medium tank design in the United States immediately after World War I went down two distinctly different paths. On the one hand, there were tanks developed by the US Army; on the other, a series of private initiatives, largely the work of Walter Christie. The 'official' designs began with a set of proposals from the Caliber Board, which put forward a plan for an 18-tonne, four/five man tank, mounting either a 57mm or a 76mm main gun and with protection enough to stop a 12.7mm/.5in anti-tank round, such as that fired by the German T-Gew, at close range. The result saw the light of day in 1922 as the Medium Tank A, or M1921, which was obsolete before it even turned a track, but which provided valuable experience to designers and engineers quite new to the task at hand. A revised version was constructed at the Rock Island Arsenal as the Medium Tank

M1922, which was basically similar to the M1921 but with a flexible track and cable suspension system along the lines of that fitted to the British Medium Mk D. The M1922 also had a considerable rise to the rear, which was intended to increase traction when the tank was climbing obstacles or out of trenches. Despite being 4 tonnes heavier than the M1921, the M1922 was 50 per cent faster, with a maximum road speed of 24km/h (15mph). It carried the same armament arrangement as its predecessor – a 57mm gun and a co-axial machine gun in the main turret and a second machine gun in an independent superimposed turret. Even though this layout made the tank tall and difficult to conceal, it was continued into the Medium Tank T1, built in 1925.

WALTER CHRISTIE'S TANKS

The T1 design reverted to the more conventional track and suspension system used in the M1921, and the single example built was used as the basis for a

■ABOVE: French tank crews popularised the practice of christening their machines. Note the unusual crew access door on this Char B1-bis, which first entered service in 1937.

testing programme. The T1 was joined, over the decade that followed, by other experimental vehicles, until a T5 design was adopted as the Medium Tank M2 in June 1939. It was provided with a 37mm main gun and no fewer than eight .30-calibre machine guns, in line with its main role of close support of infantry operations. However, less in keeping with the accepted specification for an infantry tank was its performance. A 350hp Wright radial engine gave the Medium Tank M2 a top speed of 40km/h (25mph), despite an all-up weight, with the six-man crew, of over 17 tonnes. Also unusual for an infantry tank was the vehicle's mere 25mm (1in) of armour. There was considerable concern at the meagreness of the M2's protection, and this was improved by 25 per cent in the

T-28

Armament: one 76.2mm gun, two 7.62mm machine guns
Crew: six
Length: 7.4m (24.3ft)
Width: 2.8m (9.2ft)
Height: 2.8m (9.2ft)
Armour: 10–30mm (.4–1.18in)
Engine: 500bhp petrol
Range: 220km (136 miles)
Speed: 37km/h (23mph)
Country of origin: Soviet Union

tank's successor, the M2A1, which appeared in 1940. Even this left the M2A1 lightly protected compared with similar classes of tank.

Walter Christie, meanwhile, had come to tanks via the manufacture of civilian vehicles and the design of self-propelled (SP) gun carriages. He was convinced, in accordance with the ideas of British tank officer and armoured warfare theorist J.F.C. Fuller and others, that the future of the tank on the battlefield lay not in close support of infantry operations, but in the sort of offensive manoeuvres usually reserved for the cavalry. He saw the tank carrying out long-range penetration missions, with speed, tactical agility and surprise taking the place of heavy armour-plating as a means of protection. In 1919, Christie began work on designs for a tank capable of moving at high speed over open country, rather than one optimised for operations in an environment of barbed wire, trenches and pillboxes.

M1919 TO M1921

There were two main considerations in designing such a tank – the vehicle's power-to-weight ratio and its suspension system. Even in his first tank, the M1919, Christie opted for having both wheels and tracks. Wheels were to be used for high-speed strategic transit on

the road; tracks for tactical operations across open country. The vehicle was fitted with four rubber-tyred roadwheels over which the tracks ran when in place. The tracks' tension and the vehicle's rough-terrain traction was maintained by paired, coil-sprung rollers together with a track-return roller mounted above them that could be raised out of the way when the tracks were removed for road running. Christie had in mind a versatile all-terrain vehicle when he designed the M1919. The box-like area in the centre of the vehicle, between the forward driving position and the rear-mounted engine and transmission, could be used as cargo space or to mount a turret and secondary armament. When fitted out as a fighting vehicle, the M1919 had a single, large (for its day) circular turret carrying a 57mm gun, superimposed on which was a smaller, independent, domed turret mounting a machine gun. Both turrets had 360-degree traverse. The tank had 25mm (1in) of primary armour, 7mm (.25in) of secondary protection and an all-up weight, with its crew of four, of 12.25 tonnes. It was underpowered, though, its 120hp powerplant giving it a fairly pedestrian top speed of 11km/h (7mph).

The M1919 design was extensively revised the following year, the resulting vehicle being similar only in its powerplant and track/suspension layout.

The fighting compartment had been moved to the front, while the driver and commander were positioned in the centre. The turrets were deleted in favour of a ball-mounted 57mm gun set into the front plate along with two co-axial .30-calibre machine guns. The main armour was reduced to 19mm (.75in). The lighter all-up weight doubled the M1921's top speed, while detail improvements to the suspension, including the fitting of larger-diameter roadwheels, also helped performance as well as improving the ride quality. To someone actually concerned with fighting in an armoured vehicle, the M1921 appeared as a retrograde step. Not only was its protection thinned down, but the location of its armament would have put it at a serious disadvantage in a running fight. To Christie, however, this was of secondary importance. The M1921 was never meant to be the basis for an operational tank, but was, rather, a design exercise. It excited little interest.

CHRISTIE'S M1928

Christie subsequently slipped from view for six years, resurfacing in 1928 with a new company – the US Wheel and Track Layer Corporation – and a new tank design. Gone were the paired small-diameter rollers and their accompanying track-return roller, and in their place

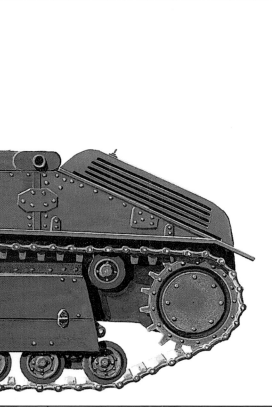

performance indeed, running at 115km/h (70mph) on its wheels on the road and at 48km/h (30mph) on its tracks across rough terrain. It also showed itself capable of crossing obstacles that other tracked vehicles of the day found impossible to negotiate. The assessors, who included a certain Major George Patton and a Lieutenant-Colonel Adna Chaffee, unanimously recommended acceptance, and Christie received an order for five vehicles, the first of which was delivered in September 1931.

The M1928 was evaluated operationally by both the infantry – still,

Tank T5 and Combat Car T2 had Vickers-type small wheels mounted on leaf-sprung bogies to begin with. Later, vertical volute springing was used, which retained the two small wheels per bogie but replaced the leaf springs with coil springs in the bogie mountings, as originally developed for the Light Tank M2A1. Christie went on designing and building tanks but never with any degree of personal success, although he did sell one, the M1937, to the British. They drew heavily on elements of its design, particularly the suspension, for their cruiser tank programme that culminated

T-40 Amphibious Light Tank

Armament: one 12.7 or 20mm gun,
  one 7.62mm machine gun
Crew: two
Length: 4.3m (14ft)
Width: 2.3m (7.6ft)

Height: 2m (6.5ft)
Armour: 10–14mm (.39–.55in)
Engine: 85bhp petrol
Range: 350km (217 miles)
Speed: 42km/h (26mph)
Country of origin: Soviet Union

appeared full-diameter rubber-tyred roadwheels, four to a side. The track, when fitted, ran over them and over smaller idler wheels at front and rear. The roadwheels were suspended on short, cranked arms, which were in turn hung on coil springs located within the vehicle's double-skinned side panels. The 385hp Liberty-engined M1928 was evaluated by the US Army in October 1930 and put up a very impressive

then, in charge of tank operations – as the Medium Tank T3 and by the cavalry as the Combat Car T1. But when Christie refused to make certain changes to the tank's design to bring it more in line with the specification, he fell out of favour. Responsibility for the US Army's medium tank project was handed over to the Rock Island Arsenal, which promptly reverted to a more conventional suspension arrangement for its designs. The Medium

in the all-round best of the breed, the A27 Cruiser Tank Mk VIII 'Cromwell'.

THE SOVIET UNION
Tank production in the Soviet Union began in 1919 with the local manufacture of a 7-tonne version of the Renault FT. The Krasno-Sormova (KS), as the little tank was called, looked virtually identical to the French original but differed from it in two respects – it had a 45hp FIAT

engine and an American-designed gearbox. That same year, the Treaty of Versailles codified the Allies' revenge on Germany for the destruction caused by the war just ended. One of its provisions banned the Germans from manufacturing or operating tanks, and to circumvent that restriction the Germans looked to two areas outside their own borders. In Sweden, the German-designed LKII light tank went into production in 1921. In the Soviet Union, meanwhile, a secret tank development establishment and proving ground was created near the city of Kazan, 600km (400 miles) east of Moscow. This centre provided the Germans with the means of sustaining a continuing armoured vehicle development programme, in return for giving the Soviet government much-needed insight into modern tank design, even though it was to be some time before the Soviets were able to capitalise on it.

SOVIET COPIES

Using the KS as a basis, the Soviet War Department Tank Bureau evolved the first Russian-designed tracked armoured vehicles, the Maily Soprovozhdieniya (MS), or 'small support tanks', series, which, not surprisingly, leaned heavily on the French NC1/NC27. The MS-1 went into production in 1928 and entered service as the T-18. Over the next three years, around 1000 of these were built in three variants. The T-18 was lighter and more powerful than the KS, and its success influenced the Soviet armour policy then being formulated.

In 1929, the first Soviet Five Year Plan was put into effect, with one of its subsidiary aims being the mechanisation of the Red Army. Accordingly, plans were drawn up for a selection of tanks, but without any really notable early success.

■ABOVE: The Soviet T-26 (like the 7TP) was an improved licence-built copy of the Vickers 6-ton light tank, although significant upgrades were made to the original armament and protection in later models. One experimental model – the AT-1 – was designed to be fitted with wings and a tailplane, and then flown into battle.

A prototype heavy tank, the T-12, was abandoned as unreliable in 1930 and was followed by a series of other designs – the T-17 and T-23, which were one- and two-man tankettes; the T-19, T-20 and T-21 two-man light tanks; the T-24 three-man medium tank; and the TG heavy tank. None of these fared much better than the T-12. As well as developing their own ideas, Soviet designers purchased several British tanks, including the Vickers Six-Ton and the Medium Mk II, as well as a variety of Carden-Loyd tankettes and carriers, and it is not surprising that elements of these vehicles' design crept into Soviet tank technology. Indeed, some vehicles were put into local production virtually unchanged in principle. The Six-Ton Tank was manufactured as the T-26, for example, the Carden-Loyd Mk VI as the T-27 tankette, and the A4E11 as the T-37/T-38 light tank. Many of these vehicles were then developed to a considerable extent. The T-26, for example, appeared with twin turrets, each mounting a single 7.62mm machine gun, and with a single turret mounting either a 27mm or a 45mm main gun as well as a co-axial machine gun. By the time it appeared in the latter form, the T-26's all-up weight had gone from just over 7 tonnes to just over 10. And since it had not been upengined in the process, its performance had fallen off a good deal. It is not surprising, either, that British

tanks bought by the Russians also found their way into German hands, and that German designers plagiarised them, too. The Russian designers also looked further afield than Britain for inspiration, though. Late in 1931, they acquired, along with two prototype Christie M1928s, a licence to the Americans' suspension system, and put a medium tank thus equipped into limited production as the first Bistrokhodny Tankoi (BT), or 'fast tank'. Fast it most certainly was, by the standards of the day. It could manage 65km/h (40mph) on its tracks and 110km/h (68mph) on its rubber-tyred roadwheels with the tracks removed. Christie's design had proved its point yet again.

The BT-1s and BT-2s were very much state-of-the-art tanks in terms of their performance, although they were design

7 TP Light Tank
Armament: one 37mm gun,
 one 7.92mm machine gun
Crew: three
Length: 4.6m (15ft)
Width: 2.4m (7.9ft)
Height: 2.16m (7.1ft)
Armour: 7-40mm (.27-1.57in)
Engine: 110bhp diesel
Range: 160km (100 miles)
Speed: 32km/h (19.9mph)
Country of origin: Poland

exercises, rather than serious attempts to field a new type of vehicle. The later variant mounted a 37mm M1930 gun, which put its combat weight up to just over 11 tonnes, but improvements to the Soviet-modified Liberty engine that powered it kept the tank's performance up to that of its lighter older brother. The first BT model to go into serious production was the BT-5 of 1935. This had an enlarged turret, which mounted an M1935 45mm L/46 gun, and a new engine, developed from a Hispano-Suiza design. The BT-5 was followed by the BT-7, with thicker armour of largely welded, rather than riveted, construction, which varied between 7mm (.25in) and 22mm (.86in). The BT-7's engine was uprated to deliver 450hp, and a version with a 500hp diesel engine was also produced in limited numbers. Christie's

suspension principles – but without the option of running on roadwheels alone – were also applied to the T-34 of 1940, the best and most important tank of its day.

THE T-28
Even while the early BTs were proving their worth in 1931, a design team at the Kirov factory in Leningrad was setting out to produce a specification for what eventually turned out to be a six-man medium tank, although at 29 tonnes it was a heavyweight by most standards. The tank's suspension, along with other features such as multiple turrets, bore a suspiciously close resemblance to the still-secret British A6 specification. Indeed, the Soviets had access to this specification, having stolen the plans. The T-28, as the resultant vehicle was known when it entered service in 1934, proved

reliable. Although it was a little slow, with a maximum speed of 37km/h (23mph), the tank seemed well protected, with frontal armour 30mm (.4in) thick and secondary armour 10mm (1.2in) thick. In addition, the T-28 had good obstacle-crossing capability and advanced features such as a stabilisation system for its 76mm main gun – something as yet unheard-of in other European designs. In fact, by the time it went into action, against the Finns and the Japanese in 1939, the T-28's armour was found to be insufficient, and the improved T-28C was developed, uparmoured to 80mm (3.15in) and 40mm (1.6in) by the application of add-on plates.

The T-28s were soon supplemented by the even heavier, 45-tonne T-32 and 50-tonne T-35 – tanks with a strong conceptual link with the British

CA.11 Medium Tank (M11/39)

Armament: one 37mm gun, two 8mm machine guns
Crew: three
Length: 4.73m (15.5ft)
Width: 2.18m (7.1ft)
Height: 2.3m (7.5ft)
Armour: 6–30mm (.24–1.18in)
Engine: 105bhp diesel
Range: 200km (125 miles)
Speed: 33.8km/h (21mph)
Country of origin: Italy

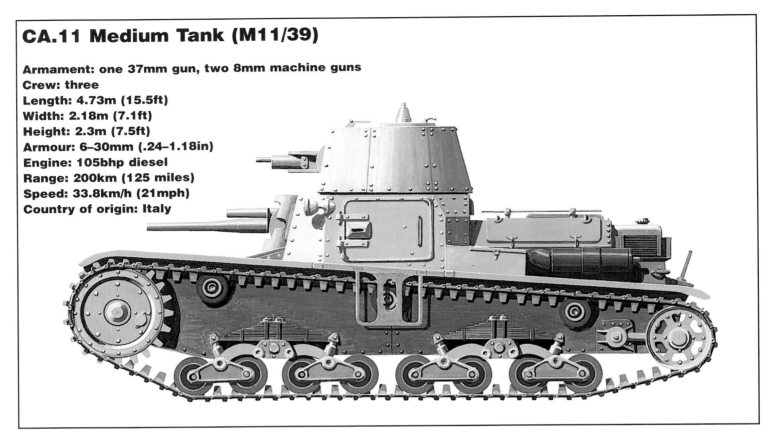

Independent. Like the A1E1, each had four secondary turrets to back up the main, which was armed with a 76mm gun. Two of the secondaries carried high-velocity anti-tank guns (37mm in the T-32; 45mm in the T-35), and the other two mounted 7.62mm machine guns. Additional machine guns in co-axial mounts were carried in the three heavy turrets and a further flexibly mounted gun was fitted in the frontal glacis plate. Enhanced-performance Liberty-derived engines (350hp in the earlier version; 500hp in the later) gave these monsters adequate performance for infantry tanks. They were eventually joined in service by the 57-tonne T-100 and the 46-tonne SMK. Both had their secondary turret superimposed on the primary. The primary, with its 76mm gun, had 360-degree traverse, while the secondary, with a 45mm gun, was capable of rotating through 300 degrees. Both tanks also had three tertiary turrets, mounting machine guns. Unsurprisingly, this arrangement led to the vehicles standing over 3m (10ft) high, and that made them extremely vulnerable. They saw action in the Winter War against Finland in 1939-40, but were soon withdrawn, as were the T-32s and T-35s. The multi-turret design, of which these Soviet tanks were by far the most exaggerated examples, was finally discredited. It was vulnerable

because of the shot-traps it created, and inefficient because of the number of men it required to crew the multiple turrets. That is not to say that tanks with more than one heavy gun emplacement then disappeared – far from it.

POLAND

The Polish Army of 1920 had small numbers of captured German A7V tanks and also some FTs acquired from Poland's ally France. Both these types played an important part in the eventual Polish victory over the Soviets in the Eastern European conflict that followed World War I. The tanks' role was not lost on the Polish High Command, and as soon as it was economically feasible, Poland embarked on a modest tank development programme of its own. The first phase, which initially called for the development in parallel of a new light tank and a 'breakthrough' medium tank, was eventually concentrated on the 12-tonne WB-10, which was to have had a 47mm gun, a top speed of 25km/h (15mph) and a range of more than 200km (125 miles). In the event, the WB-10 came to nothing and was abandoned. Then, in 1928, the Polish Army acquired a Carden-Loyd Mk VI tankette from Vickers, and this led to the development of a series of indigenous tankettes, the first of which to go into production was the TK.3. This 2.5-

tonne, two-man weapons carrier was armed with a single 7.92mm machine gun (some were later rearmed with 20mm cannon), had a 40hp Ford Model A engine and was protected by primary armour 8mm (.3in) thick. Some 300 TK.3s were delivered in all and equipped the Polish Army's fledgling armoured corps from 1930. The TK.3's designers hit on a novel means of saving on track wear if the tankettes had to travel any distance by road. They produced a four-wheel trailer that could be towed along behind the tankette, and onto which the TK.3 could be driven. Once on the trailer, the tankette's tracks were removed, and drive chains fixed between the drive sprockets and similar fixtures on the trailer's rear hubs. The ensemble was then steered by the tankette's driver via the vehicle's clutches in the ordinary way.

POLISH TKS

The TKS was an improved version of the TK.3. Its armament was still one 7.92mm machine gun but its armour was slightly heavier – up to 10mm (.4in) thick. The TKS had wider tracks, heavier-duty suspension and a locally produced FIAT engine. It went into production in 1933, and in all some 390 went into service. The following year, the TKW reached the prototype stage. The TKW was a modified version of the TKS with a small turret to

RIGHT: A command version of the PzKpfw I leads a parade of German armour through Berlin. Mussolini looks on in admiration, flanked by Reichsmarshall Göring, Admiral Dönitz and the Führer, Adolf Hitler.

accommodate the commander and a heavy machine gun. It was abandoned, and in 1936 another unsuccessful attempt to improve upon the TKS saw a 27mm Bofors anti-tank gun replace the machine gun in a strengthened front plate. The third and last stillborn development of the TKS was the TKF, which had an uprated engine and a secondary, probably 9mm, machine gun mounted as an anti-aircraft weapon.

POLAND'S TANK PLANS

The Poles were also taken with another Vickers product – the Six-Ton Tank Mk E. They manufactured a twin-turret vehicle very similar to the original Type A as the 7 TP light tank, with primary armour 17mm (.67in) thick and a 110hp Saurer diesel powerplant. This was the first time a compression-ignition engine had been fitted to a production tank. When it entered service in 1934, with a crew of three, two 7.92mm machine guns and an all-up weight just short of 10 tonnes, the 7 TP was a rather better vehicle than the original that had inspired it. It was succeeded in 1937 by a revised version, the 7 TP jw, with but a single turret mounting a 37mm Bofors anti-tank gun and a co-axial machine gun. The 7 TP jw had been uparmoured to 40mm (1.6in) and had strengthened suspension to suit.

In the 1930s, the Poles embarked on an ambitious tank design programme. The 10 TP was to have been a four-man fast tank very similar to Christie's M1928, capable of wheel-or-track operation and armed with a 37mm main gun in a turret and a second weapon in the front plate. A development, the generally similar but uparmoured 14 TP, followed the Russian practice and dispensed with the capability to run on

wheels. The heavier 20/25 TP was a multi-turreted heavy tank with 'conventional' bogie rollers, while at the other end of the scale altogether, the 4 TP was a light tank, best known in its amphibious version. All four of these

vehicles were still in the development phase when Poland was overrun in September 1939 and all such ventures came to an abrupt halt.

Like so many other countries, Czechoslovakia first satisfied its

RIGHT: Bypassing a demolished bridge, a detachment of PzKpfw I Ausf B light tanks advances deeper into France. Fast and highly manoeuvrable, the PzKpfw I had been an ideal weapon for the Blitzkrieg in Poland. However, the Führer's panzer regiments encountered stiffer opposition from the French Army in 1940.

■RIGHT: The Japanese Type 95 'Ha-Go' was produced in great numbers between 1933 and 1942, seeing service in the Japanese conflict with China in 1937 and throughout World War II.

requirement for armoured vehicles by importing Renault FTs from France, and – also like many other countries – then used the operational experience it gained to formulate a strategic 'tank policy' and a basis for design development. In the early 1920s, Josef Vollmer, formerly chief designer at the German War Department's motor vehicle section, came to Prague. He joined the armaments manufacturer Skoda and set to work on the design for a wheel/track light tank, the KH.50. The system used was different from that of Christie's in that the KH.50 had roadwheels mounted on the drive sprockets and a jockey wheel behind to keep the tracks up off the ground. Despite an impressive specification – 13mm (.5in) of armour, a 37mm turret-mounted gun and a 50hp engine capable of pushing the light tank along at 12km/h (8mph) on its tracks and 35km/h (22mph) on its wheels – the Czech Army rejected the KH.50. Even so, the army clung to

the hybrid Kolohousenka wheel/track arrangement and commissioned further design studies along the same lines. First came the KH.60, with heavier armour and a 60hp engine, and then the KH.70, with a 70hp engine and a better system for switching between wheel and track operation.

The tankette concept also caught the Czech fancy, and several examples of Carden-Loyd carriers were obtained from Vickers. Both Skoda-Tatra and

CKD/Praga pushed ahead with design studies, the S-I and the P-I respectively. The CKD/Praga design was available for evaluation ahead of its rival, and was ordered into limited production as the Tancik (tankette) T-33 even though it was essentially inferior to the S-I. The P-I was a 2.5-tonne, two-man weapons carrier, very much like the original Carden-Loyd Mk VI and the Polish TK.3. It had heavier armour than its Polish counterpart, and two machine guns, not

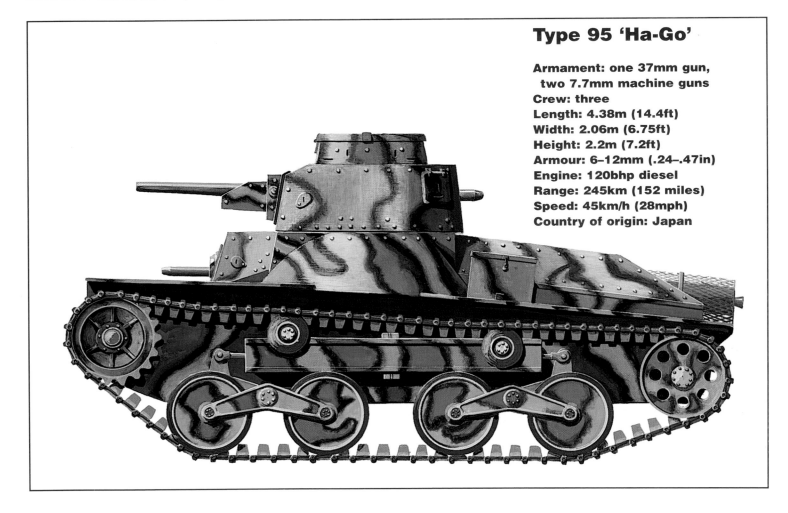

Type 95 'Ha-Go'

**Armament: one 37mm gun,
 two 7.7mm machine guns
Crew: three
Length: 4.38m (14.4ft)
Width: 2.06m (6.75ft)
Height: 2.2m (7.2ft)
Armour: 6–12mm (.24–.47in)
Engine: 120bhp diesel
Range: 245km (152 miles)
Speed: 45km/h (28mph)
Country of origin: Japan**

one, mounted in the front plate of the crew compartment. A 31hp engine limited its maximum speed to a rather mundane 35km/h (22mph), and it was widely criticised for both its poor cross-country performance and its poor ride on the road. The rival S-I (also called the T-1/MU-4) was a rather better performer, thanks to its 40hp engine, but was otherwise very similar.

THE TNHB

The S-I was later developed into the S-Id heavy tankette, with a 50 per cent more powerful engine. Despite being almost twice as heavy as the S-I, at 4.5 tonnes – thanks to having been uparmoured to a maximum of 15mm (.6in) and having a 47mm gun added – the S-Id still managed a creditable top speed on the road of 45km/h (28mph). It went into production for Yugoslavia, and later for Romania. The P-I was developed, too, into the P-II light tank, better known as the LT-34. In 1934, the LT-34 became the first true tank to have been designed and produced in Czechoslovakia to enter service with the Czech Army. Designated the TNHB, it had a crew of four, a 37mm main gun and two machine guns, plus a maximum of 15mm (.6in) of armour. The 62hp Praga petrol engine gave the 7.5-tonne vehicle a respectable top speed of 40km/h (25mph) and good off-road performance too. The TNHB's suspension system consisted of four pairs of small rollers mounted on bogies, which in turn were mounted on a leaf-sprung beam. This arrangement was later scrapped in favour of four larger-diameter roadwheels

mounted on cranked stub axles, each pair of which was in turn mounted on leaf springs. The drive sprockets were at the front and the idlers at the rear, and there were four track-return rollers initially. The large-wheeled variant had only two, with the rear roadwheel doing double duty. CKD also produced the tank for export and sold versions to half a dozen countries under a bewildering array of designations and with usually detailed but sometimes considerable differences in specification. The most important of the export orders was from Sweden, where the tank was later put into production under licence by Scania-Vabis, who also built a scaled-down two-man version, the AH-IV-Sv/Strv m/37.

CZECH EXCELLENCE

By far the most important result of the P-II/LT-34 export programme was the realisation that the vehicle was capable of considerable further development. A committee set up in October 1937 to evaluate Czech tank production recommended that a new specification for a light tank be issued, and it was an updated and modified version of the TNHB that emerged as by far the most effective candidate. The 9-tonne TNHP, or LT-38, as the production model of the new tank became known, was to be recognised as the most important light tank of its period – a classic of its type.

Unlike many of its contemporaries, the TNHP was a properly balanced vehicle, whose designers had managed to stay within the confines of their working brief in the three major areas of performance,

protection and firepower. They had traded off where necessary, but had never gone beyond the margins of workability. Certainly, the tank's 37mm L/48 Skoda-developed A-7 main gun was no world-beater, but it was effective. The 7.92mm vz37 machine gun, meanwhile, of which the TNHP had two, was probably the best gun of its type at the time and was the original of the Besa, which the British Army adopted so readily for the same role. The TNHP's 125hp EPA petrol engine gave it a top speed on the road of 55km/h (35mph), while its 225-litre (60 US gallon) fuel tank gave it a range of more than 250km (150 miles). The tank's main weakness was its riveted construction. Rivets have to be of relatively soft metal and tended, if hit full on, to turn into lethal projectiles flying around inside the tank. However, given the cost considerations and the technology available, there was little to be done about that.

THE PZKPFW 38(t)

Initially, the Czech Army ordered 150 TNHPs. Delivery did not commence until March 1939, and few if any had actually reached their units when the Germans occupied Bohemia and Moravia and placed Slovakia under their protection midway through that month. The order for TNHPs, now known as the PzKpfw 38(t) Ausf A, was completed for the German forces, and a further 325 units with minor modifications were ordered before the year's end as the Ausf B, C and D. The Czech tanks played an important role in the Battle of France in the summer of 1940, and in the light of experience gained there, further changes were ordered. Frontal armour was increased from 30 to 40mm (1.2 to 1.6in), and turret and side armour was thickened, too, while better vision slits for the driver and hull gunner were devised. Five hundred and twenty-five of what were known as the Ausf E and F were produced between November 1940 and October 1941, by which time 90 Ausf Gs had also been ordered. This model

■LEFT: With World War II looming on the horizon, it was clear that German tank technology, embodied by these PzKpfw II's, was far in advance of the rest of the world. Part of the reason for this was the fact that at least one tank in a four-tank detachment was equipped with radio, making coordinated attacks far easier.

PzKpfw IB (SdKfz 265) Befehlswagen (Command Vehicle)

Armament: one 7.92mm machine gun
Crew: three
Length: 4.45m (14.6ft)
Width: 2.1m (6.9ft)
Height: 1.99m (6.53ft)
Armour: 7-13mm (.27–.51in)
Engine: 100bhp petrol
Range: 155km (96 miles)
Speed: 40km/h (25mph)
Country of origin: Germany

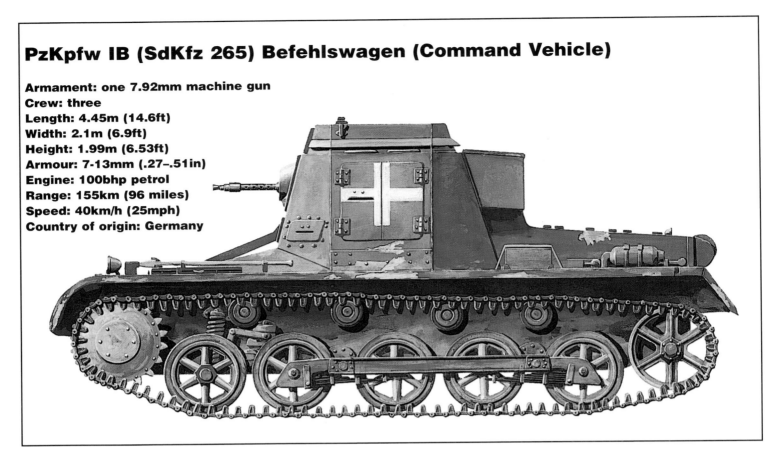

came with the frontal armour further increased to 50mm (2in) and the hull extensively redesigned so that the tank could be assembled by welding instead of riveting. The Ausf E, F and G tanks had an engine uprated to 150hp, but still suffered up to a 20 per cent reduction in top speed over earlier models, thanks to the added weight of their extra armour. Three hundred and twenty tanks ordered by the Swedish Government were also appropriated by the German Army as the Ausf S, the Swedish company Scania being granted a licence to manufacture them. In all, some 1600 TNHP/PzKpfw 38(t)s were produced, and the majority of them saw service with the German Army's Light Panzer Divisions.

ITALY'S ARMOURED PHILOSOPHY

The Italian Army's philosophy of armoured operations did not encompass any vehicle heavier than 14 tonnes until 1940, when Mussolini's ambitions of conquest led to a radical rethink of roles. A heavier tank than those then available, it was decided, was essential, and a design for a vehicle of around 25 tonnes with 40mm (1.6in) frontal armour and a 75mm main gun was commissioned. The P tank (P for 'pesante', or 'heavy') that resulted had a slow and awkward gestation. Four designs for what was to

become the P.75/40 (or P.26/40) were presented to the Inspector of Mechanised Forces, General Di Feroleto – two from the Army's own mechanisation department, the others from Ansaldo. One of Ansaldo's vehicles was chosen and ordered into production just before the end of 1940. A prototype was finally available for testing the following October. It had 50mm (2in) of frontal armour, the low-velocity 75mm L/18 gun, along with a 20mm Breda cannon in a co-axial mount, suspension taken straight from the medium tank and a 330hp diesel engine. Over the course of the next six months, the gun was changed first to the L/32 and then to the much more effective L/34, and the cannon gave way to a single 8mm Modello 38 machine gun. Production of the tank was finally authorised in May 1942. Belatedly, it was decided to substitute a 420hp petrol engine for the compression-ignition powerplant, and the changeover caused more delays. It was 1943 before production finally began, and in the event just 21 had been completed before Italy capitulated and made a separate peace with the Allies in September of that year.

The P.26/40 was technically obsolescent before it reached the units that were to operate it, although that was (and still is) far from unusual, especially

considering the protracted period between the design being submitted and production commencing. It is worth remembering, perhaps, that Italy's supplies of raw materials were severely limited, and the tank programme in general, and this segment of it in particular, had a low priority. In any case, by the time production started, plans were being drawn up for a successor – the P.43 – which had a larger, lower turret with a better ballistic profile, and a cupola for the commander; and for an improved interim version – the P.26/40 bis – with the new turret but without the cupola. Neither plan came to fruition.

Under the Treaty of Versailles, signed on 28 June 1919, Germany was forbidden to develop, manufacture or operate tanks. Nonetheless, during the 1920s, the German Government called on its major armament manufacturers to submit outline design proposals and even to produce experimental tracked vehicles.

It was the start of 1934 before a new medium tank design was commissioned as the Panzer Kampfwagen Neubaufahrzeug (PzKpfw NbFz). It had a six-man crew and mounted a large-calibre, low-velocity gun. Two versions of the prototype were constructed – the A had a Krupp turret with a 105mm gun and a 37mm gun in a superimposed co-

PzKpfw IB (SdKfz 101)

Armament: two 7.92mm machine guns
Crew: two
Length: 4.45m (14.61ft)
Width: 2.1m (6.9ft)
Height: 1.72m (5.66ft)
Armour: 7–13mm (.27–.51in)
Engine: 100bhp petrol
Range: 155km (96 miles)
Speed: 40km/h (25mph)
Country of origin: Germany

axial mounting; the B had a turret from Rheinmetall with a 75mm gun and a 37mm gun in a side-by-side co-axial mount. Both had two subsidiary turrets armed with two MG13 7.92mm machine guns and placed right-front and left-rear. The tanks had 500hp petrol engines, which gave them a maximum speed of around 35km/h (22mph). Their suspension, which was derived from the Rheinmetall Grosstraktor, was based on 10 small roadwheels paired in bogies, each of which was hung on a sprung trailing arm. Eventually, this project, too, was abandoned, though the six or eight vehicles already built were used for training purposes and saw service during the German invasion of Norway in the spring of 1940.

THE PZKPFW I

These heavy-medium tanks were one component of what was planned as an interrelated family of armoured vehicles, each with an allotted role and a specified function within the doctrine that became known as Blitzkrieg, or 'lightning war', which was even then being evolved by Wehrmacht staff officers of whom the most prominent was Heinz Guderian. The essence of Blitzkreig was a fast-moving surprise attack spearheaded by light armour, supported by mechanised

infantry and ground-attack aircraft. Initially, its most basic – and most numerous – component was to be the two-man, machine gun-armed light tank known as the PzKpfw I, designs for which were produced by five would-be manufacturers. Krupp's design for a 6-tonne tank with armour from 7mm to 13mm (.25 to .5in) thick was selected.

THE HEAVIER PANZERS

Even as the first PzKpfw Is were coming off the production line, it had become clear that the medium 'battle' tanks intended to fight alongside them – the 20-tonne PzKpfw IIIs and IVs – would take longer than anticipated to develop and produce. As a result, it was decided to build a more effective light tank than the PzKpfw I in the meantime. MAN (Maschinenfabrik Augsberg-Nürenberg) was selected to manufacture the 10-tonne PzKpfw II, which had a 130hp engine, 14.5mm (.6in) primary armour and a 20mm cannon in place of one of the machine guns carried by the PzKpfw I. By the time Hitler ordered the invasion of Poland, in the late summer of 1939, over 1000 PzKpfw IIs were in service, and it was soon clear that they were well up to the task at hand. The Ausf D and E, which Daimler-Benz produced that same year, were faster on the road, having true

Christie-type suspension with torsion bars to replace semi-eliptical springs, but had inferior performance cross country. They were soon withdrawn and converted to mount flamethrowers as the Flammpanzer II or turned into SP guns. However, in 1940 it became clear that even the best light tanks were at serious risk on the battlefield. The PzKpfw Is and IIs were eventually withdrawn to second-line service, having served the Wehrmacht supremely well.

THE PANZER IV

The PzKpfw IV support tank was planned and designed in parallel with the PzKpfw III battle tank, and was essentially similar save for its main armament. The PzKpfw IV had the 75mm L/24 gun, which could fire a much greater range of ammunition, including HE (high-explosive), HEAT (high-explosive, anti-tank), AP (armour-piercing), smoke and case (that is, anti-personnel) rounds. The PzKpfw IV Ausf A was powered by a 250hp Maybach engine, which gave it a maximum speed of 30km/h (18mph), and had suspension similar to that of the PzKpfw III Ausf C/D. The PzKpfw IV can probably be reckoned the most successful all-round tank design to come out of the Third Reich. More than 8500 were produced.

CHAPTER 3
BLITZKRIEG AND BEYOND: THE TANKS OF WORLD WAR II

In September 1939 German panzers swept through Poland, ushering in a new era in armoured warfare. By 1945 tank design had improved dramatically, and armoured formations became an integral part of American and European armies.

By the time World War II broke out, at the start of September 1939, the state of the art in tank design had changed out of all recognition from the point it had reached two decades before. The vehicles in service in the late 1930s were more capable than their predecessors and also came in various types. Most of the world's industrialised nations now had tanks of one sort or another, but very few countries had any coherent idea of how to use them, save in internal security operations. Germany was the most significant exception. In the six years that followed, however, all that changed dramatically as the tank became the linchpin of the terrestrial battlefield, be it rural or urban – the most powerful tactical weapon of its day, upon the handling of which the result of the battle often depended.

LIGHT AND MEDIUM TANKS
The light and medium tanks of the day would clearly dominate any army not prepared to resist them. Their protection, consisting of frontal armour up to 30mm

■ LEFT: The fearsome PzKpfw V Panther, pictured in the forest of Ardennes in the winter of 1944. Even at this late stage of the war, the Panther was a dangerous adversary, capable of knocking out any Allied tank at long range with its 75mm main gun.

(1.2in) thick, reducing in less vulnerable areas to around 7mm (.25in), kept the crews safe from 'ordinary' rifle and machine gun fire and from bomb and shell splinters and shrapnel. This protection allowed these tanks to overwhelm infantry units and break through defensive positions with a degree of impunity, even with the relatively small weapons they carried, making a reality of the fast-moving shock war concept. With surprise on their side – not to mention effective air cover and close support – relatively lightly armed German armoured divisions tore through the Polish defences in September 1939 like a chain saw. Yet the tanks were markedly less effective when Hitler tried to repeat the process in France nine months later. Indeed, even in the attack on Poland, German armour suffered losses. The German 4th Panzer Division, for example, lost 57 tanks out of 120 on 4 September 1939 alone. By 1940, the lighter tanks proved vulnerable to even the most basic anti-tank weapons – for example, heavy machine gun/light cannon-calibre rifles such as the British .55in Boys, the Finnish 20mm Lahti Modell 39, the German 7.92/13mm Panzerbusch PzB 38 and PzB 39 and the Japanese 20mm Model 97. And they showed themselves to be distressingly susceptible to anti-tank guns, to anti-aircraft guns used in the ground support

■ABOVE: Spring 1940. PzKpfw III tank crews take a break from the fighting in northern France. Conditions in Russia proved much harsher. During the Polish campaign the PzKpfw III had performed well, but in 1940 it was found wanting in the face of both French and British anti-tank guns.

role and to the main guns of heavier tanks. 'Light' tanks were to make something of a comeback later in the war, but by then they had grown very much

thicker skins, and deserved their classification only in relation to the new breed of medium tanks, which had put on a considerable amount of weight themselves.

THE GERMAN MEDIUMS

In September 1939, the then-current models of the German PzKpfw III and PzKpfw IV were certainly the best all-round medium tanks in the world, but they were already starting to look vulnerable. The British two-pounder gun,

for example, could knock them out at 500m (1640ft), and the French SA 35 gun was only slightly less capable. The German mediums would clearly have to be uparmoured if they were to stay ahead of the game.

Even though the PzKpfw III and IV were deployed in September 1939, it was not until a year later that they were available in anything like significant numbers. Even in the invasion of France in June 1940, of the 2500 German tanks employed, only a little over 600 were mediums. The rest were PzKpfw Is and IIs and Czech-manufactured PzKpfw 35(t)s and 38(t)s, and already, as we have noted, these were to be regarded as approaching obsolescence. A year later, when Hitler launched Operation Barbarossa against the Soviet Union, the total tank strength of the German Army and the Waffen-SS in the field had risen to about 3200, and by then, most of the tanks were PzKpfw IIIs and IVs – and more capable versions, at that.

THE PZKPFW III

The PzKpfw III Ausf H was produced between the autumn of 1940 and the end of 1941. It was a down-engineered version of the previous models with new idlers and drive sprockets, and with a conventional six-speed gearbox to replace the pre-selector originally fitted. The modifications were not introduced purely in the interests of economy, but were intended to make the tank easier to produce. The Ausf H gained bolt-on armour, spaced away from the hull proper so as to provide a measure of extra protection against hollow-charge projectiles and grenades, which were then coming into use for the first time. The tank was fitted with 400mm-wide (16in) tracks instead of 360mm (14in) versions, and this reduced the ground pressure somewhat, even with the tank's increased all-up weight. While some Ausf Es had begun to receive the more capable 50mm L/42 gun in place of the 37mm KwK 30, the Ausf H got the still better L/60 version in the spring of 1941. Tanks produced earlier got this weapon as a retrofit as and when they went for major overhaul. However, the Soviet T-34 tanks the Germans came up against in Russia that summer proved largely to be proof against the 50mm gun even in the longer, more powerful L/60 calibre, except at short range. The PzKpfw III could not take a bigger high-velocity gun, and this was the major factor in the decision to

PzKpfw 38(t)

Armament: one 37mm gun,
two 7.92mm machine guns
Crew: four
Length: 4.62m (15.15ft)
Width: 2.05m (6.72ft)
Height: 2.36m (7.7in)
Armour: 15-50mm (.6-2.0in)
Engine: 125bhp petrol
Range: 200km (125 miles)
Speed: 42km/h (26.1mph)
Country of origin: Germany

concentrate further development on the
PzKpfw IV, which could.

In order to give the PzKpfw III a
chance of getting within killing range of
the T-34s, the next version, the Ausf J,
was uparmoured to 50mm (2in), which
put its weight up by 700kg (1545lb) to
almost 22.5 tonnes. The Ausf L, which
followed hard on its heels, was basically
very similar, but had additional 20mm-
thick (.8in) spaced armour over the
superstructure. Even so, many of these
two versions of the PzKpfw III, of which
no fewer than 2600 were produced in
1942 alone, were modified in the field to
improve their protection still further. The
most common additions were extra plates
of spaced armour, along with armoured
skirts that reached up high enough to
mask the junction of hull and turret and
protected the suspension and running
gear.

THE AUSF M
Just as the Ausf H had been a simplified
version of the Ausf F, so the next model to
appear, the Ausf M, was a down-
engineered Ausf L. To make
manufacturing easier, the hull vision
ports – already reduced in the Ausf J –
and escape doors were deleted, the latter
having been rendered unusable by skirt

armour. At the same time, ammunition
stowage was adjusted to increase the
number of 50mm rounds the tank could
carry, at the cost of halving its capacity
for 7.92mm machine gun ammunition to

■BELOW: The driver of a PzKpfw 38(t)
moves cautiously across a pontoon
bridge constructed by German combat
engineers during the invasion of France
in 1940. The 38 was a Czech design.

PzKpfw III (SdKfz 141) Ausf. H

Armament: one 50mm gun, two 7.92mm machine guns
Crew: five
Length (gun forward): 5.58m (18.3ft)
Width: 2.95m (9.7ft)
Height: 2.44m (8ft)
Armour: 18-30mm (.7–1.2in)
Engine: 300bhp petrol
Range: 180km (112 miles)
Speed: 40km/h (25mph)
Country of origin: Germany

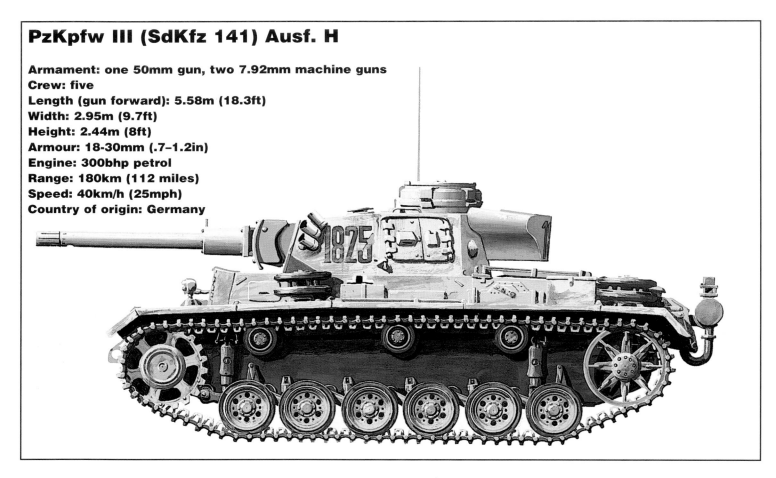

2500 rounds. The Ausf M could also 'wade' through deeper water, being able to negotiate 1.5m (5ft) instead of 0.8m (2ft 6in). It was joined in production by the final variant of the PzKpfw III, the Ausf N, in mid-1942. In place of the 50mm L/60 gun, the Ausf N was fitted with the long-obsolescent 75mm L/24 medium-velocity gun, as originally fitted to the PzKpfw IV, with its much wider range of available ammunition, and was designed to operate in the fire support role. The last 200 or so vehicles built left the factories with skirts as standard and were finished with a coating of zimmerit paste, which prevented magnetic mines from being attached. That coating became commonplace on German tanks from that time on.

TAUCHFÄHIG TANKS

As well as the 5500 PzKpfw IIIs produced as fighting tanks, a great many more chassis were produced for other purposes. More than 10,000 formed the basis for Sturmgeschütz self-propelled assault guns. These had fixed turrets that could mount 75mm and 105mm guns in a variety of lengths – larger guns than those fitted to the tanks proper. Other PzKpfw III chassis went to become Flammpanzer flamethrowers, command

tanks and armoured observation posts for artillery spotters. The most far-reaching modification of the tank itself was probably the Tauchfähig, or 'capable of submersion', version produced for the stillborn Operation Sealion, the projected invasion of Britain. The Tauchfähig tanks, with all their hatches and apertures sealed, a one-way valve fitted to the exhaust system and a flexible, floating hose to act as a breather tube, could move along the seabed under their own power at a depth of up to 7.5m (25ft), before climbing up onto the beach to achieve total surprise. Some Tauchfähig tanks were apparently employed in river-crossing operations during the early stages of Operation Barbarossa.

Originally, the PzKpfw IIIs were supported in action by the slightly heavier PzKpfw IVs, which carried the more versatile 75mm main gun. A four-company tank battalion would have three companies equipped with the PzKpfw III and one with the PzKpfw IV. As the war dragged on, and the effective protection of the Allies' tanks improved, it became clear that the support tank's greater turret capacity was a more profound factor than had earlier been supposed. It allowed the mounting of a longer-

barrelled version of the bigger gun, which could penetrate up to 92mm (3.6in) of armour with AP shot at standard angle and range and still provide fire support with HE, smoke and case rounds when necessary.

IMPROVED PANZER IVS

The first PzKpfw IV variant to receive the new gun was to have been the Ausf F, but by the time the new model was ready to go into production, the gun still was not available, and the old L/24 weapon had to be fitted instead. When the L/43 version became available in February 1942, after 460 of the 650 Ausf Fs originally ordered had been completed, the tanks that received it became known as the Ausf F2, and the originals were redesignated as Ausf F1s. The new gun was somewhat heavier than the L/24, and its extra length made the tank a little nose heavy. This problem was exacerbated when the L/48 cannon, with its 375mm (14.8in) of extra barrel length, replaced the L/43 in the Ausf H. At that point, modifications were made to the front suspension, supplementary coil springs being fitted.

The Ausf G replaced the Ausf F2 in May 1943. There were really only very minor differences between the two. Over the next 10 months a total of almost 1700 Ausf Gs were built, before this model was superseded in turn by the Ausf H in March 1943. The plan had been to phase out production of the PzKpfw IV at that point, in favour of the PzKpfw V 'Panther' and the PzKpfw VI 'Tiger'. However, the PzKpfw IV got a renewed lease of life when it became obvious that production levels of the new tanks were simply not high enough to meet basic demand. As well as the L/48 gun, the Ausf H received much improved 80mm (3.1in) primary armour. The Ausf H was also fitted with light armour skirts, similar to those field-fitted to older versions, to protect its running gear from hollow-charge weapons such as the American Bazooka rocket launcher, the British PIAT (Projector, Infantry, Anti-Tank) spigot mortar and Soviet anti-tank grenades. In all, 3775 Ausf Hs were built before July

■RIGHT: A late designation PzKpfw III in service with SS Panzer Division 'Das Reich' during the battle of Kursk in July 1943. The 'III' was no match for the 76mm gun of the Soviet T-34, and German losses were heavy.

PzKpfw III (SdKfz 141) Ausf. J

Armament: one 50mm gun, two 7.92mm machine guns
Crew: five
Length (gun forward): 6.5m (21.33ft)
Width: 2.95m (9.7ft)
Height: 2.5m (8.2ft)
Armour: 18–50mm (.7–2.0in)
Engine: 300bhp petrol
Range: 180km (112 miles)
Speed: 38km/h (23mph)
Country of origin: Germany

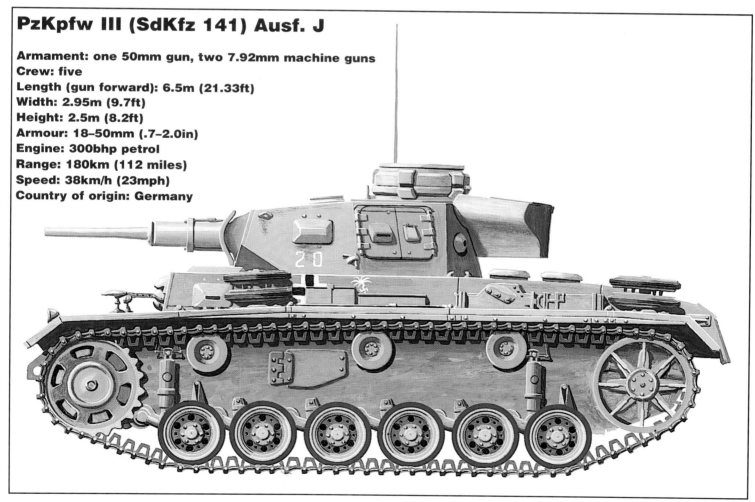

1944, when production turned over to the somewhat simplified Ausf J, which had even thicker frontal and turret armour, and whose plate burster-skirts were replaced by lighter but no less effective mesh versions. The Ausf J remained in production until the war ended 14 months later, by which time some 1750 had been produced in all.

Like most other tanks of the day, the PzKpfw IV had its 'chassis' (although technically speaking, it was a monocoque design) utilised as the basis for many other types of tracked vehicles. The best known and most effective of these were the Sturmpanzer IV, armed with a 150mm assault howitzer, the Jagdpanzer IV tank destroyer, with the 75mm KwK 40 L/48 gun, and the Flakpanzer IV anti-aircraft tank, with four 20mm cannon. The PzKpfw IV also served as a vehicle for self-propelled artillery pieces.

Although they were both good tanks, the PzKpfw III and PzKpfw IV were

■RIGHT: PzKpfw IVs were produced in greater numbers than any other German type during World War II, and it's influence is highly underestimated. This Ausf A is pictured speeding past a blazing Russian town during Operation Barbarossa in the summer of 1941.

PzKpfw IV (SdKfz 161) Ausf. H

Armament: one 75mm gun,
 two 7.92mm machine guns
Crew: five
Length (gun forward): 7.02m (23ft)
Width: 2.88m (9.4ft)
Height: 2.68m (8.8ft)
Armour: 10–80mm (.31in–3.14in)
Engine: 300bhp petrol
Range: 320km (199 miles)
Speed: 38km/h (23.6mph)
Country of origin: Germany

obsolescent, in the technical sense, by 1940. That did not stop the PzKpfw IV, in particular, from being deadly, in the right hands and with a measure of luck, right up until the final battle for Berlin. With their squared-off superstructure and turrets, and with shot-traps formed by the undercuts at the front corners, both types were cursed with what amounted to huge areas of vulnerability that could be improved only by piling on thicker and thicker armour, which inevitably meant that their all-up weight increased. With no improvement in power output available from their engines, and no room to squeeze in anything bigger and more powerful, they got slower and less agile as time went on. The last PzKpfw IVs were 5km/h (3mph) slower than the Ausf Ds had been, thanks to being almost 5 tonnes heavier. That their suspension stood up so well to the additional punishment it had to take is a credit to its original design.

BIG CATS

Even while the first prototype PzKpfw IIIs were being debugged and the initial design for the PzKpfw IV was being finalised, the German Army's Inspector of Mechanised Forces was already considering plans for a new, bigger tank that would turn the scales at over 30 tonnes. There had been interest in a tank heavier than the PzKpfw IIIs and IVs before that, but interest in that area had waned somewhat with the failure of the PzKpfw Neubaufahrzeug project. Then, on 20 November 1941, an intact Soviet T-34/76 fell into German hands (the subsidiary designation denotes the T-34's 76.2mm main gun, to differentiate it from the later T-34/85, with its bigger weapon). It became crystal clear that such a vehicle, crushingly expensive as it would be to develop, manufacture and operate, was no longer a luxury for Germany, but a necessity. Before the month was out, Daimler-Benz and MAN had been ordered to start work on designs for a new heavy tank, armed with a 75mm gun, armoured to 60mm (2.4in) on the front and 60mm (2.4in) on the turret – later increased to 100mm (3.9in) – and capable of 55km/h (35mph). Both presented their designs in April 1942. The Daimler-Benz version of the VK3002 project was basically similar to the T-34, with the turret placed so far forward that the gun mantlet was virtually a continuation of the glacis plate. It was to be powered by a diesel engine (an

important consideration at a time when fuel production was a major preoccupation in Germany) and would run on seven medium-sized interleaved roadwheels with simplified leaf-spring suspension. The authorities who evaluated the design agreed that it had considerable potential and found fault only with the chosen L/48 Krupp version of the new KwK 42 75mm main gun. An L/70 version developed by Rheinmetall was specified instead. A production order for 200 was issued, apparently on Hitler's own instruction, and construction of a prototype commenced.

ENTER THE PANTHER

The rival MAN design was much more conventional. In its layout it resembled the successful PzKpfw IV, although the flat homogenous armour plates that were welded to form the hull were angled to

■ ABOVE: To combat the threat of the Soviet T-34, with its powerful 76mm main gun, later models of the PzKpfw IV were armed with a long-barrelled 75mm main gun.

deflect incoming shot, in direct homage to the T-34 and Walter Christie. The MAN design was fitted with a more powerful petrol engine, the Maybach HL 210. This delivered more than 600hp through torsion-bar suspension and eight axles with paired interleaved large-diameter rubber-tyred roadwheels to 500mm-wide (19.68in) tracks. The turret, designed and produced by Rheinmetall to accommodate the L/70 version of the KwK 42, was set back as far as possible so that the vehicle could be operated gun-forward virtually at all times, something that was not possible with the Daimler-Benz version, especially after the L/70 gun was

PzKpfw V Panther (SdKfz 171) Ausf. A

Armament: one 75mm gun, one 7.92mm machine gun
Crew: five
Length (gun forward): 8.66m (28.4ft)
Width: 3.42m (11.2ft)
Height: 2.85m (9.35ft)
Armour: 16–100mm (.62–3.93in)
Engine: 650bhp petrol
Range: 200km (125 miles)
Speed: 46km/h (28.6mph)
Country of origin: Germany

■LEFT: The vast distances covered by German armoured divisions during the Russian campaign took their toll on both men and machinery. This PzKpfw IV Ausf D is undergoing field repairs to its Maybach engine in early 1942.

specified. With the backing of Albert Speer's Ministry of Munitions, it was this design that was finally chosen to become the PzKpfw V Panther. Fabrication of the Daimler-Benz prototype was halted, and mild-steel prototypes were ordered from MAN in May 1942 and delivered the following September. Such were the problems the German Army and the Waffen-SS were encountering on the Eastern Front that the new tank was ordered into series production straightaway – a course of action that always led to difficulties – and the first vehicles were completed in November. At the design stage, considerable thought had been put into the way the tank was to be manufactured, and this work paid considerable dividends. By the war's end, two and a half years after the type went into production, more than 5500 Panthers had been produced in all, while almost 700 more chassis were produced for other purposes. And this took place during a period in which German manufacturing resources were being stretched ever thinner.

Even during the early days of the design stage, it had been recognised that tactical requirements demanded that a heavy tank would have an all-up weight of considerably more than the 30 to 35 tonnes originally envisaged. Indeed, the production versions of the Panther topped 45 tonnes, and even with engines uprated to deliver up to 700hp, this increase in weight meant a distinct loss of performance. Top speed was reduced to 45km/h (28mph), although fording, climbing and obstacle-crossing capabilities were always well up to par.

DEBUT AT KURSK

Just 20 Ausf A Panthers were manufactured, with 60mm (2.4in) frontal armour, an early version of the L/70 gun and a 645hp engine. From the beginning, they were plagued by fundamental problems, and ironing these out was not made any simpler by the armaments ministry's refusal to halt or even slow the production programme to allow improvements to be incorporated as they were devised. The majority of malfunctions occurred in the transmission and cooling systems and in the running gear. For example, the roadwheels shed their rubber tyres with sickening regularity and replacing them meant removing as many as five wheels. The Ausf B and Ausf C were Ausf As with different gearboxes and modifications aimed at correcting the other problems, and they were produced only in very small numbers. The Ausf D was the first serious production version and began to leave the four factories manufacturing it in January 1943. All Ausf Ds were recalled for modification in April, however, and it was May before the first vehicles reached the units designated to operate them. The Panthers saw action for the first time in July 1943 at Kursk, in the biggest tank battle of World War II – and probably of all time – in which more than 6000 vehicles were committed in all. However, Panthers were not present at Kursk in sufficient numbers to outweigh the advantages the T-34 had over the PzKpfw IIIs and IVs, even if they had actually been battleworthy by that time. Clearly, introducing the untried and still unperfected Panther in small numbers, with inexperienced crews, was a major tactical error. The Red Army was allowed to glimpse the potential of the new tank prematurely and was thus presented with an opportunity to work out ways to defeat the Panthers before they came to the battlefield in meaningful strength.

The next version of the Panther first appeared around the time the Battle of Kursk was being fought out. It was designated Ausf A, while the few existing original Ausf As were redesignated Ausf D1s and the Ausf Ds became Ausf D2s. The new Ausf A had a rounded, rather than straight cylindrical, commander's cupola atop the turret, an excellent ball mount for the 7.92mm machine gun in the frontal glacis (a weapon missing from the earlier versions) and other detailed improvements. It was superseded in its turn by the Panther Ausf G at the end of February 1944. The Ausf G was essentially a stop-gap measure incorporating as many elements as possible of the design for the stillborn Panther II, but it was still a potent weapon in its own right. Much of the Panther II's design had been derived from the tried and tested PzKpfw VI Tiger, and one element from this biggest of all German tanks found its way into the Panther Ausf G – all-steel roadwheels, which solved the problem of shedding rubber tyres once and for all. The Ausf G also received better smoke dischargers, which were by now an essential part of any tank's defensive armament, plus grenade/bomb launchers and yet thicker frontal armour. This had now reached a thickness of 120mm (4.7in) and was completely impervious to any anti-tank weapon it might encounter on the battlefield. Allied tank troops, who had a lot of trouble neutralising Panthers on the Normandy battlefields in mid-1944 and after, reckoned that it took a concerted attack by four or five M4 Shermans or equivalent medium tanks to stand a real chance of stopping a Panther A or G. Even then tackling a Panther was a risky business, such was the power of the combination of 75mm L/70 gun and the tank's massive armour.

THE OUTNUMBERED PANTHER

In trying to evaluate the tanks of World War II, the Panther provides an adequate benchmark – a standard against which to judge all the rest. Indeed, many hold that, all-round, the Panther was the best tank of World War II. It was undoubtedly introduced prematurely and was rushed into action when it should have had a much longer period of preproduction testing and modification. But for all that, the Panther's basic structure and design were absolutely sound, and the matching of the 75mm KwK 42 L/70 gun with the tank's massive armour was finely judged and showed a fine understanding for what was possible within the constraints of the technology of the period. The gun was considerably more capable than that of most tanks the Panther was likely to encounter. It had a muzzle velocity of over 1000 metres per second (3280 feet per second) and fired a 6.75kg (15lb) AP round. The 75mm L/70 could pierce over 140mm (5.5in) of armour at standard range and angle and could knock out a Sherman tank at 2000m (6560ft). Yet despite all this, the gun was not impossibly heavy or unwieldy. It was 1944 before the Sherman got a comparable weapon, and even then it would not pierce the Panther's frontal or turret armour. The Panther's armour, meanwhile, was angled to throw off incoming AP rounds and was thick enough to withstand HEAT and hollow charges at the Panther's own stand-off range (the distance at which a tank can knock out a given enemy while remaining perfectly safe itself). One factor, though, was against the Panther – numbers available. Almost 50,000 Shermans were built, against fewer than 6000 Panthers. The Allied tank crews' five-to-one rule of thumb was therefore comfortably exceeded even before British and Soviet tanks comparable to the Sherman were taken into account – and they also killed their fair share of Panthers.

THE FEARSOME TIGER

The stillborn Panther II, which was to have entered production in the summer of 1945, would clearly have been even more formidable still. As noted above, it was to have been equipped with elements from the PzKpfw VI Tiger – thicker hull armour, a smaller turret with stereoscopic rangefinder and the tremendous 88mm KwK 36 gun, a further-uprated HL 230 engine and the AK 7-400 gearbox. One can only speculate on the tank's actual performance, but with 200hp extra on hand, the Panther II would have been somewhat faster than its predecessors, even though somewhat heavier. It is a moot point as to whether its reliability would have suffered as a result.

The competing prototypes of what was to become the PzKpfw VI Tiger were first demonstrated in 1942 – on 20 April, Hitler's birthday. The origins of the German heavy tank programme go back to 1937, when the 30/35-tonne tank was first discussed. The firm of Henschel received an order to develop two vehicles to that same outline specification as the Durchbruchswagen, or 'breakthrough vehicle', DW.1. A prototype was already running when the company was ordered to concentrate on an even heavier vehicle, the VK6501. This was a 65-tonne vehicle – armed with a 75mm main gun and multiple machine guns in subsidiary turrets – which it was planned to put into production as the PzKpfw VII. But the project was cancelled in 1940, by which time two prototypes had been completed and were being evaluated.

HENSCHEL'S PROTOTYPES

Meanwhile, Henschel had continued to work on the 'lighter' heavy tank and had produced a prototype, DW.2, with a realistic all-up weight of 32 tonnes, a crew of five and a 75mm L/24 gun as fitted to the PzKpfw IV. When the German armaments ministry asked Daimler-Benz, Henschel, MAN and Dr Ferdinand Porsche, head of the German tank commission, to submit plans for a 30-tonne tank in 1940, Henschel's proposal was based on the DW.2. The company was ordered to produce four prototypes for evaluation as the Vollketten Kraftfahrzeug, or 'full-tracked motor vehicle', VK3001(H). Dr Porsche was also requested to produce prototypes,

■ **BELOW: SS Panzer Division 'Viking' on the Eastern front, winter 1941–42. Armour skirts have been fitted to this Pzkpfw IV Ausf G, but they are of little use against the real enemy: the merciless sub-zero temperatures of the Russian winter.**

his to be designated the VK3001(P). Henschel duly produced two prototypes the following March, and the second pair six months later. The design was not dissimilar to that of the PzKpfw IV, but had seven interleaved roadwheels per side, mounted on torsion bars, and three track-return rollers. It was to have been armed with the 75mm L/48 gun, but when the captured T-34/76 was examined in November, the tank was deemed obsolete – even before chassis trials had been completed. The VK3001 project was promptly cancelled as a tank, and the VK3001(H) prototypes were converted to become prototype self-propelled guns instead. A similar prototype 36-tonne tank was ordered from Henschel as the VK3601(H), designed to mount the 75mm taper-bore gun. That, too, was cancelled, but for reasons of economy rather than because it failed as a design.

ENTER THE 88MM

The inadequacy of the then-current 75mm gun had been proved in action against British and French medium tanks during the fighting in France in the early summer of 1940. For example, it had conspicuously failed to knock out British Matilda IIs at Arras. As a result, Hitler had ordered work to begin on converting the 88mm Fliegerabwehrkannone FlaK 36 for a new tank that could destroy existing Allied armour at a range of 1500m (5000ft) while being able to withstand a weapon of similar power. The FlaK 36 was an anti-aircraft weapon that was also used as a towed anti-tank gun and had proved itself excellent in both roles. The armaments ministry's development team

wanted a taper-bore or squeeze-bore gun of smaller calibre that would pack the same sort of punch by dint of much higher velocity. Such weapons were already in trial as towed anti-tank guns and proved very effective indeed, but they needed tungsten for their projectiles, and tungsten was in very great demand elsewhere. The adoption of such a gun would have far-reaching consequences for the vehicle armed with it – it could be smaller and therefore lighter. However, in the end the shortage of tungsten put paid to this plan.

Single prototype tanks to mount the converted FlaK 36 gun, which was designated the 88mm KwK 36 L/56, were ordered from both Henschel and Porsche in May 1941 as the VK4501(H) and VK4501(P). Not surprisingly, both companies relied heavily on the development work they had done earlier on the 30-tonne tanks. Porsche's design utilised petrol-electric drive and longitudinal torsion bars, and also introduced other novel features. But in trials it was the more conventional Henschel tank that won out, despite being more than 10 tonnes over the stipulated weight. The VK4501(H) was ordered into production in August 1942 as the PzKpfw VI Tiger Ausf H, although as a precaution, Porsche was ordered to start work on 90 of his chassis, too, just in case the Henschel production line ran into unexpected difficulties.

THE LUMBERING ELEFANT

In the event, the Henschel production line encountered no problems, and the Porsche-designed chassis were fitted out as tank destroyers, with the 88mm Panzerabwehrkannone PaK 43/2 L/71 gun in a limited-traverse mount in a fixed armoured superstructure. The vehicle was designated the Panzerjäger Tiger (P) Ferdinand, in recognition of the vehicle's designer. The Ferdinand was later renamed the Elefant, which was what tank destroyers' crews had called them all along. These huge vehicles – more than 8m (26ft) long, almost 3.5m (11ft 6in) wide and weighing in at 65 tonnes – first saw action during Operation Zitadelle, the battle in the Kursk salient. Despite having 200mm (7.9in) of frontal armour, which was proof against any Soviet projectile, the Elefants were altogether too vulnerable to Soviet pioneers (infantrymen armed with demolition charges) since they had no defensive machine guns. They were also

mechanically unreliable and carried insufficient ammunition stocks. None ever proved its worth in battle.

Meanwhile, the Henschel Tiger was going from strength to strength. Despite its coming after the PzKpfw V Panther in sequence, the PzKpfw VI Tiger was clearly a design from an earlier period. It had none of the sloping lines of the smaller tank, bearing more of a resemblance to the PzKpfw IV, and relied for its protection on the sheer thickness of its armour. The Tiger's frontal

■RIGHT: Panzer Division 'Das Reich' received the new PzKpfw V 'Panther' in July 1943. It was undoubtedly the most capable German tank in service during the Second World War.

PzKpfw V Panther (SdKfz 171) Ausf. A

Armament: one 75mm gun, two 7.92mm machine guns
Crew: five
Length (gun forward): 8.66m (28.4ft)
Width: 3.42m (11.2ft)
Height: 2.98m (9.8ft)
Armour: 16–110mm (.62–4.3in)
Engine: 700hp
Range: 200km (125 miles)
Speed: 46km/h (28.6mph)
Country of origin: Germany

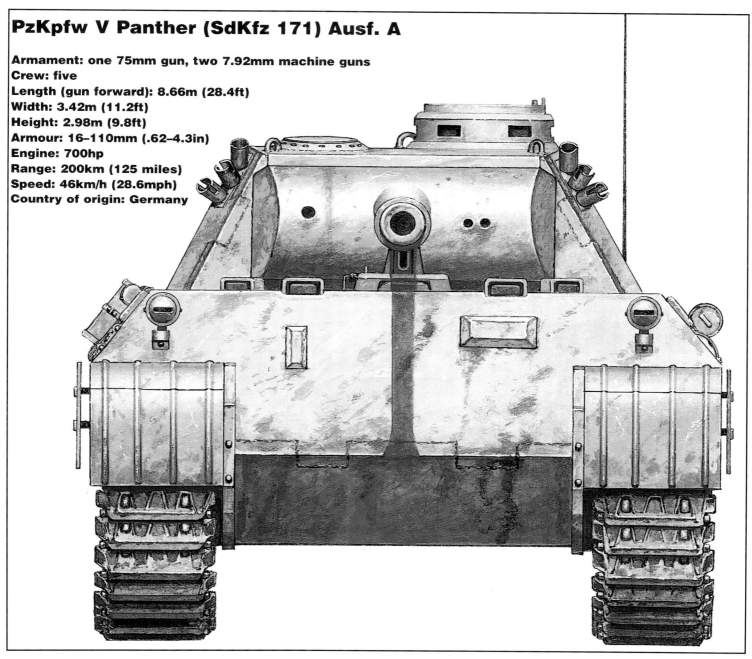

PzKpfw V Panther (SdKfz 171) Ausf. G
Country of origin: Germany

1 75mm L/70 gun
2 7.92mm MG34 machine gun
3 7.92mm MG34 machine gun
4 Ventilator
5 Commander's cupola
6 Gun cradle
7 Sighting telescope TZF 12a
8 Loading/escape hatch
9 Commander's microphone and headset
10 Wireless operator's hatch
11 Turret traversing gear
12 Elevation handwheel
13 Engine ventilator
14 Cooling air inlet
15 75mm ammunition
16 Balance/elevating gear
17 Gun compensator/balance
18 Spent 75mm cartridge bin
19 Maybach engine

20 Gun cleaning kit
21 Spare track links
22 Machine-gun ammunition
23 Gunner's seat
24 Wireless operator's seat
25 Instrument panel
26 Spent machine-gun ammunition container
27 Hydraulic traversing unit
28 Compressor
29 Brake link
30 Steering lever
31 Driver's seat
32 Machine-gun firing pedal
33 Track brake cooling duct
34 Gearbox
35 Track brake
36 Oil pressure pump

37 Batteries
38 Final drive
39 Sprocket
40 Return roller
41 Limited suspension stop
42 Shock absorber
43 Swing-arm bearing bracket
44 Suspension crank arm
45 Interleaved road wheels
46 Idler wheel
47 Torsion-bar suspension

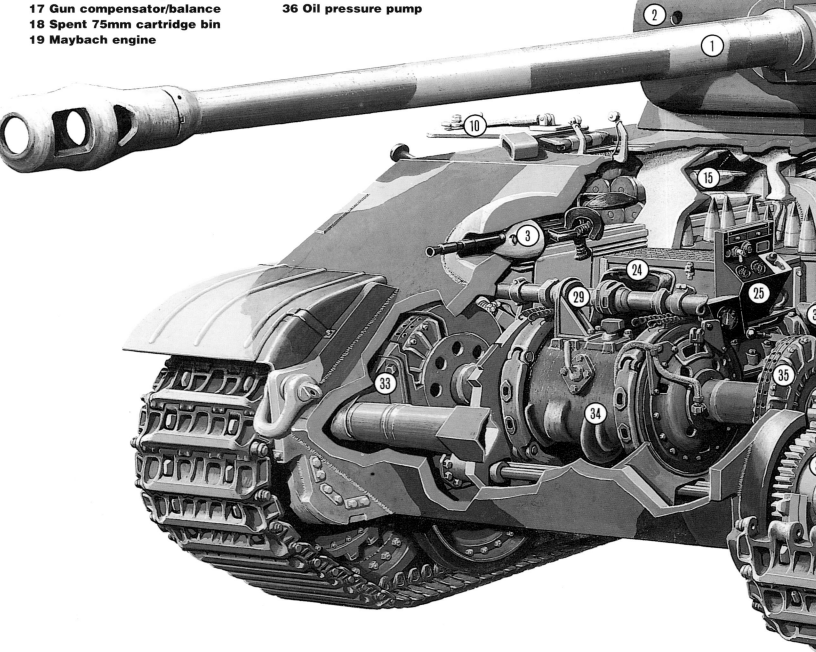

1 Microfon
1 Fernhörer
1 Microfon
1 Fernhörer

protection was 110mm (4.33in) thick, while the upper hull sides had 60mm (2.4in) and the lower hull sides 82mm (3.2in). Even the underside and turret top had 26mm (1in) plate. The armour was of all-welded construction, using the largest plates available in an attempt to improve the rigidity and stiffness of the hull, which had flexed noticeably in the prototype when the main gun was fired in anything but the straight-ahead position. The sides and rear of the turret, for example, were fabricated from a single piece of plate 80mm (3.1in) thick, bent into a horseshoe shape and completed by a flat, vertical front face 100mm (3.9in) thick and pierced to hold the 110mm-thick (4.33in) gun mantlet.

The first 250 Tigers had the 645hp HL 210 engine, but later units had the HL 230 in its simplest 700hp form (although there was actually very little difference in performance between the two), which gave them a fairly ponderous top speed of 37 km/h (23mph). Even with a capacity of 567 litres (150 US gallons), these Tigers could manage only 120km (75 miles) on the road between refuellings; cross country, the range dropped to not much over half that.

INTERLEAVED WHEELS
The lessons Henschel had learned with the suspension of the VK3001 and VK3601 proved invaluable when it came to designing the Tiger, which had eight stub axles per side, each of which carried one of the large, interleaved roadwheels.

The axles were sprung by torsion bars, and the diameter of the wheels was such as to obviate the need for return rollers. The early Tigers had rubber-tyred roadwheels, which were replaced with all-steel wheels with internal springing from February 1944. Although the Tiger Ausf H – which was subsequently retroactively redesignated the Ausf E – never had the problems with retaining tyres that beset the Panthers, its crews had a back-breaking task of their own regarding the running gear.

THE TIGER AUSF H
The Tiger Ausf H came with two sets of tracks – 725mm-wide (28.5in) combat tracks and 520mm (20in) transit tracks. In order to fit the transit tracks, the four outermost roadwheels had to be removed and then laboriously refitted when the combat tracks were replaced before the tank went into combat. The interleaved roadwheels gave an excellent, stable ride on surfaces of all types, but had one major drawback. The mud that built up between the two sets of wheels on soft going and snow froze solid if the tanks were stationary for any length of time. For example, if Tigers stopped for the night after a day's travelling in such conditions, the tanks could be immobilised by daybreak. The Red Army's tank commanders soon realised this shortcoming and timed their attacks to take advantage of their enemy's being stuck in one place. The Tiger made its combat debut in September 1942 during

the siege of Leningrad (now St Petersburg), in what would have been unsuitable terrain for any tank. The Tigers found themselves in open country, with very little cover, and facing carefully sited heavy anti-tank guns. As a result, they took considerable losses. By the time of the huge battles in the west, after the Allied landings in Normandy, the Tiger crews had learned that their vehicles were much better suited to ambush operations in close country, where they could make the most of their heavy armour and powerful gun and where their limited tactical agility, poor top speed and restricted range counted for less. As a result, in the battles to contain the Allied bridgehead in 1944, in the bocage country of Normandy, with its narrow lanes, high, thick hedges and small fields, the Tigers were at their very best. On one occasion, the British 7th Armoured Division (The Desert Rats) lost at least 25 of its vehicles to just one Tiger. Not all of the British losses were battle tanks, it must be said, although on the other hand some reports quote a much higher figure for the total number of vehicles destroyed.

MICHAEL WITTMANN
The incident took place on 13 June 1944, near the village of Villers Bocage, during Operation Epsom, which was part of the battle for Caen. The Tiger was commanded by SS-Obersturmführer (Lieutenant) Michael Wittmann of the Schwere, or 'heavy', SS-Panzer Abteilung 11. Wittmann was credited with no fewer than 119 tank kills (some reports say 138) during the course of his two-year career as a tank commander. Tigers proved their worth time and time again that winter, too, during the Battle of the Bulge, in the heavily wooded Ardennes mountains. It was here and at Caen that the Tiger won its reputation for virtual invincibility against any armoured vehicle it was likely to have to fight.

Besides the standard battle tank version, some Tigers were equipped as Panzerbefehlswagen command vehicles. They were fitted with tactical plotting boards and two extra radios – one for liaison with close air support and the other for communication with divisional headquarters – but at the cost of

■RIGHT: The legendary PzKpfw VI Tiger commanded by SS-Obersturmführer Michael Wittmann (far left). Note the rings on the gun barrel denoting the number of 'kills'.

ammunition stowage for the main gun and the co-axial machine gun. Some Tigers also served as Bergepanzer armoured recovery vehicles and as Sturmtiger assault tanks which carried 380mm Raketenwerfer rocket launchers in place of the 88mm main gun.

It is a truism that no sooner has a weapon system gone into production than it is time to start developing its successor. Certainly, no sooner had the Tiger production lines started rolling than Henschel and Porsche were ordered to start work on a design for a new heavy tank with better armament and protection. The gun was to be the same 88mm L/71 weapon (then itself still at the prototype stage) that was to go into the Elefant tank destroyer. With its longer barrel and consequent higher muzzle velocity – 1020 instead of 840 metres per second (3350 instead of 2755 feet per second) – the KwK 43 L/71 could penetrate 180mm (7.1in) of armour. Porsche's contender, the VK4502(P), was, not unnaturally, based on the same petrol-electric drive that had appeared in the earlier design exercises. It was

unsuccessful again, this time because of a strategic consideration like that which had scuppered the squeeze-bore cannon – a drastic shortage of materials, this time the copper required for the windings of the huge electric motors.

The Henschel VK4503(H) design was selected, but this time an important element from the competitor – the turret, which Porsche had designed to accept

anything up to a 150mm gun – was forced on Henschel, even though it was not perfect. A pronounced undercut in the lower edge of the face produced a nasty shot-trap. It took some time for Henschel to produce the moulds for a redesigned turret of their own, which eliminated this problem, and the first 50 of the new tanks were equipped with Porsche turrets. Save for that shot-trap, the turret

PzKpfw VI Tiger (SdKfz 181) Ausf. E

Armament: one 88mm gun, two 7.92mm machine guns
Crew: five
Length (gun forward): 8.45m (27.5ft)
Width: 3.7m (12.1ft)
Height: 2.93m (9.6ft)
Armour: 25–100mm (.98–3.94in)
Engine: 700bhp petrol
Range: 120km (75 miles)
Speed: 38km/h (24mph)
Country of origin: Germany

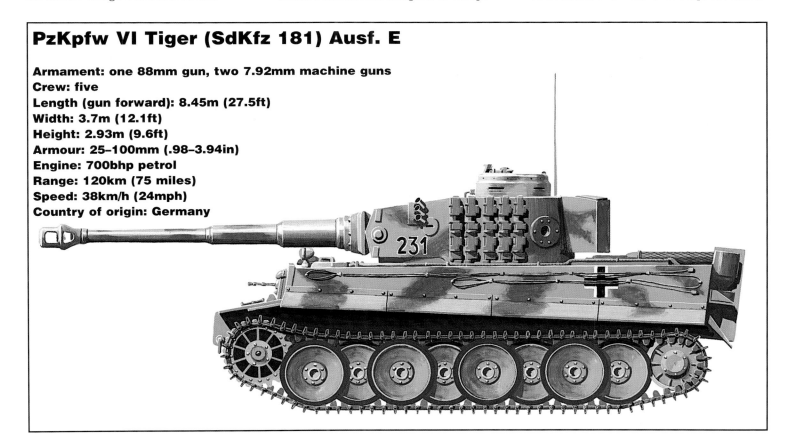

was very well shaped. Constructed out of 100mm-thick (3.9in) armour, its sides angled horizontally as well as vertically into a truncated lozenge. That shape was continued into the hull of the tank itself, which unlike its predecessor had its armour angled to throw off incoming armour-piercing rounds, incorporating the lessons learned, via the Panther, from the Soviet T-34. In fact the PzKpfw 'Tiger II' Ausf B is probably best regarded as a development of the Panther rather than of the Tiger I, since it had more in common with the former.

THE TIGER II

One thing the Tiger II shared with both its predecessors was its 700hp Maybach V-12 engine. But while that had been adequate for the 45-tonne Panther and just about acceptable for the 55-tonne Tiger I, it was hardly powerful enough for a vehicle with an all-up weight of only a

very little under 70 tonnes. The Tiger II's performance suffered badly as a result. It could still manage almost 40km/h (25mph) on the road, but its acceleration was very poor, and its fuel consumption was astronomical – 865 litres (228 US gallons) of petrol would take it barely 60km (38 miles) cross country and less than twice that on the road. Worse still, the engine was constantly being forced to operate at full power, and that spelled frequent breakdowns and malfunctions. Quite why the Maybach HL 230 engine was specified is not clear. There were

more powerful alternatives available, like the 1050hp Daimler-Benz MB509 unit fitted to the aborted 'Maus', or the even more powerful HL 234, which would have provided all the power necessary with hardly greater fuel consumption. Diesel engines of similar power were to be had, too, and they would have both reduced the specific consumption and burned fuel that was easier to obtain, being less refined than petrol.

Like the two other German heavy tanks, the Tiger II's turret was hydraulically operated, with manual

■RIGHT: The 88mm main gun of the Tiger II could easily defeat any enemy tank, but the Tiger II was produced in insufficient numbers to stop the tide of enemy armour across two fronts. This Ausf B was caught in the open by American Shermans and disabled by deliberately firing at the tracks.

Panzerjäger Tiger (Pak 43/2) Elefant (SdKfz 184)

Armament: one 88mm gun
Crew: five/six
Length (inc. gun): 10.27m (33.7ft)
Width: 3.63m (11.9ft)
Height: 2.97m (9.7ft)
Armour: 20–200mm (.79–7.87in)
Engine: 700bhp petrol
Range: 90km (56 miles)
Speed: 38km/h (23mph)
Country of origin: Germany

PzKpfw VI King Tiger Ausf. B (SdKfz 182)

Armament: one 88mm gun, two 7.92mm machine guns
Crew: five
Length (gun forward): 10.43m (34.21ft)
Width: 3.76m (12.3ft)
Height: 3.15m (10.3ft)
Armour: 25--150mm (.98in–5.9in)
Engine: 700bhp petrol
Range: 120km (75 miles)
Speed: 35km/h (22mph)
Country of origin: Germany

back-up for the times when the powerplant was shut down or, as quite often happened, the tank ran out of fuel. In fact the hydraulic system was not particularly precise, and the gunners frequently used the manual system out of choice. It took two full turns of a 250mm-diameter (10in) wheel to move the turret through one degree; that is, 720 turns for a full circle. Also like the Tiger I (or at least, the first 500 of them), the Tiger II could be fitted with a snorkel breathing tube, and with the proper preparation, which took some hours, it could stay completely submerged to a depth of 4m (13ft) for up to two and a half hours. Bilge pumps were fitted to remove any water that seeped in. One undesirable feature of the old Tiger was eliminated. The roadwheels were no longer interleaved – although they did overlap – which solved the problem of involuntary immobilisation in the depths of winter.

Besides the widespread problems of mechanical reliability caused by the underpowered engine, the Tiger II was generally popular, if only because it was truly unbeatable if fought properly. The combination of its superlative gun and

massive armour made it the most powerful tank to see combat in World War II. The Tiger II was known to its crews as the 'Königstiger', and to Allied soldiers as the 'King Tiger' or 'Royal Tiger'. Four hundred and eighty-five were manufactured in all, between the early summer of 1944 and the end of the war a year later. This rate of production was only slightly inferior to that achieved with the Tiger I, 1350 of which were produced in two years of manufacture.

KING TIGER TANK DESTROYER

Only one variant of the Tiger II was ever produced, the Panzerjäger Tiger Ausf B, a tank destroyer with 250mm (10in) of sloping frontal armour and a 128mm PaK 44 L/55 high-velocity gun firing a 28.3kg (63lb) armour-piercing round that could probably have pierced the armoured belt of the average battleship, given the chance. Weighing in at almost 72 tonnes, but still with the HL 230 engine, the vehicle was very underpowered, and largely as a result of that its reliability was even worse than that of the tank from which it sprang. Considerable energy was devoted in Germany during

the latter half of World War II to the development of weapons and vehicles that often never struggled past the prototype stage and that a more rational mind than Hitler's (for the Führer himself was often either the instigator or the champion of such projects) would have rejected long before that. Armoured vehicles were by no means immune from this process, and as early as 1942, Ferdinand Porsche came up with the idea of a truly massive tank. This monster was to weigh upwards of 150 tonnes, thanks to armour that was at the lightest 40mm (1.6in) thick and at the heaviest 350mm (13.8in) thick, and it was to be armed with one 150mm or 128mm high-velocity gun and a co-axial 75mm gun. Power was to come from a 1200hp petrol engine, driving the tracks through electric motors. The tank was to have the longitudinal torsion bar suspension that Porsche always specified and would run on 24 small roadwheels per side, which were to be arranged in fours on bogies and partially interleaved.

When the first 'Mammut', or 'mammoth', prototype appeared in December 1943, it was evident that the

PzKpfw VI Tiger (SdKfz 181) Ausf. E
Country of origin: Germany

1 88mm L/56 gun
2 7.92mm MG34 machine gun
3 7.92mm MG34 machine gun
4 7.92mm machine-gun ammunition
5 Smoke generator discharger
6 Escape hatch
7 Commander's seat
8 Commander's traverse handwheel
9 Revolver port
10 Traverse gearbox
11 Commander's shield
12 Gunner's traverse handwheel
13 Gunner's elevating handwheel
14 Gunner's seat
15 Machine-gun firing pedal
16 Binocular telescope
17 Air cleaning system
18 Maybach engine
19 Radio set
20 88mm ammunition bins
21 Hydraulic traverse foot control
22 Hydraulic traverse unit
23 Disc-brake drum
24 Steering unit
25 Steering wheel
26 Gearbox
27 Driver's seat
28 Handbrake
29 Accelerator
30 Foot brake
31 Clutch
32 Shock absorber
33 Torsion bar suspension
34 Overlapping bogie-wheels
35 Commander's cupola
36 Fan drive clutch lever
37 Air-intake valve control
38 Petrol primer
39 Petrol tap
40 Machine-gun ammunition
   storage

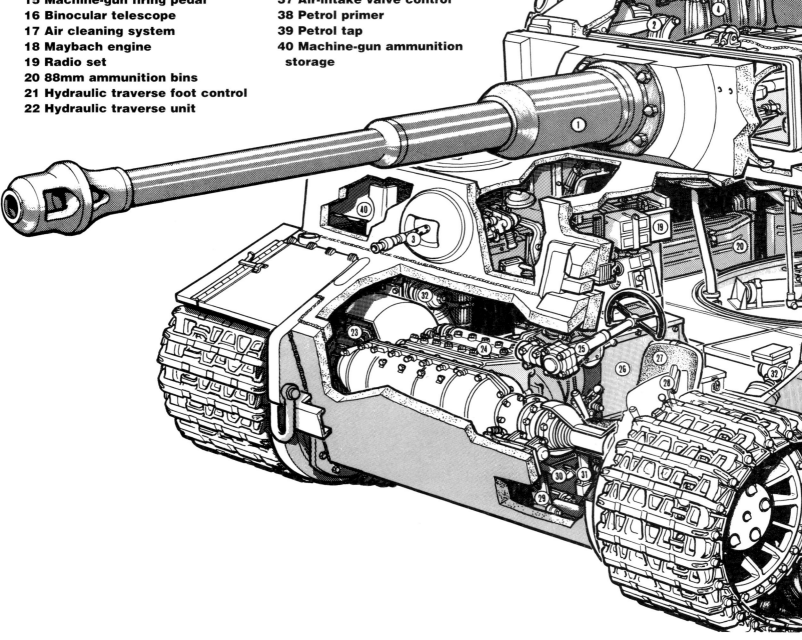

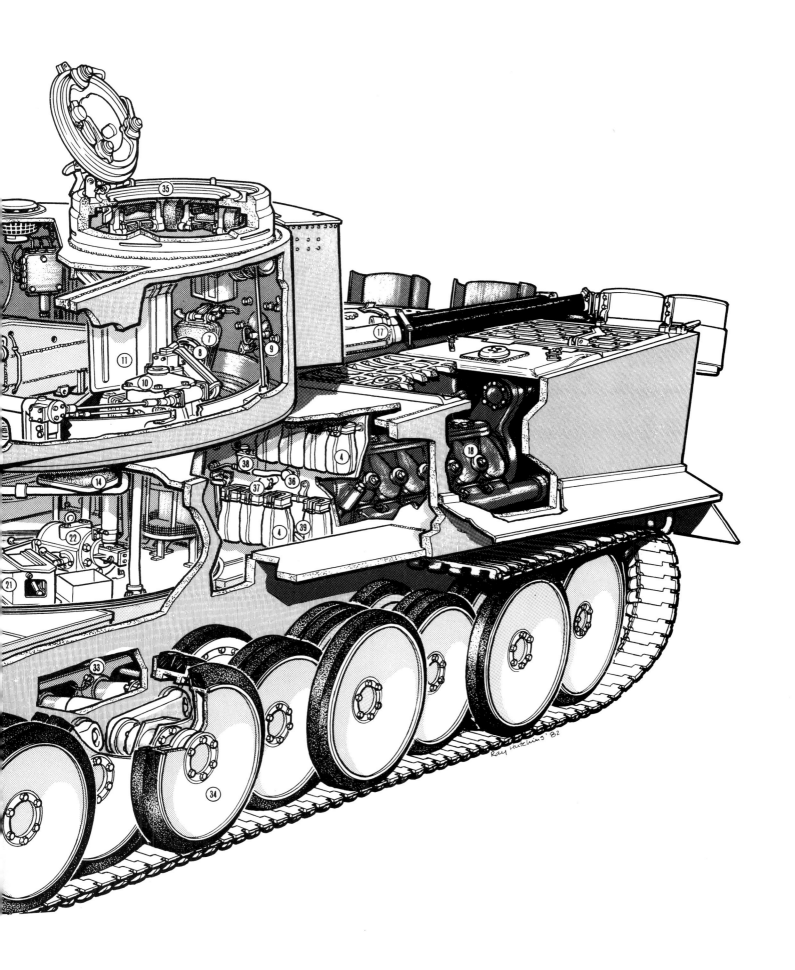

finished tank would weigh something like 190 tonnes with its turret and armament. But, for all that, the prototype actually performed fairly well on test, much to the surprise of its critics in the German High Command, the OKW. It attained a maximum speed of 20km/h (12mph) with an admittedly underpowered Daimler-Benz 1080hp engine in place of the 1200hp unit that had been specified. The Maus, or 'mouse', as the tank became known, somewhat ironically, was far too heavy to use conventional bridges, and so it was provided with the capability to run submerged to a depth of 8m (26ft), with both crew and engine breathing through rigid snorkel tubes. As one expert has put it, 'no coherent tactical use was ever formulated' for the Maus, but that did not prevent nine prototypes being constructed before the collapse of the Third Reich put a stop to the project, by which time 150 of the colossal tanks had actually been ordered into production.

For a variety of reasons, the German Army High Command, the OKH, was opposed to the development of Porsche's Maus, and they reacted just as the French Service Technique Automobile had against the Schneider Char d'Assaut in 1916. They commissioned a competitor,

the E100. It was developed at Henschel and hardly surprisingly was to have looked rather like a bigger version of the Tiger II, armed with a 150mm KwK 44 L/38 gun with a co-axial 75mm, just like the Maus. The E100 was rather lighter in construction than the Maus – although the term is strictly relative – with

armour from 50mm (2in) to 200mm (7.9in) thick and a gross weight calculated at 140 tonnes. One prototype was in the course of construction when the war ended. It was never completed.

Without a doubt, the medium and heavy tanks with which Germany finished World War II were among the

KV-1A

Armament: one 76.2mm gun,
 three 7.62mm machine guns
Crew: five
Length: 6.9m (22.61ft)
Width: 3.25m (10.66ft)
Height: 2.67m (8.75ft)
Armour: 30–75mm (1.18–2.95in)
Engine: 600bhp diesel
Range: 225km (140 miles)
Speed: 35.3km/h (22mph)
Country of origin: Soviet Union

best the world had ever seen. They were beaten not by vehicles that were of a superior construction or by more effective tactics and more advanced fighting skills, but simply by sheer weight of numbers. The Americans built more than twice as many of one marque of tank alone – the M4 Sherman – as the Germans had

tanks altogether. In addition to this, the Soviet Union probably built a total of some 40,000 T-34s during the war. Given the remarkable quality of German World War II tanks, it is hardly surprising that so many elements of tank design perfected by Daimler-Benz, Henschel, Krupp, Rheinmetall and other German

firms found their way into postwar armoured vehicles.

THE TANKS OF THE RED ARMY

The tank that most influenced wartime German armoured vehicle designers was the Soviet T-34, itself derived from Walter Christie's work. In this way, the American could be said to have had an impact on armoured vehicle design out of all proportion to his own personal success in the field. Using as a starting point the BT series of tanks that the Soviet Union evolved from Christie's M1928, the Soviet designer Mikhail Koshkin, working with Aleksandr Morozov and Nikolai Kucherenko at the Komintern plant at Kharkov, turned his attention to a 20-tonne medium tank. The A-20 had Christie's wheel-or-track capability, inclined armour on hull and turret, a 45mm L/46 gun and a powerful and reliable 450hp diesel engine that gave it a top speed of 65km/h (40mph). The A-20 showed itself clearly superior to rival designs in everything but its main armament, and this was changed to the short 76.2mm L/26.5 gun. The A-30, as the tank was now known, went into production in 1939.

THE T-34

Koshkin was not convinced that a tank's being able to run on wheels, as per Christie's original plan, was necessarily worth the limitations this placed on the running gear; in particular on track width. In his next design, which was to become the T-32, he did away with the provision. He was able to fit wider tracks and achieve lower ground pressure and improved traction as a result. The T-32 was basically very similar to the A-20/30 except that it ran on five instead of four roadwheels per side, the wheels being big enough now to make track-return rollers unnecessary. It was marginally slower than the A-20/30, which was also deemed to be better protected and armed. Koshkin believed the T-32 to be the better vehicle, though, and capable of much greater development. He therefore used it as the basis for the design that was to become the T-34.

Uparmoured somewhat, to a maximum thickness of 45mm (1.75in), and with a

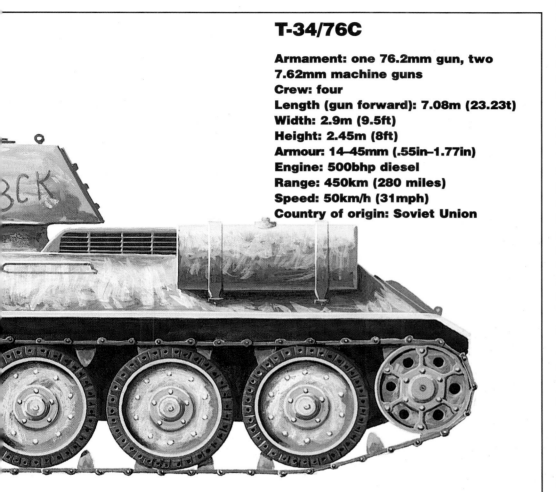

T-34/76C

Armament: one 76.2mm gun, two 7.62mm machine guns
Crew: four
Length (gun forward): 7.08m (23.23t)
Width: 2.9m (9.5ft)
Height: 2.45m (8ft)
Armour: 14–45mm (.55in–1.77in)
Engine: 500bhp diesel
Range: 450km (280 miles)
Speed: 50km/h (31mph)
Country of origin: Soviet Union

■LEFT: The first versions of this KV-1 heavy tank were tested in combat during the Russo-Finnish War. The KV-1C pictured had uprated frontal armour and a more powerful (600bhp) engine.

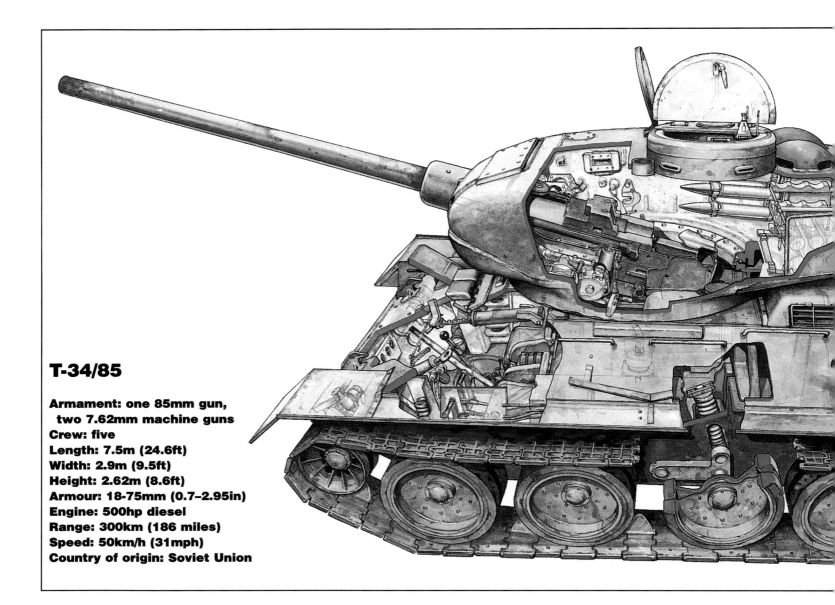

T-34/85

**Armament: one 85mm gun,
  two 7.62mm machine guns
Crew: five
Length: 7.5m (24.6ft)
Width: 2.9m (9.5ft)
Height: 2.62m (8.6ft)
Armour: 18-75mm (0.7–2.95in)
Engine: 500hp diesel
Range: 300km (186 miles)
Speed: 50km/h (31mph)
Country of origin: Soviet Union**

slightly more powerful version of the V-2 engine, the prototype T-34 first ran in 1940, just before Koshkin died of pneumonia. Morozov took over as chief designer and saw the tank into production. It had a more capable version of the 76.2mm gun, with a longer L/30.5 barrel, which achieved a muzzle velocity of 610 metres per second (2000 feet per second). Such a velocity was sufficient for its 6.25kg (14lb) AP projectile to pierce upwards of 55mm (2.2in) of armour at standard angle and range, and kill the contemporary PzKpfw IIIs and IVs at twice that distance, even head on. Two 7.62mm Degtyareva machine guns were fitted – one mounted co-axially, the other in the glacis plate. Broader tracks than were to be found on any other tank of the period, running on unequally spaced double roadwheels whose coil-spring suspension was inside the hull, allowed the T-34 to continue where its opponents foundered. And 615 litres (162 US

gallons) of fuel – a quarter of it in externally mounted tanks that could be jettisoned when empty – gave the tank a remarkable 450km (280-mile) range. All in all, the T-34 was a superlative vehicle, even in its original form, and got better and better as the war wore on. Yet it did have faults. The final drive was known to be prone to failure – a problem that was soon rectified by redesigning it. There were also problems with the turret. The commander's hatch was both too big and opened in the wrong sense, being hinged on its forward edge, while the welded turret itself, with its very distinctive cast gun cradle, was too small and had a shot-trap under its pronounced rear overhang.

T-34 VARIANTS

The first production T-34s were delivered to the Red Army in June 1940 from factories in Kharkov, Leningrad and Stalingrad, although only a total of some 120 units were produced that year. When

Hitler attacked the Soviet Union in the summer of 1941, the Kharkov and Leningrad plants were seen as vulnerable and were moved, along with most of the rest of Soviet strategic industry, to locations east of the Ural mountains. The tank plants relocated to Chelyabinsk, where they were combined with an existing tractor factory to become Tankograd, where Soviet tank production was to be centred until the collapse of the USSR in the early 1990s. The first variant of the T-34 was known in the west as the T-34/76A and remained in production until 1942. By that time a more powerful version of the Model 1939 gun – the Model 1940 F34 – had become available. Its barrel had been increased in length to 41.2 calibres and its muzzle velocity increased to 680 metres per second (2230 feet per second) in consequence. As well as the new gun, the T-34 also acquired heavier armour and a cast turret to become the T-34/76B. That

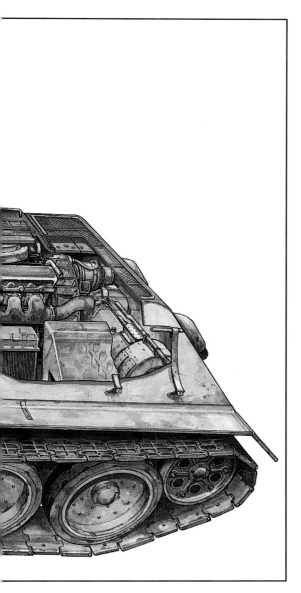

■ABOVE: Few weapons had as decisive an impact on the outcome of World War II as the T-34. More than 40,000 were produced, and its crews played a major part in halting the German advance in the East.

year, a total of some 5000 were produced. In 1943, the T34/76C began to appear, with heavier armour, a redesigned turret hatch and other detail improvements. That year production topped 10,000, and it did not drop below that figure until the war's end.

THE STALWART T-34/85

By 1943, a radical revision of the original design was well advanced that would allow the tank to mount the much more powerful 85mm D-5T85 gun. But a decision was taken to continue the T-34/76's development, too. This became clear when the T-34/76D variant appeared, with a new hexagonal welded turret that was bigger than the previous unit, giving much-needed increased elbow room inside, and also did away with the potentially dangerous overhang at the rear. The T-34/76E was very similar, but had a raised cupola for the commander, while the T-34/76F had the same design

of turret, but it was of cast construction instead of fabricated by welding.

In order to accommodate the much bigger 85mm gun, the improved T-34 needed a completely different turret. Krylov, who had by now taken over from Morozov as chief designer, chose a unit that could also be fitted to the KV-1 heavy tank that had gone into production at around the same time as the original T-34. The new turret was much more commodious all round and had room for a fifth crewman, which freed the commander from the secondary and tactically distracting duty of loading the gun. The gun itself was in every sense the equal of the 88mm KwK that had gone to arm the Tigers. In its early form the gun had a barrel 51.5 calibres long and fired its 9.36kg (20lb 8oz) solid shot at a muzzle velocity of 792 metres per second (2600 feet per second). The improved ZIS-S53 gun that superseded it had a barrel 3.1 calibres longer and achieved 800 metres per second (2625 feet per second) to penetrate 100mm (3.9in) of armour at a range of 1000m (3280ft). The T-34/85, as the improved tank was known, went into production in

December 1943, and in the first month alone almost 300 units emerged from Tankograd. Eleven thousand more were produced in 1944, and another 10,000 before the end of the war. It has been estimated that another 10,000 units at least were constructed after that, with production continuing until 1964.

SOVIET HEAVIES

The T-34/85 stayed in frontline service with the Red Army and the armies of the Warsaw Pact countries well into the 1950s before being relegated to the training role, and more than 50 years after it was first produced, it was still to be found in the armed forces of some Third World states. During World War II, T-34s of both major types were modified as flamethrowers. Others were converted for the armoured recovery role, either by simply deleting the turret or by adding a winch and crane jib. After World War II, some T-34s were equipped with bulldozer blades and mine-clearing rollers, and some in Czech service were fitted out as bridgelayers. Some Syrian T-34s were refitted as SP guns, with a D-30 howitzer in place of the turret, while some North Vietnamese tanks received modified turrets mounting twin 37mm anti-aircraft guns.

As was noted in the previous chapter, the heavy tank concept found considerable favour in the Soviet Union during the 1930s, with first the T-28 and

■LEFT: Prior to World War II, elements of the British Army were deployed far across the globe, charged with policing the Empire. The Vickers-Armstrong Light Tank Mk VI seen here patrolling the Egyptian desert was the standard light tank used by the British throughout the war. Armament was the venerable .303in Vickers heavy machine gun, which had been in service since the Great War.

T-35 and then the T-100 and SMK being developed, all of which had multiple turrets and harked back to an earlier philosophy. While these designs were less than successful, the idea of a heavier tank than the T-34 found considerable acceptance. Early in 1939, designers at Leningrad's Kirov factory, led by Kotin, began work on a new vehicle, the KV-1. It was named after Marshal Klimenti Voroshilov and was to be basically similar to the T-100/SMK but without the subsidiary machine gun turrets and with but a single large-calibre gun in a conventional single turret. The prototype was ready for evaluation in September 1939, and the new tank was ordered into production towards the end of the year, at the same time as the T-34. The KV-1 had an all-up weight of 47.5 tonnes through having primary hull armour 77mm (3in) thick, but could attain 35km/h (22mph) powered by a V-2K V-12 diesel engine uprated to deliver 600hp. Its turret was large enough to accommodate three men and was welded from plate 75mm (2.9in) thick at the sides and 30mm (1.2in) thick on top, with a cast mantlet to protect the breech of the 76.2mm gun. In 1943 the design was updated, and the original chassis was fitted with a new turret, which it shared with the T-34/85, to accommodate the 85mm gun. In the meantime, three KV-1 variants had been produced with more armour. The KV-1A and KV-1B had appliqué panels on the hull front and turret, while the KV-1C had fundamentally thicker armour. A fourth variant, the KV-1s (the 's' stood for 'skorostnoy', or 'fast'), also appeared. It

had less armour than the original KV-1 and could manage 45km/h (28mph) with a combat weight reduced to 43 tonnes.

STALIN'S TANK

The same design team that had been responsible for the KV series tanks was allocated the task, in early 1943, of planning a successor. The new tank's running gear used the system developed for the T-100/SMK. Each side had small roadwheels on six stub axles sprung by torsion bars, along with three track-return rollers. Three prototypes were ready for trials in the autumn, and it was soon apparent that the vehicle had the makings of a very superior tank indeed. Its all-welded hull was armoured to a maximum of 120mm (4.6in), while the turret was the same cast unit as was to be found in the KV-85 (the upgunned KV-1) and the T-34/85. The tank was designated the IS-85. IS stood for Iosef Stalin, and in keeping with western notions of transliteration, it is sometimes rendered as JS. The main difference between the IS series and the KV series was that the former had its running gear mounted lower, which meant decreased track rise and a deterioration in the tank's ability to cross obstacles. At the same time, though, it allowed the superstructure to overhang the tracks and keep the vehicle's overall height down, thus permitting the incorporation of a larger turret ring. In combat trim, the IS-85 was actually 2 tonnes lighter than the KV-85, thanks to careful design and despite the fact that its armour was 50mm (2in) thicker in the crucial places.

The IS-85 went into limited production as the IS-1, and the design team was charged with producing an upgunned version, to mount first a 100mm main gun and later the 122mm D-25. The latter fired a 25kg (55lb) AP round at a muzzle velocity of 780 metres per second (2560 feet per second), which could penetrate 160mm (6.23in) of homogenous armour at a range of 1000m (3280ft). The D-25-armed tank was developed as the IS-122, and went into production as the IS-2 at the end of October 1943. By the end of the year, some 100 had been delivered, and by the end of 1944, more than 2200 had been produced. It was clear that the IS-2 was a formidable vehicle. Yet development did not stop there.

THE IS-2

Petrov, who had been responsible for the original cast turret to take the 85mm gun and who had improved upon that for the IS-2, now conceived a turret with a still better shape. The shallow inverted bowl, varying in thickness between 25 and 230mm (1 and 9in), is still recognisable on Soviet tanks as modern as the T-80 – which was produced up until the end of the 1980s – and was also copied by the People's Republic of China for its light tanks and main battle tanks. The hull of the IS-2 was also completely redesigned and uparmoured, receiving its distinctive feature – the inverted 'V' form of the glacis plate. Nevertheless, the combat weight was still kept below 46 tonnes – well over 10 tonnes lighter than the Tiger I and 20 tonnes lighter than the Tiger II. The IS-3, as the improved tank became, had a ground-pressure value exactly the same as that of the T-34/76A, which was an important factor considering the scope for rural operations in the extensive wetlands that the former Soviet Union contained. The IS-3 was certainly superior to either of its two German rivals, both in terms of firepower – though it had a slower rate of fire – and protection. If the IS-3 had a shortcoming

A12 Infantry Tank Mk II Matilda II

Armament: one 2pdr gun, one .303in machine gun
Crew: four
Length: 6.02m (19.75ft)
Width: 2.59m (8.5ft)
Height: 2.36m (7.74ft)
Armour: 20–78mm (.79–3.07in)
Engine: 2 x 87bhp diesels
Range: 260km (161 miles)
Speed: 24km/h (15mph)
Country of origin: United Kingdom

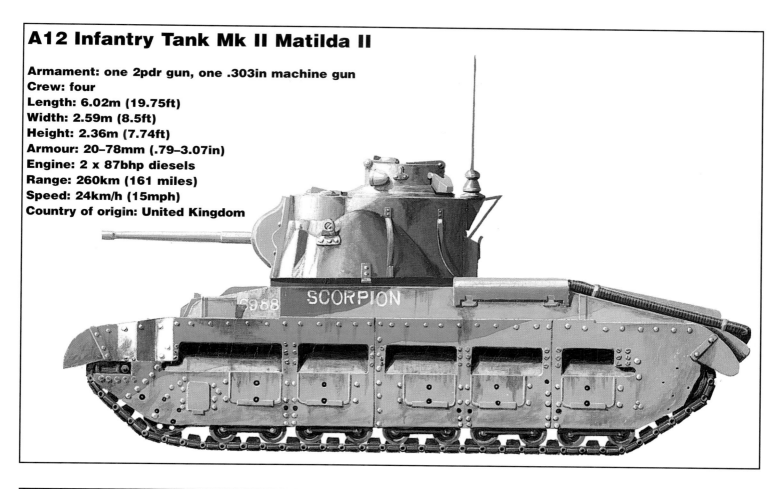

■LEFT: Built by Vickers to a strict budget, in response to a 1934 British General Staff requirement for a tank 'to support infantry in the attack', the Mk I Matilda was hopelessly outmoded by 1940. Although well armoured, the tracks are extremely exposed, and top speed was a miserly 12.8km/h (8mph).

at all, it was that it had a cramped interior – despite the crew having been reduced to four men – and poor ammunition reserves, with just 28 rounds for the main gun. Both the IS-2 and IS-3 had long frontline service with the Soviet Union and its client states, in some cases well into the 1970s. Syria still operated some when it went to war with Israel in 1973, and the Israelis reckoned them hard to kill even then. Many variants were produced, including self-propelled

guns and mortars of up to 420mm and both tactical and intercontinental missile launchers. The final evolution of this remarkable vehicle entered service with the Red Army in 1957 as the T-10.

BRITISH WORLD WAR II TANKS

Although Britain declared war on Germany on 3 September 1939, it was the following spring before British armour was involved in any serious land battle. In the 1940 German campaign in

the west, which led to the capitulation in short order of Holland, Luxembourg, Belgium and France, it soon became obvious that both Paris and London had horribly and recklessly underestimated the brute power of the revitalised German forces, even though all the signs had long been there for all to see. Much of the small British Army at home was committed to the defence of France, and after a campaign that lasted less than a month this army was very nearly captured or annihilated in its entirety. Only a most remarkable set of circumstances, hinging on Hitler's scarcely credible orders to his armies to halt in place on 26 May, and not to advance and crush the Allied remnant at Dunkirk, enabled 338,000 of its men (a full third of them Frenchmen and Belgians) to escape to fight another day. A makeshift rescue armada, the like of which the world had never seen before,

■ABOVE: The Mk II Matilda was a huge improvement on its predecessor and served the 8th Army with distinction in North Africa until 1943. This picture of January 1941 shows crews in England familiarising themselves with camouflage techniques.

snatched the men from the piers and beaches of Dunkirk, while the gallant French First Army, itself without a hope of any sort, screened the operation. But although almost 350,000 men constituted a great army by any reckoning, it was now one without much of its heavy equipment. After all, tanks cannot be embarked on destroyers, much less on tiny pleasure craft.

VICTORY AT ARRAS

The British had one armoured division – the 1st – in Europe, and another – the 7th – in Egypt during the early months of 1940. The divisions were equipped with Light Tank Mk VIs, Infantry Tanks Mks I and II and Cruiser Tanks Mks I, II, III and IV. Of these the most effective were the Mk III and Mk IV cruisers and the Mk II (Matilda) infantry tank. Much of

the 1st Armoured Division went to France with the British Expeditionary Force (BEF) and there fought its first battlefield engagement in 23 years – at Arras, a name that held no particular joy for British tankers – on 21 May. The division fielded 58 Matilda Is, armed only with machine guns, and 16 Matilda IIs, armed with two-pounder guns, together with an unknown number (perhaps a dozen) of Light Tanks Mk VIB.

The British tanks arrived on the battlefield after a slow 190km (120-mile) journey on their tracks from the defensive positions they had taken up near Waterloo in Belgium, many of the units using maps bought along the way. That all but one of the tanks that started reached their objective despite regular attacks by aircraft of the German Air Force was a considerable surprise, not least to the tanks' crews. The infantry tanks proved resilient to German 37mm anti-tank guns, too, and although they took some casualties, the tanks quickly and literally overran the German gun positions. When they were then attacked by tanks of the 7th Panzer Division, led by Irwin Rommel, they responded by

destroying six PzKpfw IIIs and three PzKpfw IVs, as well as an unknown number of PzKpfw IIs. The victory was short-lived, and was marred by what the British Army of a later time was to call a 'blue on blue' incident, when the Matildas came under fire from French SOMUA S-35s whose crews had mistakenly identified them. In the end, the Germans disabled the Matildas with armour-piercing Panzergranate rounds fired from 88mm anti-aircraft guns, which were essentially the guns that later equipped Tiger tanks.

MATILDAS AND CRUISERS

The Matilda IIs, with their 78mm (3in) of primary armour, were certainly tough, but unfortunately they were also slow, having sacrificed speed in the power-to-weight trade-off. On the other hand, the Cruiser Tanks Mks III and IV, which did have satisfactory performance, were clearly both underarmed, with the two-pounder QF gun, and underarmoured, even though the later tank received extra bolt-on panels. Unfortunately, combat experience soon demonstrated that the same was true of the next generation of heavy cruisers, too. The A15 Cruiser Tank Mk VI 'Crusader' was rather similar in outline and basic design to the Cruiser Tank Mk V Covenanter, but with the tried-and-tested (and rather long in the tooth) 350hp Nuffield Liberty engine in place of the flat-12 Meadows. The Crusader also had an extra roadwheel per side. Yet it still had the same main armament, although a subsidiary machine gun turret was fitted alongside the driver's position. This turret was subsequently deleted when the tank was uparmoured – much to the relief of the men who had been stationed there – as was a second hull machine gun operated by the driver.

The 19-tonne Crusader, like the Covenanter before it, had been ordered into production straight off the drawing board, before a prototype had ever turned a track, and once again this was to be the cause of mechanical unreliability on a fairly massive scale. The Crusader first saw action during Operation Battleaxe, the abortive British two-pronged offensive of June 1941 against Sollum and Halfaya Pass in the Western Desert. It is said that more Crusaders broke down than were knocked out by superior PzKpfw IIIs and IVs. The Crusader's own two-pounder gun continued to

demonstrate how the state of the art in tank design and construction had moved on since it had been adopted in 1934. Later versions of the Crusader got a 57mm six-pounder gun with a barrel 42.9 calibres long. This gun had a muzzle velocity of 853 metres per second (2800 feet per second), sufficient for its projectile, which was actually rather over six pounds (2.75kg) in weight, to penetrate 80mm (3.1in) of armour at standard range and angle. It was superior to the 50mm guns fitted to the PzKpfw IIIs and was not that inferior to the L/43 variant of the 75mm gun fitted to the later PzKpfw IVs. The 57mm six-pounder gun became the standard main armament for British tanks until it was superseded first by a 75mm version and then by the very much more powerful 17-pounder.

The final form of the Crusader – the Crusader III, which had armour up to a thickness of 51mm (2in) – was ready for deployment at the Battle of El Alamein of October and November 1942 and acquitted itself quite well. By the time of the Allied invasion of Italy the following year, however, the Crusader III was starting to look decidedly inferior and was rarely seen in action after that. In all, some 5300 Crusaders were built, and

the chassis was also used as the basis for armoured engineering tractors, armoured recovery vehicles, mobile anti-aircraft batteries and observation posts. With its passing also went the 'cavalry' tank concept, according to which the Crusader had been designed. The cavalry tank idea had now, finally, proved itself to be false, as the progressive uparmouring and upgunning of the Crusader had demonstrated. From then on, British medium tank design fell more in line with German practices, although the truth of the matter is that both nations' tanks developed along the only possible lines, as did American and Soviet tanks. The resilience of their armour and the penetrating power of their armament chased each other to gain a brief supremacy before being overtaken again, with reliability and performance the other competing factors.

THE BRITISH INFANTRY TANK

The cavalry tank was only one weapon in Britain's armoured arsenal. The infantry tank – ponderous, heavily armoured and lightly armed – was still very much alive at that point. The Infantry Tank Mk III 'Valentine' (according to some it was named in honour of John Carden, whose middle name that was) was loosely based

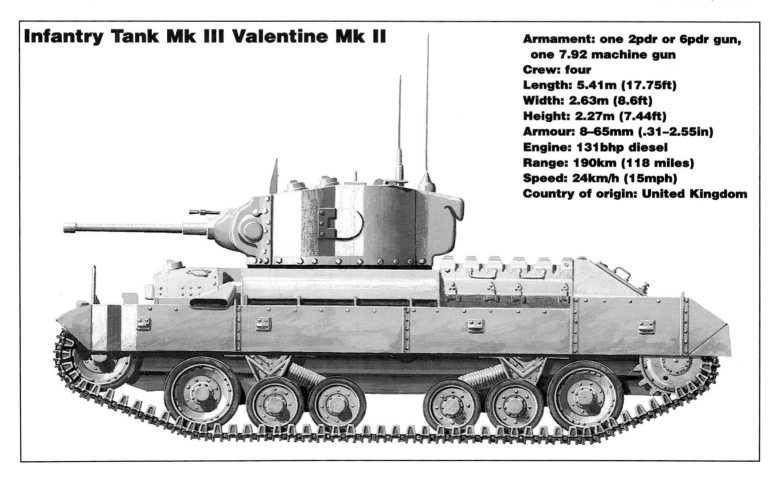

Infantry Tank Mk III Valentine Mk II

Armament: one 2pdr or 6pdr gun, one 7.92 machine gun
Crew: four
Length: 5.41m (17.75ft)
Width: 2.63m (8.6ft)
Height: 2.27m (7.44ft)
Armour: 8–65mm (.31–2.55in)
Engine: 131bhp diesel
Range: 190km (118 miles)
Speed: 24km/h (15mph)
Country of origin: United Kingdom

■LEFT: The compactness and heavy armour of the Matilda made it ideal in the close-quarter support role, especially during the Pacific conflict. Australian infantrymen are seen here advancing cautiously through the Bougainville area supported by the 2/4th Australian Armoured Regiment.

discarded in favour of the much more potent 76.2mm weapon, which made the turret even more cramped than ever. The Valentine's strongest feature was its extreme reliability, which went a long way towards compensating for the compromises that had been made in its design. The Valentine chassis formed the basis for a series of armoured support vehicles, including bridgelayers, mine-clearing tanks with both rollers and flails, armoured engineering tractors and flamethrowers. It was also the foundation for the stop-gap Bishop SP gun, with a 25-pounder gun/howitzer, and for the rather more successful Archer tank destroyer, which mounted a 17-pounder anti-tank gun. The Valentine chassis was also used to develop the Straussler Duplex Drive, which performed so well during amphibious operations.

on the Cruiser Tank Mk II but with elements taken from the Cruiser Mk I and the Matilda I. The Valentine was thus something of a compromise. It had armour between 8 and 65mm (.314 and 2.52in) thick, which was somewhat thinner than was held to be desirable for an infantry tank. It was powered by a 135hp petrol engine, which was soon swopped for a 131hp diesel and later for a 165hp version. The tank's turret was a cramped two-man affair mounting the ubiquitous two-pounder gun, which later grew into a cramped three-man turret, eventually mounting a six-pounder gun and finally a 75mm weapon. The Valentine used the 'Bright Idea' three-wheeled-bogie running gear that Carden designed for the Cruiser Tanks Mks I and II, weighed just over 16 tonnes and had a top speed on the road of 24km/h (15mph), just half that of a contemporary cruiser tank. Curiously for an infantry tank, the Valentine had no hull-mounted machine gun, only a co-axially mounted one. This machine gun was deleted when the first six-pounder guns were fitted, but later reinstated. The later Valentines also gained a Bren gun in the commander's hatch for use against aircraft.

Vickers offered the design for what became the Valentine to the War Office in February 1938, but it was 16 months before it was accepted. It has been suggested that the reason for the delay concerned the two-man turret, which

went against the sensible Tank Corps doctrine of leaving the commander free to concentrate on the tactical situation. Vickers, in fact, had a self-loading two-pounder gun available that would have solved that problem, but curiously it was never specified for the tank. When the design was finally accepted, the company was instructed to deliver 275 tanks with the shortest possible delay. No prototype was ever built, which was a reasoned and reasonable decision taken at a time of deepening crisis, being based on the fact that all the essential components of the tank had been proved in other vehicles. The first Valentines came off the production lines in May 1940. They were too late to see action in France but in plenty of time to fight in the very different environment of the Western Desert. They also fought in small numbers in the Pacific, and six Valentines, along with six Tetrarchs, were involved in Madagascar in the first British amphibious assault involving armoured vehicles. The Infantry Tank Mk III Valentine passed through 11 versions between mid-1940 and early 1944, when manufacture ceased after a total of 8275 had been built in Britain and a further 1420 in Canada by the Canadian Pacific Railroad Company. Most of the latter plus 1300 of the Vickers-built vehicles went to the Soviet Union, where more often than not the two-pounder guns were promptly

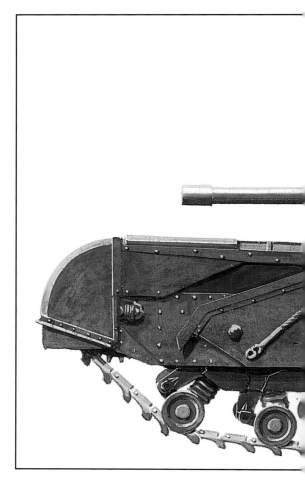

The Valentine was succeeded by what was eventually, after the worst possible start, to become the most significant British infantry tank of World War II – the A22 Infantry Tank Mk IV 'Churchill'. The forerunner of what was to become the Churchill was conceived in 1939 as an up-to-date version of the heavy tanks of World War I. The expectation was that the coming war would be similar in character to that of 20 years before, so a requirement was envisaged for a tank that could cross deep, wide trenches and scale obstacles, was immune both to shellfire and anti-tank weapons, and was armed for close-support operations against hardened defensive positions. In a very real sense, as originally postulated the new tank was little more than a modernised Tank Mk V, complete with rhomboidal tracks and unditching beam and its armament mounted in side sponsons. A feasibility study was undertaken by the British Army's Mechanisation Board and Vickers-Armstrong, which resulted in a rather more conventional specification, the A20, being issued to Harland and Wolff. The company developed a prototype that used the Meadows flat 12 engine produced for the Covenanter – a 300hp diesel engine

being developed by Harland having fallen way behind schedule – and the turret from the Matilda II. Two pilot tanks in mild steel were ordered, but by the time the first was ready for trials their champions' notion of how modern war would develop had been overtaken by reality.

RUSHED PRODUCTION

That same month, May 1940, a revised specification – the A22 – for an infantry tank was put to the Defence Committee and approved. It was issued to Vauxhall/Bedford, who had done some work on the A20, including the production in almost no time at all of a powerful alternative flat 12 engine by the simple expedient of mating two existing straight sixes to a common crankcase. Within two months, Vauxhall/Bedford came up with an A22 design using substantial elements of that evolved by Harland and Wolff for the A20. It incorporated the suspension system, for example, with its 11 small, coil-spring-mounted wheels per side. Small wheels gave an inferior ride cross country but had the redeeming merits of being both cheaper to produce and easier to replace than large-diameter wheels, as well as

having a greater measure of redundancy when damaged. On 1 July, a production order was placed, and the Prime Minister, whose name the tank would eventually bear, himself insisted, across the protests of the Director of Tanks and Transport, that no fewer than 500 be produced by the following March. The attitude of the engineers responsible for carrying out this blatantly impossible task can perhaps be summed up by the response one made on being told that there would be no prototype. 'On the contrary,' he said, 'there will be five hundred of them!'

INITIAL PROBLEMS

Against all the odds, Vauxhall/Bedford actually had the first vehicle ready for testing in December 1940, less than six months after the detailed design work had commenced. Unfortunately, the Department of Tank Design, which had responsibility for the turret, was not so quick off the mark, and a less than ideal unit was initially installed that was big enough only for the two-pounder gun. The second component of the tank's main armament was the three-pounder howitzer mounted in the hull front plate, but this was soon deleted. The Churchill Mk II had a Besa machine gun in its

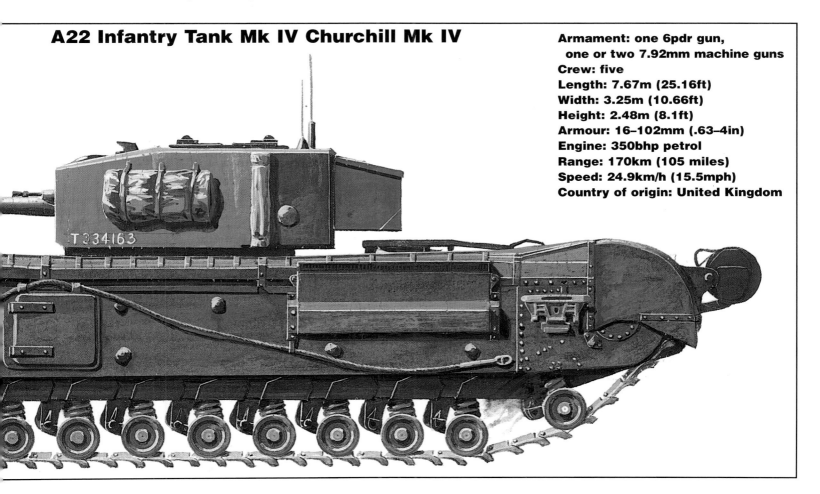

A22 Infantry Tank Mk IV Churchill Mk IV

Armament: one 6pdr gun,
  one or two 7.92mm machine guns
Crew: five
Length: 7.67m (25.16ft)
Width: 3.25m (10.66ft)
Height: 2.48m (8.1ft)
Armour: 16–102mm (.63–4in)
Engine: 350bhp petrol
Range: 170km (105 miles)
Speed: 24.9km/h (15.5mph)
Country of origin: United Kingdom

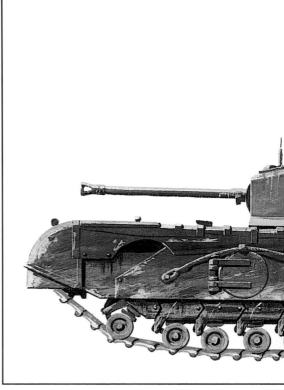

■ABOVE: In June 1940, with the Battle of France at its height, British tank factories were working round the clock. The model in production is the Mk IV Cruiser tank.

place. The Churchill was 7.5m (25ft) long and 3.25m (10ft 8in) wide and was actually something approaching roomy inside in consequence. With armour varying between 16 and 102mm (.6 and 4in) thick, the Churchill weighed in at over 39 tonnes. It is hardly surprising that its 350hp engine would only drive the tank along at 24km/h (15mph) and that it was overstretched and notably

A22 Churchill Mk III AVRE (carpet laying device)

Armament: 290mm spigot mortar
Crew: five
Length: 7.67m (25.16ft)
Width: 3.25m (10.66ft)
Height: 2.48m (8.1ft)
Armour: 16–102mm (.63–4in)
Engine: Bedford 350bhp petrol
Range: 100km (62 miles)
Speed: 24.9km/h (15.5mph)
Country of origin: United Kingdom

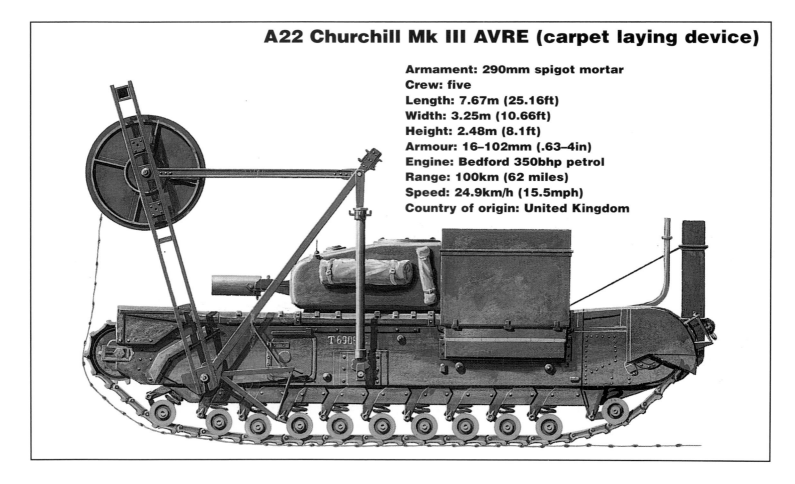

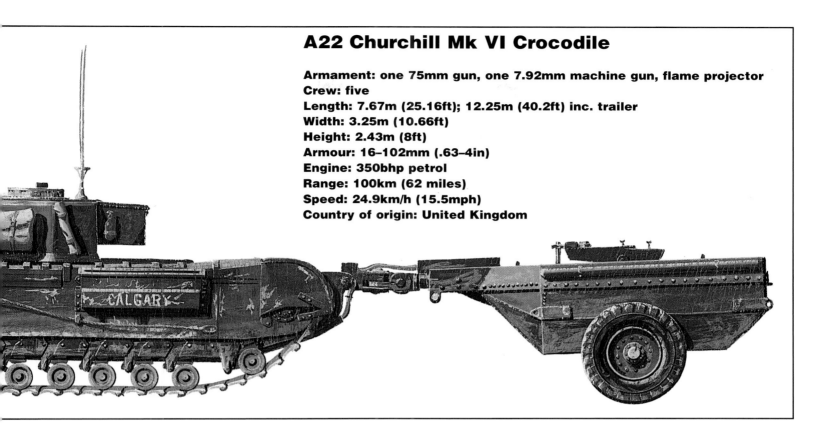

A22 Churchill Mk VI Crocodile

Armament: one 75mm gun, one 7.92mm machine gun, flame projector
Crew: five
Length: 7.67m (25.16ft); 12.25m (40.2ft) inc. trailer
Width: 3.25m (10.66ft)
Height: 2.43m (8ft)
Armour: 16–102mm (.63–4in)
Engine: 350bhp petrol
Range: 100km (62 miles)
Speed: 24.9km/h (15.5mph)
Country of origin: United Kingdom

unreliable as a result. In addition, the engine bay was so designed that the entire powerplant had to be removed for even quite minor tasks to be performed.

The first production Churchills were issued in the summer of 1941 and must have broken the heart of many a dedicated tank soldier. In terms of their overall design, they were clearly capable of mixing it with the best, but they were so prone to mechanical failure and so undergunned that they were actually next to useless. The frustration was probably only further increased by the excellence of some components of the tank's design. The Merritt-Brown regenerative steering system, for example, allowed the tank to turn in a tighter and tighter radius the slower it went, until while stationary it could turn in its own length. Under normal circumstances, all the problems of reliability would have been sorted out at prototype stage, before the first production tanks ever left the factory, as Vauxhall Motors pointed out in an unprecedented addendum to the tank's Operation Handbook. Slowly though, the problems were solved, although that necessitated the first 1000 or so vehicles being returned to the factory for no fewer than six substantial modifications. The Mk III and Mk IV versions finally got the long-delayed six-pounder gun, the former in an inadequate welded turret, the latter

in a cast unit that was not all that much better. Still, by October 1942 – by which time, the Tiger had already been in action for three months, and the first Panthers were coming off the production lines – the Churchill was in such bad odour that further production was cancelled and the tank was declared obsolescent. The tank's reputation had not been improved by the poor performance of the Churchills landed at Dieppe on 19 August 1942 on their operational debut.

THE CHURCHILL'S RECORD
Remarkably, however, the Infantry Tank Mk IV Churchill not only stayed in production but eventually turned into a winner, by means of gradual refinement and the progressive deletion of faults. It never matched the German tanks of the period, but at least three Tigers were destroyed by Churchill guns. One Tiger was also captured, almost intact, and today rests in the British Army's Tank Museum as a result. By the time the Churchill reached its seventh variant, the tank had been substantially redesigned, with 150mm (5.9in) of frontal armour, a new cast/welded turret mounting a 75mm gun and stronger suspension. However, it never did get a more powerful engine, just a more reliable version of the original. The Churchill finished the war a firm favourite with its crews and the infantry it supported alike. It stayed in

service with the British Army until 1952 and was still in use elsewhere into the late 1960s. A total of 5640 were produced, some of which were converted for special purposes such as recovery, mine clearing, bridge laying and road laying (using rolls of hessian reinforced with scaffolding pipes. Churchills were also converted into flamethrowers by means of the Crocodile installation, which was also employed in other tanks in British service. By 1943, plans for an improved Churchill were being laid, but it was January 1945 before the first of six prototypes was completed. The A43 'Black Prince', as it was known in a departure from the British practice of giving their tanks names beginning with 'C', was to all intents and purposes a British Tiger. It was 50 tonnes in weight and had the 17-pounder gun introduced with the A30 'Challenger'. The Black Prince never saw action, and the project was cancelled at the war's end.

The desert fighting in North Africa exerted a considerable influence on British thoughts concerning tank design. It was recognised soon enough that the existing cavalry tanks were too flimsy, and the infantry tanks too ponderous, to make the necessary contribution to the battle. There was the question of reliability to be addressed, too, of course, but that was a different matter. Early in 1941 a specification for a heavy cruiser tank, the A27, was issued, demanding 70mm (2.75in) of armour and the six-pounder gun in a turret set on a 1520mm (60in) ring. The tank was to weigh around 25 tonnes and was to be powered by the as yet still unavailable Rolls-Royce/Leyland Meteor engine developed from the very successful R-R Merlin that powered many of the Royal Air Force's best aircraft. At 27 litres (1648 cubic inches), the Meteor was of similar capacity to the Liberty engine (although rather smaller overall), but produced up to 600hp compared with the Liberty's approximately 400. It was the supply of the Meteor engine that held up the new tank's progress, and in the interim, a stop-gap specification, A24, was issued to Nuffield Mechanisations and Aero. It still bore the code name 'Cromwell', although it later became the Cruiser Tank Mk VII 'Cavalier'. The resulting tank was another inadequate design. It shared many features of the Crusader, including its Christie transmission (which was satisfactory), its Liberty engine (which decidedly was not) and its hull (which was marginal, at best). The only real difference lay in the A24's angular turret, which was big enough to mount the six-pounder gun. The A24 was never to see action as a gun tank, although many

were later used as observation posts for SP artillery batteries and as recovery vehicles. Its main contribution was perhaps in putting a stop, once and for all, to the practice of ordering tanks off the drawing board.

THE CENTAURS

By early 1942, the Meteor engine was still not ready to go into full production, and so an interim A27 specification was issued for the hull and turret to the new design combined with the old Liberty engine and the Crusader's suspension. This became the A27L Cruiser Tank Mk VIII 'Centaur', and was largely used for training purposes. When the Meteor engine finally came on stream, most of the A27Ls were converted to A27M specification, and thus became Cromwells. Perhaps the best of the Centaurs was the Mk IV, which was fitted with a 95mm howitzer that could fire a wide variety of ammunition, including a hollow-charge round that could penetrate 110mm (4.33in) of armour at standard angle and range. The Mk IV Centaur was conspicuously successful in the close-support role during the Normandy landings in June 1944. The Royal Marine Armoured Support Group started firing before their Centaurs had even left their

landing craft and maintained a steady barrage up the beaches and out into the countryside beyond, far exceeding their expected performance and going way beyond their allotted role.

No one really expected the Centaur to be entirely effective in the combat role, for it was always going to be slow. With just 395hp available to pull the 28 tonnes it weighed by the time it was ready to go into battle, the Centaur had a maximum speed of just 44km/h (27mph). But with a minimum of 20mm (.8in) and a maximum of 76mm (3in) of armour, it at least offered much improved protection over the Crusader, and had the much improved gun too. The Mk III was even better off in this respect, for it was fitted with the still more powerful 75mm gun. This gun was essentially a bored-out six-pounder, which made the task of mounting it in existing turrets very simple and straightforward. The 75mm could also chamber American ammunition as used in the M3 Grants and M4 Shermans, thus making the logistical system simpler. The A27M Cromwell (the 'M' was for its Meteor engine) first appeared in prototype form in January 1942. It was a full year before it was accepted for service, not because there were an unusual number of faults

A27M Cruiser Tank Mk VIII Cromwell Mk V

Armament: 75mm gun, two 7.92mm machine guns, two .303 AA machine guns
Crew: five
Length (gun forward): 6.42m (21.1ft)
Width: 3.1m (10.2ft)
Height: 2.49m (8.2ft)
Armour: 8–76mm (.31–3in)
Engine: 600bhp petrol
Range: 275km (171 miles)
Speed: 56km/h (35mph)
Country of origin: United Kingdom

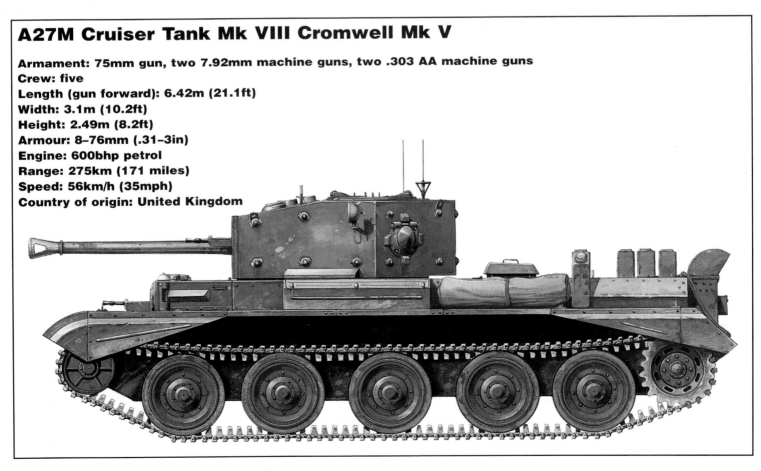

A27M Cruiser Tank Mk VIII Cromwell Mk V

Armament: 75mm gun, two 7.92mm machine guns, two .303 AA machine guns
Crew: five
Length (gun forward): 6.42m (21.1ft)
Width: 3.1m (10.2ft)
Height: 2.49m (8.2ft)
Armour: 8–76mm (.31–3in)
Engine: 600bhp petrol
Range: 275km (171 miles)
Speed: 56km/h (35mph)
Country of origin: United Kingdom

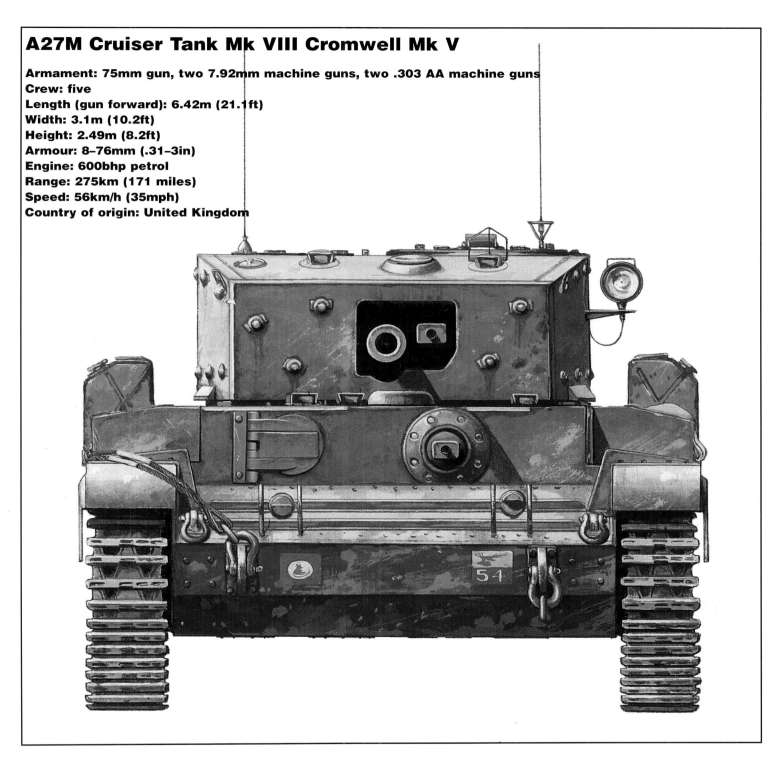

in the pilot tanks or further delays in the Meteor programme, but rather because of a new-found determination in the British War Office to get the new weapon right before issuing it to its fighting men. And right it was.

For the first time, the British Army's armoured divisions had an indigenous tank that they could rely on and put faith in. It was capable of up to 60km/h (38mph) and had a main gun capable of knocking out the enemy on contact. The Mk I and II Cromwells had six-pounder guns, while the Mk III and IVs were re-

engined six-pounder-armed Centaurs. The Cromwell Mk V had the 75mm gun as standard, and the Mk VI was the close-support version, with the 95mm gun. Like every British tank from the Matilda II onwards – with the exception of the Churchill, which had electrical operation – the Cromwells had hydraulically operated turrets. But the system was never quite fine enough in operation to please most gunners, who often preferred to wind the turrets around by hand. It took about 10 seconds to traverse through 90 degrees. In terms

of protection, the first version of the Cromwell had armour up to 76mm (3in) thick, and from the Mk V onwards the hulls were of welded, rather than riveted, construction. There were eight versions of the Cromwell altogether, along with various sub-types. Mks VII and VIII were updates of earlier Cromwells with the thickness of the primary armour increased to 101mm (4in). They also had widened tracks and some detail changes, including a lower final-drive ratio to cut the vehicle's top speed and thus prolong the period between major services.

THE CHALLENGER

The considerable delays in getting the Cromwell into production meant that it was rather overshadowed by the M4 Sherman, which by the time the Cromwell made its operational debut, on D-Day, had been issued in large numbers to British as well as to American units. The Cromwell was to fight through the rest of the war, however, and even if it was not a real match for the Tigers – and nothing was under the right circumstances – it was a workmanlike vehicle that punched its not inconsiderable weight. Fairly early on in the evaluation process, a decision was made to use the Cromwell as the basis for a tank to mount the much more potent 76.2mm 17-pounder anti-tank gun, which was the equal in every way of the German 88mm. The 76.2mm could penetrate 130mm (5.1in) of armour 1000m (3280ft) away, and even when cut down from 55 calibres to 49, it could still go through 102mm (4in) at that range. This new tank was to become the A30 Challenger. It was essentially a Cromwell lengthened by adding another roadwheel and equipped with a 1780mm (70in) turret ring. The larger ring enabled a turret to be fitted that was big enough not only to house the breech of the much larger gun, but also a fourth man to help handle the ammunition. The crew was kept down to five by deleting the hull machine gun. More than 250 Challengers were produced in all, despite being decidedly inferior in protection to the tanks they were to fight and even to those they were to support. The thickness of their armour had been reduced considerably to keep their weight down and their performance up to scratch. That was only the Challenger's main defect, however. It was also very difficult to steer, thanks to the length-to-width ratio of track in contact with the ground being far outside the acceptable norms. The 'simple expedient' of lengthening the tank had proved not to have been so expedient after all. Still, in the absence of anything

■RIGHT: The 2pdr gun that was a standard feature of British tanks prior to 1941 was completely outclassed in terms of range and penetration by the Germans' 50 and 75mm weapons. By the time the new 6pdr main gun (shown here mounted in a Mk VI Cruiser) had been introduced in 1942, German tanks had been further upgunned.

more satisfactory, Challengers were issued to units equipped with Cromwells to give them added firepower. Their casualty rate in the last months of the war was very low, suggesting that they were not fought very enthusiastically.

A STEP BACKWARDS

Whatever their merits may or may not have amounted to, the Cavalier, Centaur, Cromwell and Challenger all seemed to have taken a step backwards in design terms from the Crusader and Covenanter, in that none of the four made use of angled armour. Instead, they relied on sheer thickness of plate for protection. This was in contrast to the Soviet and German practice of the same period and at variance with the sort of designs the Americans had been producing for medium tanks ever since the M3 entered service in 1941. However, throughout the entire period there was controversy over the effectiveness of angled armour. The argument centred around the ineffectiveness of angling the armour at 30 degrees and the likelihood of tanks meeting at different attitudes and thus either negating or compounding the effect.

The designers of the A33 Heavy Assault Tank project in 1943 continued to steer clear of angled armour, increasing the protection on their new tank by adding more metal. Based on the later Cromwells, but with differences in the wheels, the A33 had its frontal armour increased to a maximum of 114mm (4.5in). This increase put the all-up weight up to almost 46 tonnes and cut

the tank's top speed to 45km/h (28mph), although this would probably have been acceptable in view of its projected tactical role. In any event, the 'Excelsior' was abandoned at prototype stage. The A39 Heavy Assault Tank got no further either. The A39 was actually a tank destroyer to rival the similar variants of the Tiger, with its gun – a massive 94mm 32-pounder – mounted in a fixed superstructure with a traverse limited to 20 degrees. Design work started in 1942, but it was 1947 before a prototype was delivered, by which time the need for such a monster had evaporated.

THE COMET

The last British cruiser tank, the A34 Comet, was also worked up from the Cromwell and was a very much more acceptable vehicle for the 17-pounder gun than was the makeshift A30. The Comet had distinctly better lines than the Cromwell, a new turret with electrical instead of hydraulic traverse and a modified suspension system that was on the basic Christie pattern but used smaller roadwheels and four track-return rollers. Because the tank's weight had increased to 33.5 tonnes, the Meteor engine, which was to remain the standard powerplant for British medium tanks until well after the war was over, could give the Comet a top speed of only 52km/h (32mph). A 527-litre (140 US gallon) fuel capacity, meanwhile, gave the tank a range of around 200km (125 miles), much the same as those of other Meteor-engined mediums and of most other petrol-engined tanks of the day. In

fact, the Comet's cross-country performance was such that it was widely held to have been the first tank to be limited only by what its crew could withstand. The Comet prototype first ran in February 1944, and production tanks reached the frontline units early the following year, to immediate wide acclaim. Such approval was deserved, for the Comets were excellent tanks, even if they did still have the square-set front plate. About 1200 Comets were produced in all, and some stayed in British Army service until 1958, while tanks sold on to other users were still going strong two decades later.

If the Cromwell and its derivatives were good tanks (and as has been observed, some were and some were not), there was much better to come before the war was over, in the shape of the A41 'Centurion', which will be discussed later. By and large, though, an analysis of British achievements in the field of tank

design throughout the early part of the period makes slightly sickening reading.

At no time did the British ever beat the Germans to the punch in terms of weaponry, protection or performance, and they lagged a long way behind the Soviet Union too. Had it not been for the sheer number of armoured vehicles available from across the Atlantic, the British would never have been able to come to terms with their main enemy. The dithering attitude to tank production and design that characterised the 1930s was carried on into the war years themselves, and all too frequently this procrastination resulted in British soldiers being sent into battle in vehicles that really stood extremely little chance of fighting through. Thankfully for Britain's integrity and the morale of its various armies, that situation was slowly but surely put right.

ENTER THE AMERICANS

The turning point in British fortunes came with Hitler's decision to declare war on the United States in the days after Japan's surprise attack on Pearl Harbor. Indeed, Churchill made a declaration of his own when he heard the news – that the war was won. He was right, but it took a further two and a half years to prove it. Until Hitler went to war with the United States, the Americans had been supplying Britain with weapons and equipment readily enough – despite considerable opposition from isolationists and pro-German elements – first on a 'cash-and-carry' basis and later under the Lend-Lease Agreement. But the hardware supplied was never quite state of the art. The United States' entry into the war changed that. Soon enough, British armoured divisions started to receive modern American equipment in large quantities – as, of course, did those of the Soviet Union. By the time of the invasions of Sicily and Italy, the Allies in

Light Tank M3A3 (Stuart Mk V)

Armament: one 47mm gun, three .3in machine guns
Crew: four
Length: 4.53m (14.9ft)
Width: 2.23m (7.32ft)
Height: 2.5m (8.2ft)
Armour: 25–38mm (.98–1.5in)
Engine: 250bhp petrol
Range: 140km (87 miles)
Speed: 54.7km/h (34mph)
Country of origin: USA

the west had begun to learn their lessons, and the Americans, to quote one of their heroes from a different war, had only just begun to fight.

When the US Army got the final version of the M2 Light Tank, the M2A4, in 1939, it was already clear that the design was not going much further, thanks to the limit imposed by the width of its hull. Nonetheless, when the first M3s appeared the following year, they

were little more than developments of the earlier vehicle. The M3s had more armour, which took the vehicle's weight up to 12.5 tonnes, and simple modifications to the suspension system, but they retained the five machine guns of the earlier model. Over the next two years, around 5800 M3s were produced, and many of them found their way to the British Army as part of the Lend-Lease Agreement. These latter were fitted with

the Guiberson 220hp nine-cylinder diesel engine in place of the original Continental 250hp petrol engine. The British eliminated the two fixed forward-facing machine guns in the above-track sponsons and used the space thus freed for storage. They designated the tanks 'General Stuart' I and II, nicknamed them 'Honeys', and used them enthusiastically right through to the end of the war, even though the tanks were

Medium tank M3 (early prototype)

Armament: one 75mm gun, one 37mm gun, two .3in machine guns
Crew: four
Length: 5.64m (18.5ft)
Width: 2.72m (8.88ft)
Height: 3.12m (10.25ft)
Armour: 38–50mm (1.5–1.97in)
Engine: 340bhp petrol
Range: 160km (100 miles)
Speed: 42km/h (26mph)
Country of origin: USA

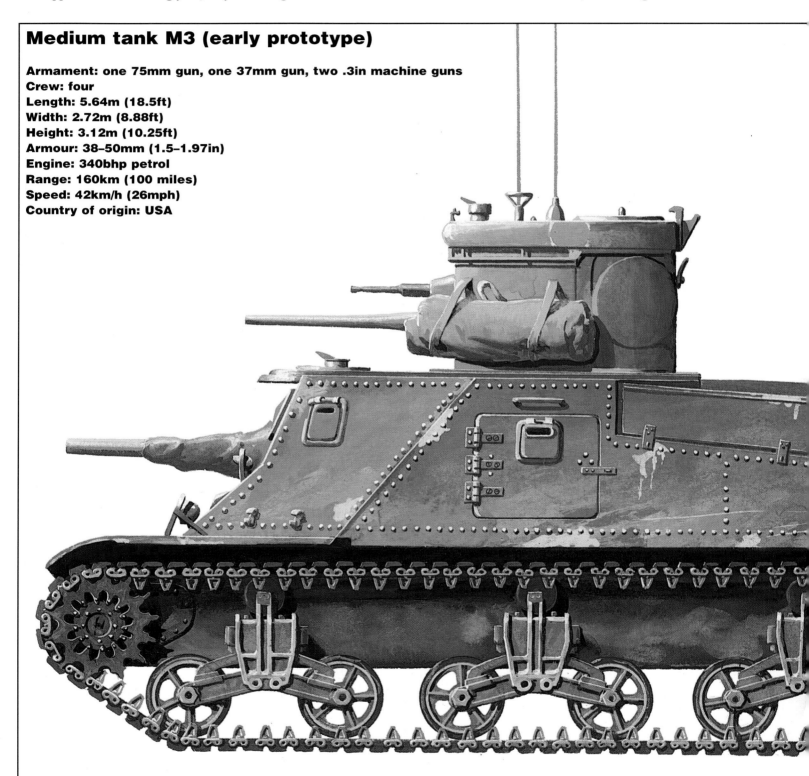

■ABOVE: Known to American forces as the M5, and to British operators as the Stuart Mk VI, the M5 was designed for a fast reconnaissance role. A gyro-stabiliser allowed the 37mm main gun to be fired accurately at speed.

very vulnerable by that point.

To start with, the British used their Stuart Is as cruiser tanks. They were almost on a par with the A13s and Crusaders, and much more reliable. Their new owners were prepared to put up with the inadequate performance of the 37mm L/50 gun for the sake of a top speed of 55km/h (35mph) and armour up to 64mm (2.5in) thick. The Stuart Is could hardly be described as roomy. The four-man crew, two in the turret and two down in the driver's compartment at the front of the hull, saw to that, and further space was taken up by the transmission shaft running forwards through the middle of the tank from the hub of the high vertically set radial engine to drive the front sprockets. Besides the space constraints it caused, this arrangement was undesirable in itself, since it put the return run of the track under tension.

The problem of space actually got worse, at least in the fighting compartment, with the introduction into the M3A1 of a turret basket – a false floor that rotated with the turret and therefore needed to be set entirely above the drive shaft. No mechanical traverse was fitted to the original M3, and in fact the entire procedure for turning the turret was complicated. The gunner could not reach the actuating wheel, but had to shout instructions to the commander above the clamour of the machine instead. The M3A1s got hydraulically operated turrets, which by now were welded castings instead of being riveted. The hulls were not made of welded castings until the final version, the M3A3, which also had a further improved turret. Some 5300 M3A1s (Stuart IIIs and IVs to the British) were built, and almost 3500 M3A3s (Stuart Vs), making the type the most widely used light tank of World War II. Incidentally, there never was an M3A2. The tank was cancelled before it ever went into production.

M3 AND M5 VARIANTS
The M2 and M3 light tanks were

M3 General Lee Mk I

Armament: one 75mm gun, one 37mm gun, four .3in machine guns
Crew: six
Length: 5.64m (18.5ft)
Width: 2.72m (8.9ft)
Height: 3.12m (10.23ft)
Armour: 12–57mm (1.47–2.25in)
Engine: 340bhp petrol
Range: 195km (121 miles)
Speed: 42km/h (26mph)
Country of origin: USA

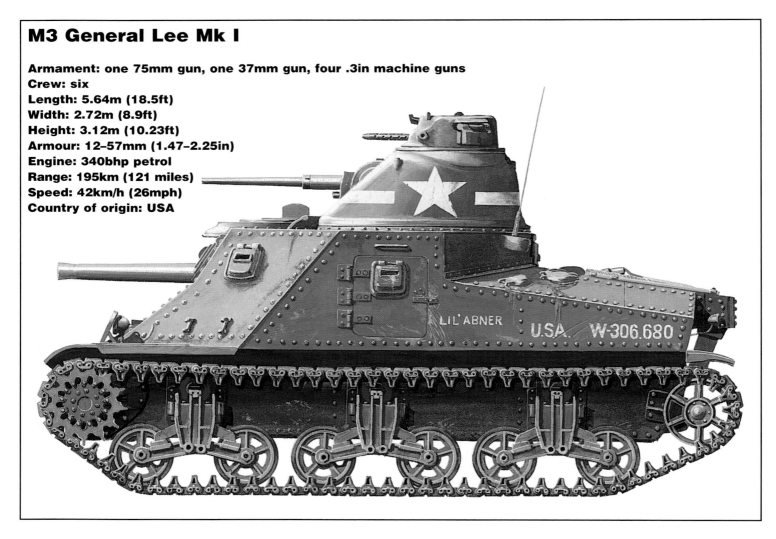

developed at the Rock Island Arsenal and produced by companies specialising in heavy engineering. But in 1941, the Cadillac Division of General Motors converted an M3 to accept a pair of V-8 automobile engines coupled to a standard Hydra-Matic automatic transmission. Fairly widespread beliefs that the revision would not stand up to the task were stifled when the prototype M3E2, as it was initially known, was driven the 800km (500 miles) from the factory to the proving ground. Detailed changes were made, and in February of the following year the design was accepted as the Light Tank M5. Besides the change of powerplant, the 'new' tank had longer superstructure, a raised rear deck and an angled glacis plate in place of the original square front. The M5A1 followed with the turret developed for the M3A3. By the time production of the M5 ceased in late 1944, a total of some 8900 had been produced. They, too, were used extensively by the British, who called them the Stuart VI. By 1944, a 'light' tank was very much bigger and heavier than the equivalent class of vehicle just a

decade before. The M3A3 turned the scales at almost 14.5 tonnes, and the M5A1 was a tonne heavier still. Nonetheless, both could still manage a very respectable 58km/h (36mph). If they were light in any sense it was in their armament, having main guns of just 37mm. But since their role was to reconnoitre and gather intelligence, rather than to get involved in firefights that they were doomed to lose, a light armament was deemed, officially anyway, to be not too much of a drawback. In fact, during the last two years of the war, British Stuarts were often to be found minus their turrets, serving as reconnaissance cars and as armoured carriers for casualty evacuation and resupply. They were faster without a turret, and their lower profile made them easier to conceal. M5s were also converted into Howitzer Motor Carriage M8s, with a 75mm pack howitzer in the turret. The wide popularity of the M3/M5 series seemed to validate the light tank's continued presence on the battlefield, and the US Army actually commissioned two more – the M7, which never got past the

prototype stage, during which it grew into a medium tank anyway, and the M22, which the British, who were the only ones to operate it in combat, and then only once, called the 'Locust'.

THE AIRBORNE M22

The M22 was the American counterpart of the British Tetrarch, intended for use by airborne forces. As commissioned, it was to weigh just over 7.5 tonnes, be crewed by three men, mount a 37mm gun and three .30in machine guns and have armour up to 25mm (1in) thick. A design by Marmon-Herrington was selected. Marmon-Herrington was an agricultural tractor manufacturer that had also produced the T-16 light tank for export and had built some armoured cars. The prototype M22, the T9, appeared in the autumn of 1941. At 8 tonnes it was judged too heavy and underwent a slimming process that involved changing from an all-riveted construction to a welded hull and a cast turret. The slimming-down also required the removal of the hydraulic traversing gear, the gyrostabiliser for the gun and the hull

■LEFT: Under the terms of the 1940 Lend-Lease Act, the powerful and well-armoured M3 Medium Tank became available to British armoured divisions, so helping to redress the balance between Allied and Axis tank forces. To reduce the overall silhouette, the British version seen here was built without a turret cupola.

machine guns. The result, powered by an Avco-Lycoming air-cooled engine developing 162hp, could achieve 65km/h (40mph).

The delivery method envisaged for the M22 was somewhat bizarre. Specially adapted C54 Skymaster aircraft, the military version of the four-engined Douglas DC4 airliner, were to carry a vehicle each as underslung loads, the turret first having been removed and placed inside the fuselage via an enlarged cargo door with a built-in hoist. Somewhat surprisingly, the loading operation could be carried out comfortably by six men in half an hour. The vehicle was positioned beside the cargo door, and the hoist attached to the turret, which was then winched up and swung inside. Meanwhile the tank's hull was driven to a point between the sets of landing wheels, beneath the aircraft's centre of gravity, where a second hoist, attached to four points on the vehicle's extremities, elevated it until four sprung hooks in the airframe located with four lugs on the tank. When the aircraft reached its destination, the sprung hooks were released, dropping the tank the 35cm (14in) to the ground. The driver could then climb aboard his vehicle and drive around to the cargo door, where the turret was reunited with the hull. The whole unloading process took a mere 10 minutes.

INTO ACTION IN 1944-45

The drawback was that the DC4 was not capable of operating on a rough field, and the unloading process could hardly be carried out under fire. This meant inevitably that the M22 could be delivered only to rear-echelon airfields, which rather negated its value. The British Airborne Forces used a much simpler system that delivered their light tanks to the battlefield itself. They commissioned the General Aircraft Company to build the biggest glider ever to see active service, the Hamilcar, with a wingspan of 33.5m (110ft) and an 8-tonne payload. The entire nose of the glider was hinged to allow an M22 or a Tetrarch to simply reverse up a ramp to load and then drive off again at the destination. The Tetrarch was the first tank to be deployed by air, with more spectacle than real effect, on the evening of D-Day, and Locusts of the 6th Airborne Division delivered by glider saw combat during the Rhine crossing operations in March 1945, the only time they went into action. By that time, having been designed to meet 1941 criteria, the Locusts were hopelessly vulnerable. A total of 830 were built, plans for a further 1100 having been cancelled. The Light Tank Mk VIII Harry Hopkins, which was designed as a successor to the Tetrarch, was too heavy for the glider at 8.5 tonnes and consequently never saw service.

The final American wartime venture into the field of light tanks was a rather more workmanlike exercise. In April

1943, a programme to develop a successor to the M5 was put in train by the US Ordnance and Cadillac. It was to use the powerplant of the M5, still with its automatic transmission, and the Christie running gear of the M18 Motor Gun Carriage built by Buick, another arm of General Motors. The M18 was the only American SP gun of World War II to be designed as such and not modified from an existing armoured fighting vehicle. Prototypes of the M5's successor were delivered in October, and the new tank was standardised as the M24 in July 1944, after it had been in production for three months. The British Army acquired a few M24s during the final months of the war, and both the British and the Americans used them during the Rhine crossings and later. M24s also saw service during the Korean War and in French hands in Indochina. The British called them 'Chaffees', after Adna R. Chaffee, the 'Father of US Armoured Forces'. Chaffee, whom we last glimpsed alongside George Patton at the trials of Christie's M1928, had died of cancer in August 1941, and the US Army was quick to adopt the name itself. Experts – and by now that included a lot of tankers – called the Chaffees superb.

THE CHAFFEE
At 18.5 tonnes combat-ready, the M24 Chaffee stretched the original definition of a light tank way out of shape. And while its maximum of 25mm (1in) of armour on the hull front and 38mm (1.5in) in the turret, powerful 75mm M6 main gun and 55km/h (35mph) top speed certainly met the specification for a cavalry tank well enough, that type had been effectively obsolescent for a good while by 1944. Yet despite what looks like immediate obsolescence, a total of perhaps 5000 M24s were built, four-fifths of them in the single year up until the end of the war. They were still in service with a score of nations, in one form or another, until the late 1970s and after, often with quite sophisticated fire-control systems added. GIAT, the French

M4A3 (76)W HVSS Sherman IVY

**Armament: 76mm (3in) gun,
two .3 machine guns,
one .5in AA machine gun
Crew: five
Length: (gun forward) 5.9m
(19.35ft)
Width: 3m (9.8ft)
Height: 2.97m (9.746ft)
Armour: 12–110mm (.47–4.33in)
Engine: 500bhp petrol
Range: 161km (100 miles)
Speed: 42km/h (26 mph)
Country of origin: USA**

national arms manufacturer, took up the Chaffee and modified it very extensively in partnership with a Norwegian company, Thune-Eureka, supplying a number to the Norwegian Army in 1975-76. The conclusion to be drawn is that perhaps there's always room for a 'good little 'un'.

AMERICAN MEDIUMS

On the outbreak of war in Europe in September 1939, the US Army, which was not to be directly involved for a further two years and more, had a pair of extremely similar tanks, one light and one medium, in general service. It did not take long for the realisation to dawn that the M2 Medium Tank – with its 32mm (1.25in) primary armour, 37mm gun and small turret ring – was both hopelessly outclassed by the tanks being used in Europe and incapable of much in the way of any improvement. In 1940, a new tank specification, armoured up to 38mm (1.5in) and mounting a 75mm gun, was worked up. In the absence of anything like a suitable turret, it was decided to use the Phase III Medium Tank T5, which carried its main armament in a limited-traverse mount in a starboard-side sponson, as the basis for the new vehicle. It was to be suitably uparmoured and given a turret with all-round traverse atop the superstructure. This turret mounted a 37mm gun, and a secondary turret mounting a machine gun was to be placed above it. The side sponson main gun mounting was a stop-gap solution, certainly, and as the tank's

■**ABOVE: The M4 Tankdozer, one of the diverse tasks the M4 Sherman was adapted for as part of the Allied invasion of Europe in June 1944.**

users were to discover, it unfortunately was next to useless when engaged in combat with other tanks, although it proved satisfactory enough in the assault/support role. Nonetheless, in the late summer of 1940, a recently placed order for 1000 M2A1s was converted to tanks of the new specification, to be known as M3 Medium Tanks.

THE M3

The new M3 looked rather different from the M2A1 – which was a cluttered, angular, ugly design, full of shot-traps – but shared many of its elements. The suspension and running gear, for example, consisted of three twin-wheeled bogies on vertically set volute springs with a track-return roller mounted at each of their upper attachment points. The rear-mounted 340hp Wright Continental radial engine – somewhat surprisingly substituted for the 400hp version found in the earlier tank – drove the front sprockets via a shaft that passed through the centre of the fighting compartment, although this arrangement mattered less here than it did in the light tanks, since the M3 was that much bigger. Indeed, it was considered fairly roomy, even with a full six-man crew on board. In its initial form, the M3 weighed a little over 27 tonnes, and in combat terms its best feature, even if it was not

mounted particularly cleverly, was its dual-purpose M2 75mm gun, derived from the original French 75mm 'Soixante-quinze' and better than anything either Britain or Germany had in the field at the time. It was able to fire HE shell as well as AP, the latter with a muzzle velocity of 567 metres per second (1860 feet per second), which enabled the gun to pierce 60mm (2.4in) of armour. In fact, the M2 L/38 gun was an interim model. Its successor, the M3, had a 38-calibre barrel that achieved 700 metres per second (2300 feet per second) and pierced an extra 10mm (2.4in). The M3 gun was fitted to later M3 tanks, as well as to some M4 Shermans and the M24 Chaffee.

THE BRITISH ORDER THE M3

The placement of the order for 1000 M3s coincided with the arrival in Washington of the British Tank Mission. It consisted of three members: Michael Dewar, an industrialist, L.E. Carr, a design specialist, and Major-General Douglas Pratt, who had commanded the British tanks at Arras and probably knew as much as anyone else in Britain about actually fighting tanks in the field. These three men were to play a vital role in seeing American tanks adopted by the

■ LEFT: 'Virgin', a Sherman V clearly yet to be tested in combat, comes ashore at Gold Beach during the Normandy landings, 6 June 1944. The Sherman was without a doubt the most important tank in service with the British and American armoured forces during World War II. The US automotive industry alone produced nearly 40,000.

British Army, but when Pratt first saw the M3 he was quite taken aback. Admittedly the main gun was attractive, but its mounting was not, even if it – and that of the turret-mounted 37mm gun – was gyrostabilised in azimuth in order to keep the barrel steady and guarantee reasonably accurate shooting even while the tank was at speed. The tank's overall height of 3.1m (10ft 3in) was daunting, and the supermounted turret-cum-cupola was very vulnerable. Besides all that, the M3's armour was flimsy for a tank of its size, and the riveted joints were not properly sealed against 'splash' from the molten lead core of incoming small arms rounds, a hazard that had existed since the days of the very first tanks. Nonetheless, there was very little choice – it was M3s or nothing. Dewar got permission from London to order 1250 of them on the understanding that their manufacturers would modify them where possible to suit British requirements. He promptly more than doubled the order, to 3000, on the further understanding that he would have to take only 1500 if a better tank went into production while the M3s were being manufactured. Dewar thereby assured continuing production of medium tanks for the British Army at a crucial time, albeit at the cost – when spares and components for other armoured vehicles, particularly the Valentines, were included – of virtually every penny of British Government investment in the United States: a total

Sherman VC Firefly
Country of origin: USA/UK

1 **17pdr gun**
2 **.30-calibre M1919 machine gun**
3 **.50-calibre M2 machine gun**
4 **Commander's cupola**
5 **Commander's periscope**
6 **Loader's hatch**
7 **Wireless set**
8 **Signal pistol**
9 **17pdr ammunition stowage**
10 **Commander's seat**

11 **Loader's seat**
12 **Escape hatch**
13 **Driver's periscope**
14 **Portable fire extinguisher**
15 **Driver's seat**
16 **Chrysler 425hp multibank petrol engine**
17 **Range finder**
18 **Two 12-volt batteries in series**
19 **Power train**
20 **Gearshift lever**
21 **Parking brake lever**
22 **Steering levers**
23 **Five-gallon water containers**
24 **Equipment chest**
25 **Ventilator**
26 **Radio antenna**
27 **First-aid box**
28 **3.5in-thick gun shield**
29 **1.5in-thick mantlet**
30 **Binoculars**
31 **Periscope**
32 **Air cleaner manifold**
33 **Clutch assembly**
34 **Fan assembly**
35 **Radiator**
36 **Final drive housing**
37 **Track return rollers**
38 **Suspension bogie**
39 **Track drive sprocket**
40 **Track idler**
41 **Volute spring**
42 **2in bomb-thrower on loader's
side of turret (not shown)**

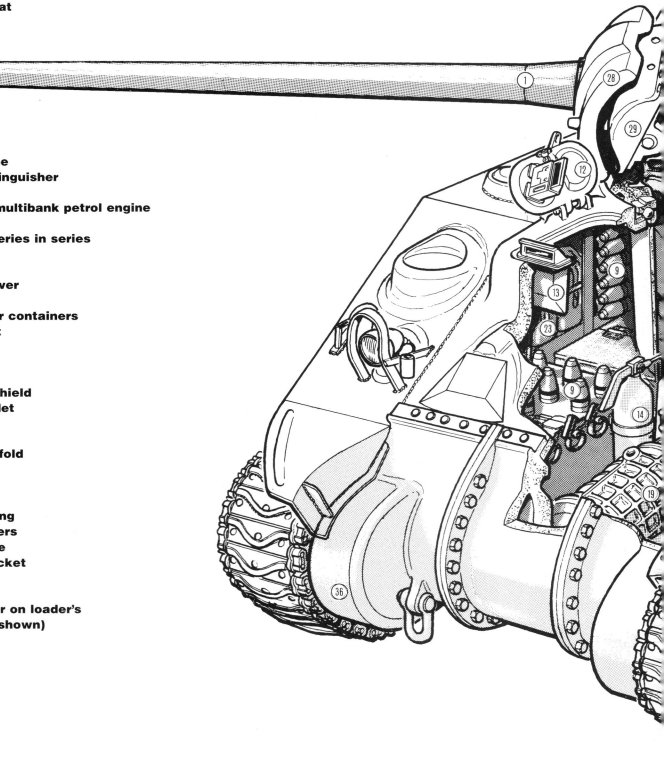

M4 Sherman Crocodile (Flamethrower)

Armament: one 75mm gun, one flamethrowe‹ (range 40m), two .3in machine guns
Crew: five
Length (with trailer): 11.35m (37ft)
Width: 2.66m (8.72ft)
Height: 2.74m (9ft)

of some $240 million. The problem that this created led ultimately to the substitution of Lend-Lease for the original cash-and-carry policy in March 1941.

Although it was current for just 18 months, from April 1941 to October 1942, the M3 was to go through a somewhat confusing array of variants, particularly when modifications to the tanks to go to Britain were taken into account. The M3 was manufactured in one form or another by heavy engineering concerns Baldwin Locomotives, American Locomotives, Pressed Steel and Pullman. But the biggest number – 3350 out of the total production of 6250 – came from Chrysler. This represented the first, but by no means the last, serious involvement of the American automobile industry in the World War II tank manufacturing effort. The most important difference between the American and British vehicles was in their turrets, although not all the tanks issued to the Royal Armoured Corps were actually to the British specification. This was reflected in the fact that there were

■RIGHT: March 1944. Although a capable and reliable machine, the M4 (Sherman I) medium tank was no match for the German Tiger tanks that Allied forces encountered at Cisterna, near the Anzio beachhead in southern Italy in early 1944.

two names for M3s serving with British units. Those M3s and variants with American turrets were known as 'General Lees', whereas M3s and variants with the British turret – with its much thicker, heavier front face and with the superimposed turret deleted – were called 'General Grants'.

GENERALS LEE AND GRANT

The original M3 had a riveted hull and either the Wright radial engine or a similar Guiberson diesel. The four main variants (excluding the M3A2, of which only 12 were built) were the M3A1, with a similar engine and a cast upper hull from Alco, the only producer capable of casting such a large component; the M3A3, with paired GMC 6-71 diesels and a welded hull; the M3A4, with a riveted

Armour: 12–51mm (.47–2in)
Engine: 400bhp petrol
Range: 180km (111 miles)
Speed: 40.2km/h (25mph)
Country of origin: USA/UK

hull and the bizarre Chrysler A-57 multibank engine, created by mating no fewer than five car cylinder blocks to a common crankcase/crankshaft; and the

M3A5, which had a riveted hull and the twin GMC engine layout. All five common variants were to be found under the General Lee identity in the British Army from the spring of 1942 onwards, but only the M3 and M3A5 appeared with the Carr-designed turret, as the General Grant I and II. The first M3s weighed just over 27 tonnes, and the weight changed very little from model to model save for the M3A4, which came to 29 tonnes, being 350mm (14in) longer to accommodate the engine installation. M3s first went into action at Gazala in May 1942 and made a decisive contribution to the British victory at El Alamein in the closing months of the year. By that time they had become popular with their crews, largely because they could knock out a PzKpfw IV at stand-off range. By mid-1944, the type had disappeared from frontline service almost as quickly as it had appeared, totally eclipsed by the M4 Sherman.

One interesting development of the basic M3 took place in Canada. The Ram, as it was known, used the underframe and running gear of the American tank and mated it with a new, cast upper hull and a fully traversing turret that mounted a two-pounder gun when the tank was first developed in 1941.

CANADIAN RAMS
The turret had been designed originally to accommodate the six-pounder gun and had a suitably sized removable plate bolted into the turret face. As soon as supplies of the six-pounder became available, the gun was incorporated into what became the Ram II. On the whole, the Canadian tank was an improvement over the original, though it incorporated some outdated features such as hull-side escape hatches and a small turret for the hull machine gun. But it was never used in action, since by the time it was ready the tanks it would have met were already largely proof against six-pounders, and the Ram could not be further modified to take the 75mm gun. Some 1900 Ram IIs were built and used for training purposes, however, and the tank was later used as the basis for a wide variety of specialist vehicles, such as the Ram Kangaroo armoured personnel carrier (APC) and the Sexton SP gun.

A rather less successful tank from the British Empire – at least in terms of its operational achievements, if not of its innovative qualities – was also originally to have been based on the M3's running gear, but in the end events intervened to prevent that. The announcement that Australia, which had no experience of

M4A2 Sherman III DD 1

Armament: 75mm gun, two .3in machine guns
Crew: five
Length: 6.35m (20.83ft)
Width: 2.81m (9.22ft)
Height: 3.96m (13ft) (screen erect)
Armour: 12–51mm (.47–2in)
Engine: 410bhp diesel
Range: 240km (149 miles)
Speed: 40.2km/h (25mph) or 4 knots
Country of origin: USA

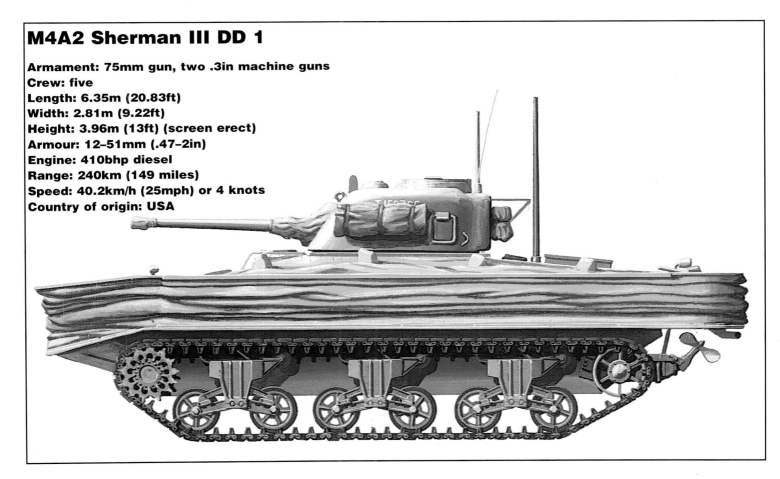

M24 Chaffee

Armament: one 75mm gun, two .3mm machine guns, one .5in AA machine gun
Crew: five
Length: (gun forward) 5.5m (18ft)
Width: 2.95m (9.7ft)
Height: 2.5m (8.2ft)
Armour: 12–38mm (.47–1.49in)
Engine: 2 x 110bhp petrol
Range: 280km (174 miles)
Speed: 42km/h (25mph)
Country of origin: USA

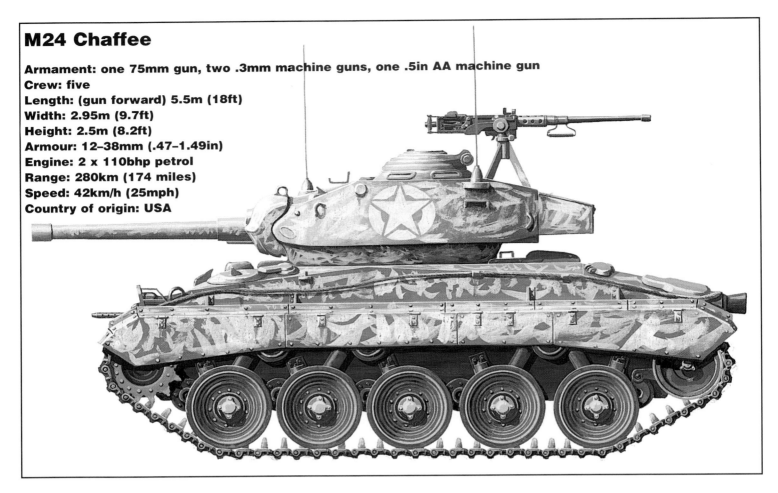

tank design, was to build the AC 1 Sentinel Cruiser Tank came as something of a surprise. The result, however, when it appeared in 1941, was more akin to a knockout, since the Bradford & Kendall Ltd engineers working on the project had succeeded where most others in the world had so far failed and had cast an entire hull half (and in this case, the more complex upper part) in one single piece. The American suspension system was eventually abandoned in favour of one based on that developed in France by Hotchkiss for the H-35. The Wright radial engine and its associated gearbox were unavailable and had to be replaced by three cross-linked 115hp Cadillac Model 75 engines, two abreast and one behind, driving the front sprockets through a locally produced five-speed crash gearbox. The only gun available in 1941 was the two-pounder, which was mounted in a one-piece cast turret. Three prototypes of the AC 1 were made. They were put to the test in January 1942 and exhibited minor, but correctable, faults. However, real problems came when an attempt was made to put the tanks into series production using components and assemblies built all over the vast sub-continent. In the end, it became clear

that only a purpose-built factory to produce the entire tank under one roof would serve, and one was built, at Chullora in New South Wales, where 66 AC 1 Sentinels were manufactured. They were all used for training purposes.

THE BIRTH OF THE SHERMAN

Not a moment too soon, the M3 was succeeded by the M4 Sherman. In view of the dominant role this tank was to play in Allied operations in Western Europe from its introduction in 1942 onwards, it is perhaps appropriate that the variety of Shermans produced should be even more bewildering than the range of M3s manufactured. It is frankly impossible in the space available here to compile a truly comprehensive list of variants and sub-variants. Instead, descriptions of the basic types will be given, along with the main alternatives in terms of armament, construction, powerplant and suspension, as well as accessories such as the Crab flail and the Duplex Drive. Design of what was to become the Medium Tank M4 commenced the day after the M3 was ordered into production in late August 1940. At this moment, Britain was stealing itself to fight off the threatened German invasion, and Belgium, France

and Holland were trying to come to terms with foreign rule. Little could the men who sat down to the task have realised that they were about to create the tank that would be largely responsible for freeing Europe of Nazi tyranny. One thing was certain. Whatever else the design might stipulate, the new tank's hull would be surmounted by a fully traversing turret fitted with a stabilised dual-purpose gun. In the event, the prototype got the M2, and production models were fitted with the M3. At a stroke, this turret arrangement would solve most of the problems associated with operating the M3 Lee/Grants. The realisation that that was so led the team to settle on the powerplant, running gear and suspension of the earlier tank, assuming, quite correctly, that it would be tried and tested in combat before the new model was ready to go into production, at which time any unforeseen problems could be solved. The T6, as the tank was known up until it was standardised, emerged in two forms. One had a rather angular welded upper hull and became the M4; the other had a cast upper hull – which was rather more difficult but quicker to produce, although without any other pronounced benefit or drawback –

and became the M4A1. The two types continued in production roughly in parallel, the 10 factories involved choosing to manufacture one of the two variants according to their own capabilities and facilities. Both versions had frontal armour 50mm (2in) thick, a cast turret and the 400hp version of the Wright Continental radial engine. Their respective weights were roughly the same, at a little over 30 tonnes, and their top speeds were equal at a rather leisurely 35km/h (22mph). There were, however, detailed differences between individual tanks. A tank might be given hydraulic or electrical turret traverse, for example, depending on what was available, and some were equipped for a .50in Browning M2 AA machine gun in the commander's hatch. In addition, some 20 per cent of M4s received a 105mm howitzer in place of the M3 gun and were to operate in the close-support role. The

■LEFT: An M4A3 (Sherman IV). The Allied advance through France throughout 1944 was greatly aided by the speed and reliability of its Ford 500hp V-8 engine, the first to be designed specifically for a tank.

Cruiser Tank RAM Mk II (early model)

Armament: one 6pdr gun, two or three .3in machine guns
Crew: five
Length: 5.79m (19ft)
Width: 2.77m (9.08ft)
Height: 2.67m (8.76ft)
Armour: 12–75mm (.47–3in)
Engine: 400bhp
Range: 200km (124 miles)
Speed: 34km/h (21mph)
Country of origin: Canada

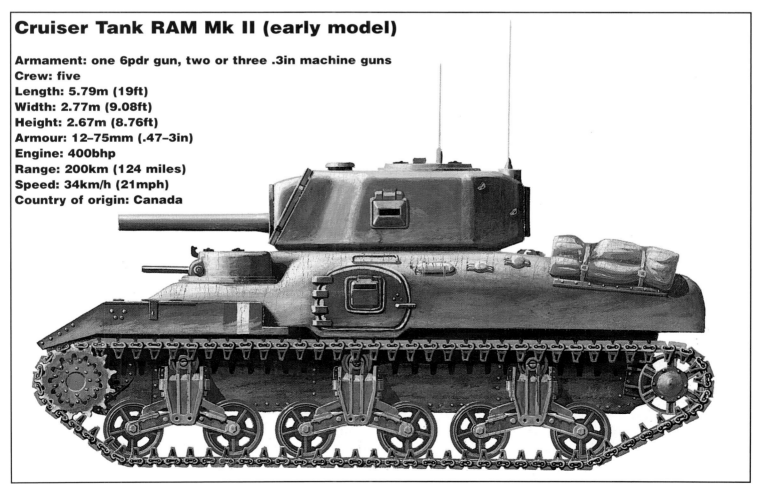

British, who could barely contain themselves at the thought of getting their hands on a medium tank that worked, named the M4 after William Tecumseh Sherman, the base model becoming the Sherman I and the M4A1 the Sherman II. A 'B' suffix was allotted to the close-support tanks, and that same system was used for all the successive versions. The US Army later adopted the name Sherman for its own M4s. In all, some 8400 M4 Sherman Is were produced, and 9700 M4A1 Sherman IIs. Two-thirds received the 75mm M3 gun; the rest the 76.2mm high-velocity M1. This weapon was more capable than the M3, but was still inferior to both the British 17-pounder and the German 88mm. Like its German counterpart, the M1 gun was developed from an anti-aircraft weapon.

THE SHERMAN FIREFLY

The new cannon, which fired a 7kg (15lb 8oz) AP round, could penetrate 100mm (3.9in) of armour at 1000m (3280ft), which was not enough to be sure of killing a Tiger or even a Panther. The M1 would not fit the original turret, and so the turret from a tank under development as the T23 was used instead. The T23 was to have carried a 90mm gun, and its turret fitted the Sherman turret ring without modification. Incidentally, the British 17-pounder would not fit the original turret either, but the gun was shoe-horned in anyway to produce what was probably the most effective Sherman variant of them all – the Firefly. The 75mm gun also later found its way into many marks of M4, and in British service, tanks carrying it were identified by an 'A' suffix after the mark designator (for example, Sherman IIA).

The second Sherman variant, the M4A2, was powered by twin GMC diesel engines geared to a common transmission in the welded hull and had any one of the three main guns. The third variant, the M4A3, was also based on the welded hull but with the angle of the front glacis increased to 47 degrees. The M4A3 was powered by a new engine specially designed and produced by Ford, the 500hp GAA V-8. This engine proved to be a significant improvement over its

predecessors, having greater reliability and better all-round performance. The GAA V-8 pushed the slightly heavier vehicle's top speed up to a much more acceptable 50km/h (30mph). The new engine was probably the most significant factor in the M4A3's becoming the most important Sherman variant. Almost 11500 were built, 5000 with the 75mm M3 gun, 3500 with the 76.2mm M1 and the rest with the 105mm M4 howitzer. Most stayed in service with the US Army. A small number – 254 all told – were produced with an additional 102mm (4in) of armour welded to the hull front and 152mm (6in) added to the face of the turret. Designated M4A3E2s, these tanks were for use in the assault role during the Allied invasion of France. As a result of the additional armour, they weighed 7 tonnes more than the normal tank, and their top speed went down to that of the original M4 as a result, but they were very difficult to stop. Some M4A3s had horizontal, rather than vertical volute springs, together with 585mm (23in) rather than 420mm (16.5in) tracks. The changes were introduced to improve flotation and simplify maintenance, but in fact the greatest improvement was probably in soft-ground performance,

thanks to much reduced ground pressure. Tanks thus modified were designated M4A3E8s by the US Army, and indicated by the suffix 'Y' by the British.

SHERMANS WITH MORE PUNCH

The M4A4, which was to become the most common Sherman in British service as the Sherman V, was an M4 with the Ford engine replaced by the inferior Chrysler multiblock found in some of the M3s. Once again, the use of this engine meant that the tank's hull and therefore its track run needed to be lengthened, this time by 280mm (11in). Eight thousand were constructed in all before production ceased in favour of models with Wright or Ford engines. A few – less than 100 – were fitted with Caterpillar 500hp diesels and designated the M4A6. The majority of M4A6s, which were all E8 variants, went to the Soviet Union, where diesel engines were the norm.

When the 76mm gun was demonstrated to the British Tank Mission, early in 1943, there was considerable disquiet. If this was the best the Sherman would be able to do, it was thought, then the tank was clearly not going to be a match for the Panthers or Tigers it would meet in increasing numbers as the war against Hitler in the west moved out of North Africa, where it was still localised, and into Europe. In general, the experts were right. As has been observed, the Sherman never was a match for the big German tanks. Yet it still won – by sheer weight of numbers. Nonetheless, in 1943, the British wanted a bigger gun. It had been demonstrated that at stand-off range – 3000m (almost 2 miles) – the 17-pounder gun fitted in the otherwise unsatisfactory A30 Challenger could penetrate a PzKpfw IV Ausf H's 50–60mm (2–2.5in) frontal armour, while a solid shot from the German tank's long-barrelled 75mm gun would bounce off the Challenger's own armour, inadequate though it was. And that set some middle-ranking British tankers thinking of ways to insert the gun into a Sherman's turret.

On 30 December 1943, the decision was taken to modify 2100 precious Sherman Vs to what was to be called the Firefly configuration. In the event, the hull-mounted machine gun was also deleted and the space it and its gunner occupied was used to hold 15 extra rounds of ammunition. Thus was born the only American or British tank able to

confront the Panthers and Tigers on anything like their own terms during the desperate fighting through France and the Low Countries and on into Germany in 1944 and 1945. Curiously, the

■ **ABOVE: Before D-Day, Allied armoured divisions were issued with wading kit that enabled them to disembark from landing craft offshore. Note the roundel on the roof for aerial indentification.**

Carro Veloce L.6/40

Armament: one 20mm cannon, one 8mm machine gun
Crew: two
Length: 3.84m (12.6ft)
Width: 1.85m (6.1ft)
Height: 2.03m (6.66ft)
Armour: 6–30mm (.23–1.18in)
Engine: 70bhp petrol
Range: 200km (124 miles)
Speed: 42km/h (26mph)
Country of origin: Italy

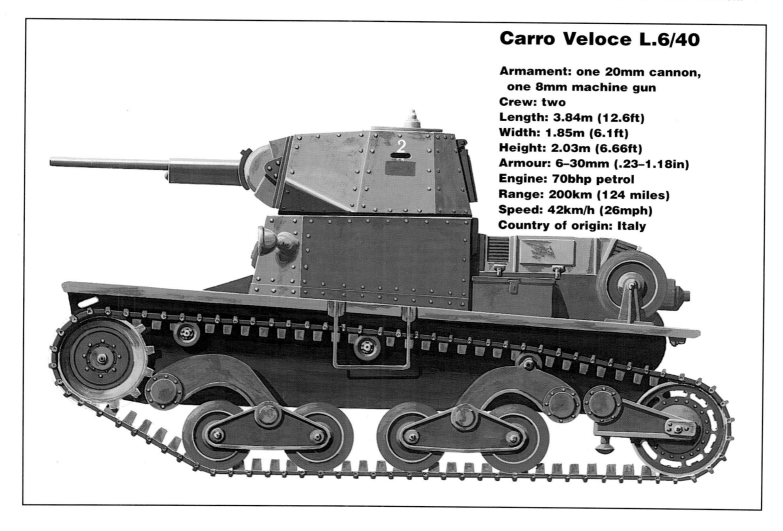

Americans were never convinced of the superiority of the 17-pounder gun over their own 76mm M1 and steadfastly refused to have anything to do with the Firefly concept, even when its worth was proved to them time after time. They found their own M4s severely undergunned and unnecessarily vulnerable as a result. M4s, which stayed in frontline US Army service until 1956, never had anything bigger than the M1 gun, whereas those of some of the many other nations to employ it had the British 17-pounder. The Israelis went even further and, among other modifications, fitted a French 105mm gun to tanks that they used in battle as late as 1973.

Shermans fought through North Africa from before El Alamein to the capitulation, then played a vital role first in the rapid suppression of the Axis forces in Sicily and then in the slow progress northwards through the Italian peninsula. The American, British and Canadian forces that took part in the D-

■RIGHT: August 1940. Although the Italian armoured forces in North Africa outnumbered the British by three to one, Italian tanks such as this captured M 13/40 were poorly armoured, and proved easy prey for the Matildas of the 7th Armoured Division, the famous 'Desert Rats'.

Day landings on 6 June 1944 had many more Shermans at their disposal than any other type of tank. By that time, the Sherman had become the basis for a range of 'funnies', as they were commonly called, modified for special purposes and to meet special needs. The British set up an entire armoured division, the 79th, ahead of D-Day, to develop and operate such vehicles. The division was under the

command of Major-General Sir Percy Hobart, formerly Inspector General of the Tank Corps and commander of the 7th Armoured Division in Egypt.

Perhaps the best known, and possibly the most important, of the funnies was the Sherman DD, with Nicholas Straussler's Duplex Drive, which was developed originally for the Valentine. The 'Duplex' in the name derives from

Fiat Ansaldo L35/Lf (flamethrower)

Armament: Flamethrower gun, one 6.5 or 8mm machine gun
Crew: two
Length: 3.2m (10.5ft) (tank only)
Width: 1.4m (4.6ft)
Height: 1.3m (4.2ft)
Armour: 6-13.5mm (.23-.53in)
Engine: 43bhp petrol
Range: 120km (75 miles)
Speed: 42km/h (26mph)
Country of origin: Italy

Type 97 'Te-Ke'

Armament: one 37mm gun
 or 7.7mm machine gun
Crew: two
Length: 3.7m (12.1ft)
Width: 1.8m (5.9t)
Height: 1.8m (5.9ft)
Armour: 4-16mm (.15-.62in)
Engine: 65bhp diesel
Range: 250km (155 miles)
Speed: 40km/h (25mph)
Country of origin: Japan

the system's giving the tank a second method of propulsion. Besides being able to travel on land in the normal way, Sherman DDs could 'swim' through water, by means of propellers, the tank floating thanks to the added displacement provided by a lightweight watertight skirt, or screen, secured all round the vehicle just above the return track run.

It would be fitting enough to be able to end this account of the tanks of World War II with the Sherman, since it was the tank that won the war in the West. But the Sherman was not the final design the US Army was to be issued with before the end of the war in Europe in May 1945. In April 1943, work started on two more medium tank projects, the T25 and T26, both to be armed with the M3 90mm gun, which fired a 10.9kg (24lb) AP round at 1020 metres per second (3350 feet per second). Development of the two projects continued in parallel for a year before the T26 emerged as a clear leader. Its primary armour was 115mm (4.5in) thick, which meant an all-up weight of

more than 40 tonnes, and the tank's 470hp Ford GAF engine, driving through a Torquematic automatic gearbox, could push it along at almost 40km/h (25mph). The T26 rode on six medium-sized roadwheels, each independently suspended on a torsion bar, and, in an attempt to minimise ground pressure, had 610mm-wide (24in) tracks. It was standardised for limited production as the M26 'General Pershing'. Just 310 Pershings reached the US Army's armoured divisions in northwest Europe before the war's end. The new tank found itself up against Panthers, Tigers and King Tigers and quickly proved itself to be just as resistant to punishment as the best of them. The type received its baptism of fire at the battle for the Remagen Bridge across the Lower Rhine on 7 March 1945, acquitting itself well against the best tanks of the war.

CHAPTER 4
TANKS IN TRANSITION, FROM POTSDAM TO VIETNAM

The tank's achievements during World War II ensured armour's role in future strategic plans. The conflicts which spanned the subsequent Cold War period, plus advances in technology, ensured that the tank became one of the most decisive weapons on the battlefield.

One of the immediate results of World War II's coming to a close, halfway through 1945, was the downsizing of the western Allies' armies and the consequent withdrawal, either into storage or for disposal, of huge numbers of vehicles and weapons. Some of what remained of the weapons and equipment of the defeated German Army and the Waffen-SS went for scrap, but some was appropriated by the Allies (particularly France), and some found its way into the 'second user' market. Redundant Soviet equipment, what there was of it, went to equip the USSR's client states. All this was to be expected. The same armies had, by and large, gone through the same process a quarter of a century before, but there was one big difference between the circumstances in 1945 and those of 1919. This time, there was to be no reconstitution of small independent states on the dissolution of powerful empires. Instead, exactly the reverse was to take place, as the Red Army, far from marching out of the countries it had overrun in its pursuit of the Nazis, dug itself in to stay. Winston Churchill warned of Soviet expansionism in a

■**LEFT: The Vietnamese jungle was difficult country in which to operate tanks, but US commanders were quick to exploit the devastating mobile firepower of the flamethrower M60.**

speech he made in Fulton, Missouri, on 5 March 1946, in which he said: 'From Stettin in the Baltic to Trieste in the Adriatic, an iron curtain has descended across the continent [of Europe].' The western Allies' response to the Soviets was to set up the North Atlantic Treaty Organisation (NATO) in 1949, with the United States in a pre-eminent role. The 'Cold War' that ensued was to last for some 40 years and ensured that progress in weapons technology and in the development of new ways and means of waging war hardly slowed at all.

AGEING AMERICANS
Had it come to immediate all-out war between NATO and the Warsaw Pact countries, as the eastern bloc became known, there is little doubt who would have won, for, to misquote Belloc's paen to an earlier weapon that changed the world, 'Whatever happens, we have got/The atom bomb, and they have not'; in other words, NATO had nuclear weapons, the Russians did not. However, that state of affairs was not to last, and once parity had been reached at the top of the weapons tree, a struggle began for supremacy lower down. And nowhere was this battle for the upper hand more bitterly fought than in the area of tanks.

The vast majority of the tanks in US Army service at the war's end were M4 Shermans of one variety or another. The

M24 Chaffee

Armament: one 75mm gun,
  two .3in machine guns, one .5in AA
  machine gun
Crew: five
Length: (gun forward) 5.5m (18ft)
Width: 2.95m (9.7ft)
Height: 2.5m (8.1ft)
Armour: 12–38mm (.47–1.5in)
Engine: 2 x 110bhp petrol
Range: 280km (174 miles)
Speed: 42km/h (25mph)
Country of origin: USA

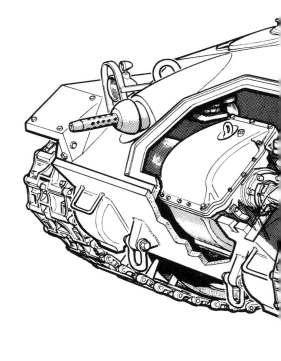

Sherman was a tank designed in 1940 according to principles established during the previous decade, and it was very clearly obsolescent by this time and badly in need of replacement. In the short term, at least, the replacement would be a vehicle based on the Sherman's successor, the M26 Pershing, which was now classified as a medium tank again after a brief spell as a heavy. In the light tank category, which still seemed to have a degree of validity, thanks largely to the increased destructive power of new types of ammunition, the US Army had the M24 Chaffee. This also needed replacing, even though its design was considerably more 'modern' than that of the Sherman. Finally, there was a need, identified but as yet unfulfilled, for a true heavy tank to be able to stand up to the massive IS-3s of the Red Army.

US CLASSIFICATIONS

It is perhaps worth examining what was meant by the terms 'light', 'medium' and 'heavy' at this time. In 1945, the US Army Ground Forces Equipment Review Board (AGFERB) set weight limits for these categories at 25, 45 and 75 tonnes respectively (and also talked of a 150-tonne superheavy category, at least for experimental purposes, although that concept was soon deleted from the agenda). The so-called Stilwell Board – named after its president, General 'Vinegar Joe' Stilwell – ratified the categorisation, at the same time recommending that the development of tank destroyers and towed anti-tank guns be terminated. Stilwell's report highlighted the importance of continued development in the four main areas: new and more powerful guns and ammunition; new types of armour and new ways of employing it; engines specially developed for armoured vehicles, including both multifuel units and gas turbines; and improved running gear and suspension to allow heavier vehicles to move faster.

AMERICAN LIGHT TANKS

As a first stage towards replacing the M24 Chaffee, a four-man light tank project, designated T37 and conforming to the norms established by the AGFERB, was instigated soon after the war's end. By 1949, and by now known as T41, it had gone through three phases. In Phase I it had a stabilised 76.2mm M32 gun. In Phase II it had a redesigned turret, a new mantlet, a bore evacuator, an integrated fire-control system and a stabiliser for the main gun. In Phase III it received an automatic loading system for the M32 gun and an improved stabiliser, neither of which was adopted for the production tank, which was standardised as the Light Tank M41 'Little Bulldog' in 1950. Before it was ever issued to troops, however, the tank was renamed the 'Walker Bulldog' in honour of General Walton H. Walker, ground forces commander in Korea, who died in a jeep accident two days before Christmas 1950.

The way the Walker Bulldog was designed had one point of particular interest. Whereas all previous American tanks had been designed around a gun, and a suitable engine selected later, the starting point for the Walker Bulldog had

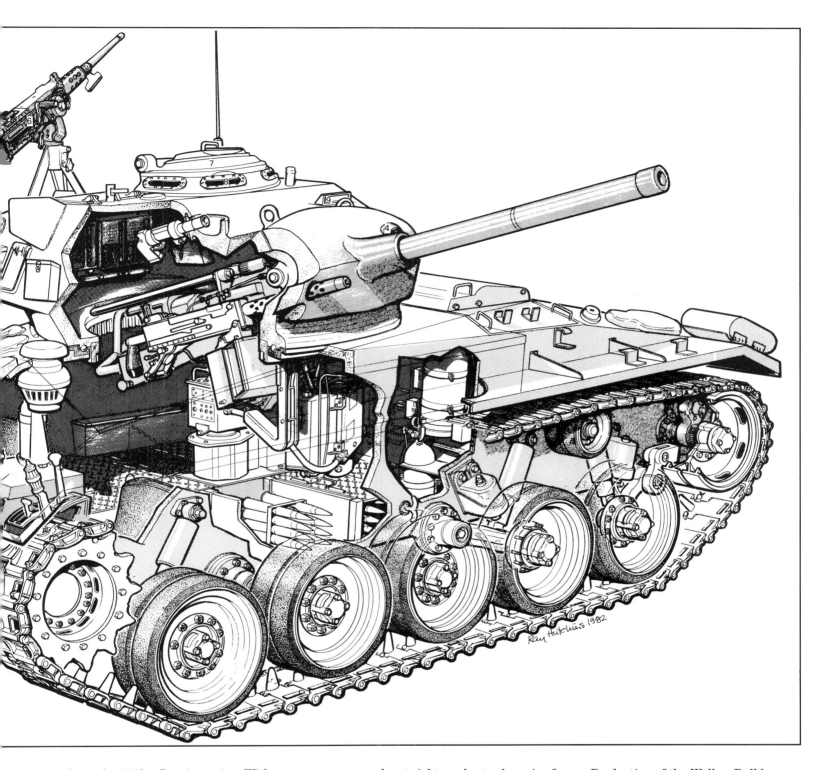

been the 500hp flat six engine. With an all-up combat weight of 25 tonnes firmly in mind, the designers decided to first specify the amount of power they would need to achieve a certain performance goal – a road speed in excess of 65km/h (40mph) and a range of 160km (100 miles) on 530 litres (140 US gallons) of petrol. Torsion bar suspension was selected, with five medium-sized roadwheels per side and three track-return rollers. The rear sprockets were driven by means of an Allison cross-drive system, so called because it was mounted

transversely, at right angles to the axis of the engine's crankshaft. It was an early version of the sort of transmission that was to pass into the motor car as the transaxle, although very much more complicated. In keeping with the tank's general character, the armour was relatively light – 25mm (1in) thick on the glacis and the turret face, 12 to 19mm (.5 to .75in) thick elsewhere. In addition to the main gun, there was a co-axial M1919A4 machine gun and a heavier .50in Browning M2 on an anti-aircraft mounting in the turret hatch.

Production of the Walker Bulldog began before the end of 1950 at the Cleveland Tank Plant run by General Motors' Cadillac Division, which had by now bid to make light tank manufacture in the United States its preserve. In all, some 5500 Walker Bulldogs were to be produced there. Coming as it did at the start of a period of transition, it is not surprising to discover that the M41 was used as a test-bed for different turrets and armaments, including the 90mm M36 gun from the M46A1/M47/M48 Pattons. The M41 Walker Bulldog also

M41 Walker Bulldog

Armament: one 76mm gun, one .3in
  machine gun, one .5in AA machine gun
Crew: four
Length: (gun forward) 8.2m (26.9ft)
Width: 3.2m (10.5ft)
Height: 2.7m (8.85ft) (to cupola)
Armour: 12–38mm (.47–1.5in)
Engine: 500bhp petrol
Range: 160km (100 miles)
Speed: 72km/h (45mph)
Country of origin: USA

formed the basis of the M42 'Duster' anti-aircraft tanks, the M44 and M52 SP guns and the M75 armoured personnel carrier (APC). It was to be supplied to around two dozen client states, and as the turn of the century and the M41's 40th birthday approached, it was still in service with many of them. Sometimes it was serving in something close to its original form, but more often than not it had received significant enhancements, including diesel engines, more powerful main guns, improved fire control and infra-red driving and fighting systems.

TANK AND SP HYBRID
In January 1959, a preliminary feasibility study was launched aimed at providing the US Army with a replacement for both the M41 Walker Bulldog light tank and the M56 self-propelled anti-tank gun. By December 1961 both a full-scale mock-up and an automotive test rig had been produced by General Motors Detroit Diesel Allison Division, and a decision in principle had been taken to arm the new vehicle with the 152mm M81 combined gun and missile launcher, which was then in development. A turret to take this hybrid weapon was developed and mounted on a Walker Bulldog hull, and tests, during which 590 MGM-51

■ABOVE: North Korean infantrymen emerge from a bunker shattered by the 90mm gun of an American M47 during the Korean War. The commander points out another pillbox to US infantrymen.

'Shillelagh' missiles were fired, seemed to indicate that the concept was viable. Twelve prototype XM551s, as the new tank was designated, were produced between 1962 and 1965, and the vehicle was then type classified (that is, standardised) and put into limited production as the M551 'Sheridan' Light Tank/ Reconnaissance Vehicle.

The most interesting innovation of the Sheridan – which was named after American Civil War infantryman turned cavalry leader, General 'Little Phil' Sheridan – was its use of aluminium armour for its hull and aluminium alloys for its engine and transmission casing. The powerplant itself was a six-cylinder turbo-charged diesel and produced 300hp to give the 16-tonne tank a top speed of 70km/h (43mph) on the road. With a flotation screen deployed, the tank became amphibious, with a maximum speed through the water of 6.5km/h (4mph), propelled by its tracks. The turret, which mounted a 7.62mm co-axial

machine gun and a heavier .50in Browning as an anti-aircraft weapon in the commander's cupola, was of welded steel. A laser range-finder was later developed, and most of the 1700 Sheridans completed before 1970, when production ceased, were retrofitted with infra-red searchlights mounted above the gun tube/launcher. The M551 was issued to airborne and light formations, but by 1979 it had been withdrawn from all but the 82nd Airborne Division. It was withdrawn from service entirely soon after, aving failed to live up to its original promise.

AMERICAN MEDIUM TANKS
As a first step towards developing a new medium tank, the US authorities decided to improve the existing M26 Pershing design. They substituted an air-cooled 800hp Continental AV-1790 V-12 engine and a beefed-up version of the Allison

■RIGHT: December 1950. An M26 General Pershing and US Marines cross the bleak winter landscape near Chosin, Korea. The freezing conditions played havoc with tank engines.

cross-drive transmission and steering system for the Pershing's Ford GAF and Torquematic transmission. The improved tank also received a new model of the M3 gun with a fume extractor (bore evacuator) and muzzle brake. Although these improvements probably did not warrant a change of designation, the upgraded tanks were reissued as the M46 'General Patton', in honour of George 'Blood and Guts' Patton, who had died of heart failure just before Christmas 1945.

ALLISON'S DRIVE SYSTEM
The Allison CD-500/CD-850 cross-drive system, as fitted to the M41 and M46 respectively, actually contained

M47 Patton 1

Armament: one 90mm gun, two .3mm machine guns, one .5in AA machine gun
Crew: five
Length: (gun forward) 8.5m (27.9ft)
Width: 3.51m (11.5ft)
Height: 2.95m (9.7ft) (to cupola)
Armour: 13–115mm (.51–4.5in)
Engine: 810bhp petrol
Range: 150km (93 miles)
Speed: 48km/h (29.8mph)
Country of origin: USA

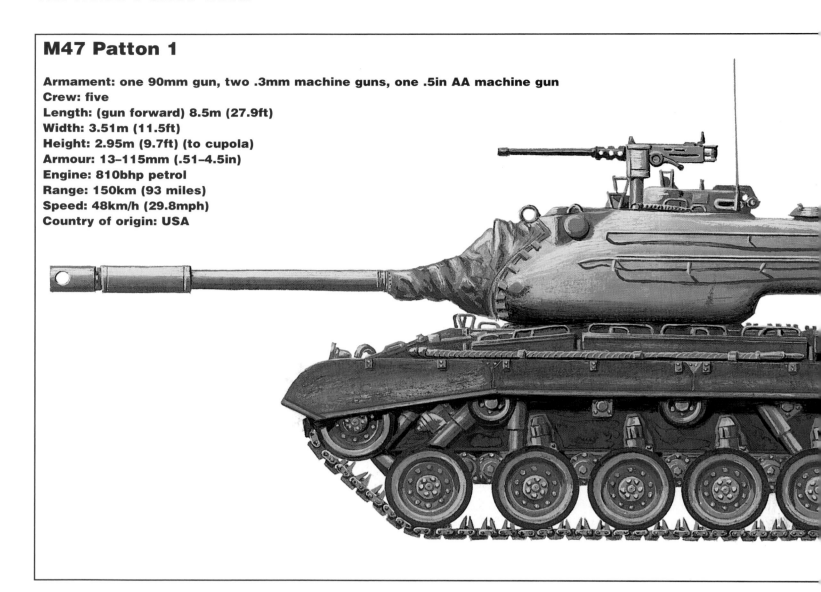

transmission, steering and brakes all in one and was a considerable improvement on the simpler systems that had gone before. It utilised two forward speed ranges and one reverse, each hydraulically selected, and in both senses, part of the engine's power output was transmitted via the hydraulic torque converter or fluid flywheel and the remainder through a conventional mechanical path. The power from both transmission trains was available to both output paths when the tank was proceeding in a straight line, but when the 'wobble stick', or joystick, was actuated, all the mechanically transmitted power was applied to just one track. The wobble stick acted on a hydraulically controlled differential – moving it to one side while the tank was moving caused more power to be applied to one track; the same action while the driving gearbox was in neutral caused the two tracks to move in opposite directions and spin the tank on its axis.

(The Merritt-Brown system of World War II achieved the same end, but the Allison system was simpler to use.) Disc brakes, operated by a foot pedal, were installed in each drive shaft. Later models of the CD-850 had a split hydraulic power train instead of the hydraulic/mechanical path found in the original, but the principle remained the same.

THE M47 PATTON

At the same time as the T41 light tank programme proper got underway, two further American tank projects were initiated – one to lead to the development of a new medium tank, known as T42; the other for a heavy tank, designated T43. T42 was seen from the outset as a development of the M26 Pershing/M46 Patton, in particular concentrating on redesigning the turret to improve its ballistic performance, but making some changes to the hull and running gear too. In the event, the T42 project was overtaken by the Korean War, which

began in June 1950, and it turned into a crash programme to produce medium tanks to supplement those already in service. The only major segment of the T42 programme already substantially complete was the redesign of the turret, and the decision was made to mount the new turret, with its improved 90mm M36 gun, on the slightly modified M46 hull. In fact, the modifications were similar to those already made to the M46 hull in an earlier improvement programme, since cancelled, known as T40, in which the reangled profile of the frontal glacis was the most important change, and the increase in size of the turret ring to 1850mm (73in) probably the most far-reaching. In addition, two track-return rollers were deleted and a tensioning roller added between the sixth roadwheel and the drive sprocket at the rear. The result of marrying the new turret with a modified hull was a significantly improved vehicle at minimal cost, both in money and time. The tank thus created,

refurbished them, fitting some with 105mm guns either of French or of British origin. One weakness of the M47 was its poor range – just 150km (80 miles) on 885 litres (235 US gallons) of fuel – and some second users, notably Austria, Iran, Israel, Pakistan and Spain, tried to improve on that by fitting their M47s with diesel engines. Others converted M47s to support purposes, including bridge laying and recovery, the latter being the only alternative use to which the US Army put the vehicle.

THE PATTON'S SUCCESSOR

Even as the tooling-up process to produce the M47 began in the summer of 1950, the Ordnance Board design team was working on its replacement. In fact, limited development work continued on the original T42 programme, in the hope that it might lead to a lighter, more economical medium gun tank. The T42's basic fault was a lack of power, thanks to a 500hp engine as fitted to the much lighter M41 having been rather optimistically specified. Prototype T42s became test-beds for various major modifications, the most important of which was the introduction of an

■**BELOW: The Indo-Pakistan War, 1971. Early M24 Chaffees were only lightly armoured, and those in Pakistani service were easily knocked out by the 105mm main gun of Indian Centurions.**

oscillating turret, complete with an auto-loading 90mm gun capable of delivering 18 rounds per minute. In this guise the T42 was known as the T69. The entire T42/T69 programme was finally cancelled only in 1958.

It was the T48 programme, announced in February 1951, that was to provide the M47's successor. The T48 tank was to be armed with a new version of the 90mm gun with a quick-change barrel. It was also to have a minimum of 25mm (1in) of armour, with a maximum of 110mm (4.33in) on the hull front and 120mm (4.72in) on the turret front for a total dry weight of 41 tonnes. This specified weight proved to be only a little unrealistic. The first production tanks weighed 42.25 tonnes before being loaded with fuel and supplies, 60 rounds of main gun ammunition and 6000 rounds for the machine guns. The T48 had a crew of four, the deletion of the hull machine gun (for the first time in an American tank) along with the introduction of the new transmission and steering system allowing the elimination of the second driver-cum-machine gunner. The space he occupied was given over to ammunition storage instead.

THE T48'S RADICAL DESIGN

The basic form of the T48 was taken from that of the heavy tank T43, the most important feature of which was its cast, elliptically shaped armour, as designed by

its combat weight increased by around 12 per cent over that of the Pershing to just over 46 tonnes, was designated the M46A1 Patton in the case of conversions of existing vehicles, and the M47 Patton 1 for newly produced tanks. It was always seen as a purely interim solution and entered service with the US Army in mid-1952.

The M47 Patton 1 (also known as the Patton 47) was a considerable success, despite its short operational life with the US Army. Around 8600 were produced altogether before manufacture ceased in November 1953, Large numbers were shipped to client states under the Military Aid Programme. South Korea, not surprisingly, was a major user; so was France and the newly created West German Army. Many of the M47s that went abroad continued in service until the mid-1970s, sometimes undergoing some further slight modification in the process. Both GIAT in France and Oto-Melara in Italy bought in old tanks and

M48A3 Patton 2

Armament: one 90mm gun, one .3mm
machine gun, one .5in AA machine gun
Crew: four
Length: (gun forward) 7.44m (24.4ft)
Width: 3.63m (11.9ft)
Height: 3.12m (10.23ft) (to cupola)
Armour: 12.7-120mm (.5–4.72in)
Engine: 750bhp diesel
Range: 465km (289 miles)
Speed: 48km/h (30mph)
Country of origin: USA

Joseph Williams, who had also played an important part in designing the M41 and the turret of the T42. Williams had produced the original drawings as long ago as 1948 and had clearly been influenced by the Soviet IS-3. In order that this design could be taken up for the T48, the turret ring of the medium tank was increased in size still further, to 2160mm (85in). In terms of the tank's shape, the main effect of the enlarged turret ring was to allow the turret walls to slope down smoothly to the hull top, eliminating shot-traps to a considerable extent. Further homage was paid to Soviet designers in the forward location of the turret ring, with the large 'bustle', where the radio and ventilation systems were housed, balancing the 48-calibre barrel of the M41 main gun. This housing also protected much of the top deck above the engine when the gun was pointing forward, although the normal attitude while travelling was for the turret to be reversed, a feature the tank shared with its predecessors and all later designs, both in the United States and elsewhere.

M48 was the first of the modern main battle tanks (MBTs), although in every way a development of the M26/M46/M47 vehicles.

As originally specified, the M48 was powered by the same engine as the M46/M47s, and despite being somewhat heavier, at 45 tonnes all up, it was a little faster. The M48 paid for this in reduced range, with its 757-litre (200 US gallon) fuel capacity being enough for no more than 115km (70 miles). The Allison cross-drive transmission was only marginally modified from earlier installations, with the wobble stick replaced by a steering wheel. The wheel worked in the conventional way when the tank was in motion, but with the gearbox in neutral, a full turn of the wheel in either direction set the tank spinning around on its own axis, its tracks contra-rotating. The running gear was virtually identical to that of the M47, too, the main difference being the reinstallation of the second and fourth track rollers that had been deleted from the original M26/M46.

THE M48'S FAILINGS

The worst failing the M48 had was the truly appalling rate at which its AV-1790-5 and AV-1790-7 series engines consumed fuel – they got through almost 9 litres per kilometre (4 US gallons per mile) cross country. The first attempt to alleviate the problem saw four 210-litre (55 US gallon) drums of fuel mounted on a rear rack, their outlets connected to the fuel filler cap. The drums were unprotected, but could be jettisoned from within the vehicle in an emergency. A better solution was an improved version of the engine, the API-1790-8 – with fuel injection in place of carburettors – together with an improved transmission, the XT-1400. These modifications not only raised the top speed by almost 20 per cent to 48km/h (30mph), largely thanks to a change in the final-drive ratio, but also more than doubled the tank's range to 260km (160 miles). The chief reason for the increased range was that the new engine occupied less space, leaving room for bigger fuel tanks. Fuel capacity went up to 1270 litres (335 US gallons). A modified rear deck was necessary to accommodate the new engine, and it was decided that an attempt should be made to reduce the tank's infra-red signature at the same time. This was the first time such a precaution had been contemplated, and it resulted in the exhaust grilles being

The development contract for the T48 went to the Chrysler Corporation, and the first prototypes began their trials in the early months of 1952. Although the design was still not perfect – new range-finder sights and fire-control systems, in particular, were slow to be developed and delivered – the tank was ordered into production that March. It was

standardised as the 90mm Gun Tank M48 Patton 48 (or Patton 2) on 2 April 1953, by which time some 900 examples had already been produced. A total of around 11,700 M48s were to be produced before manufacture ceased in 1959, many of them being extensively modified perhaps as many as three times during the course of their operational lives. The

RIGHT: An M48 of the 1st Tank Battalion, US Marine Corps, patrolling a South Vietnamese beach in late 1968. The M48 was designed to rectify the problems of its predecessor, the M47.

moved from the upper deck to the rear of the tank. Modifications were also made to the running gear, including the deletion once again of the second and fourth track-return rollers, while the commander gained a redesigned enclosed cupola with an integral housing for the Browning M2 machine gun that had originally been externally mounted. The tank went through two evolutions during this period, the majority of the changes coming in the M48A2. The later M48A2C variant had a modified fire-control system, and some early M48s were uprated to this standard.

There followed the M48A2E1/M48A3, which were rebuilt M48A1s and M48A2s fitted with a 750hp AVDS-1790 diesel engine, which gave a much improved maximum road range of 465km (290 miles) on 1420 litres (375 US gallons) of fuel with no reduction at all in performance. The M48A3 was then improved in its turn by the substitution of a 105mm M68 main gun for the original 90mm M41, a move that was necessitated by the appearance of the Soviet T54/T55 series, with their 100mm armament. A total of 1210 M48s were converted to this new standard, a task which took three to four months, depending on the modification level of the vehicle when it arrived. This modification programme, which ran from 1972 to 1975, resulted in the M48A5 – a tank that fell only a little way short of the M60 specification. M48 tanks were to serve with 14 nations altogether and saw extensive combat in American and South Vietnamese hands in Southeast Asia and in those of the Pakistani and Israeli Armies during their wars against their neighbours in the 1960s and 1970s.

INFRA-RED LIGHTS

The M48 was used to try out many new items of equipment and ideas. This is not surprising, for the period of the tank's currency was one of considerable technological innovation right across the board. Infra-red driving lights were already fairly commonplace, but infra-red fighting systems were only just coming into use. These systems could be passive, or they could be active in the form of 'black' searchlights that emit radiation in

that portion of the spectrum and whose light is invisible to the naked eye as a result. The US Army used both the M48 and the M41 for active infra-red trials, the 2.5kW xenon searchlight that was the light source – in both the infra-red and visible portions of the spectrum – being co-axial and positioned just above the gun mantlet. It had an effective range of 2000m (6560ft), the same as that of the tanks' AT armament.

New types of anti-tank ammunition were being developed too, the most innovative being the high explosive, squash-head (HESH) round, which was invented in the United Kingdom and is known to the US Army as the high explosive, plastic (HEP) round.

NEW ARMOUR

In the field of armour, research had already indicated that glass or ceramic armour was effective against the HEAT round, with its hollow charge. Now similar material, combined with conventional steel armour, was shown to be equally efficacious against both HESH and kinetic energy (that is, solid shot) AP rounds. Fused silica (silicon dioxide, or common sand) was used as the core of this new form of armour, which was known, logically enough, as 'siliceous

M60A1

Armament: one 105mm gun, one .5in machine gun, one 7.62mm machine gun
Crew: four
Length: (gun forward) 9.3m (30.5ft)
Width: 3.63m (11.9ft)
Height: 3.27m (10.7ft)
Armour: 25–127mm (.98–5in)
Engine: 750bhp diesel
Range: 500km (312 miles)
Speed: 48km/h (30mph)
Country of origin: USA

cored armour'. This form of protection proved to be as resistant to anti-tank rounds of all types as solid homogenous steel armour of the same dimensions, but 40 per cent lighter. Shaped plates – to be applied to the forward hull of the M48 as and when required – were produced but never adopted for general use. Production of the M48 had ceased before the manufacturing technique for producing whole castings for hull and turret could be finalised. Grilles were also tested that could be applied to the hull front and turret in order to offer some protection against both HEAT and HESH rounds.

M48 TURRETS

Electronic, rather than mechanical, ballistic computers, aimed at providing a first shot kill capacity, made their first appearance in tanks at this stage. However, the state of the art in computer technology had not yet reached a point where a sufficiently powerful device could be housed in the confined space of a tank's turret. Protection against nuclear, biological and chemical (NBC) weapons was provided as standard for the first time in the M48 Patton 2. A system of

filters was fitted on the crew compartment air intakes, along with ventilator fans that ensured that the passage of air would always be from within to without. This sort of installation became standard in main battle tanks from this period on.

One experiment carried out with the M48 was far-reaching enough to deserve a development designation of its own – the T54/T54E1/T54E2, which centred on mounting new turrets on the M48 hull. The three turrets were one-piece castings carrying the 105mm T140 gun. One was to be of the innovative oscillating type, as tested in the T69, and the others were to be conventional rigid turrets. Oscillating turrets are relatively rare, although as the remote control of armoured vehicles becomes a more realistic possibility, there is every reason to believe they will eventually become more popular.

At the time of writing, however, only two types of tank with oscillating turrets have gone into production, though neither are MBTs. These are the French AMX-13 – classed as a light tank – and the Austrian Steyr SK105/A1 Kurassier – classed as a tank destroyer – both of

which mount the same French-built turret. A 'conventional' turret houses a main gun mounted on trunnions – a pair of large pins or shafts, which are fixed to the gun at right angles to the axis of the bore. The trunnions are placed diametrically opposite one another at the centre of balance of the gun, and when mounted on them the gun is free to pivot in the vertical plane within the limits imposed by the design of the turret. This allows the gun muzzle to be elevated and depressed. The movement in azimuth is provided by the turret turning within its mounting ring. By combining the two movements, the gun can be pointed anywhere within the swept zone, which is usually from something like 8 to 10 degrees below the horizontal up to 20 degrees above it, with unrestricted traverse.

OSCILLATING TURRETS

An oscillating turret differs in one particular: the gun is fixed within it, and the turret itself is mounted on trunnions. Thus the entire turret is inclined in order to elevate and depress the tube and usually through a more limited range

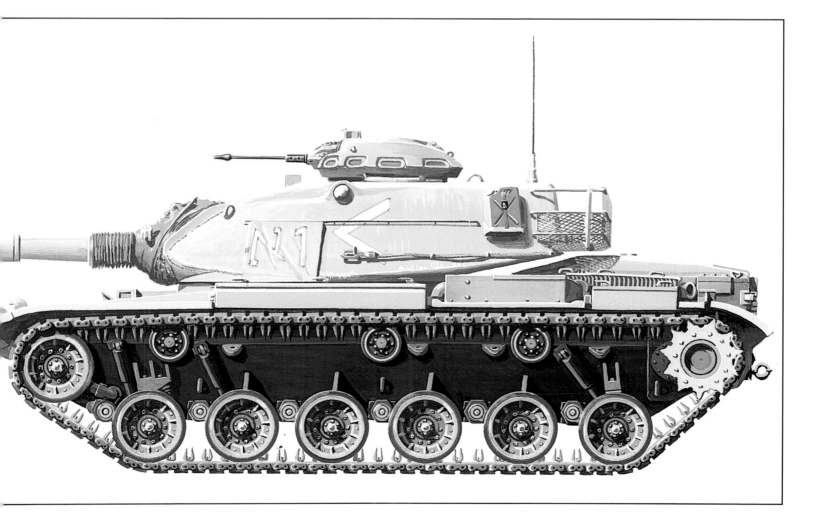

US Army M-911 tank transporter with M60A3 MBT (for specifications see page 108)

than is available in the conventional turret. The main advantage of the oscillating turret is to simplify the installation of an auto-loading mechanism, since the gun now moves independently of the turret only in recoil. The installation of the fire-control system is simplified, too, since the system can be fixed to the fabric of the turret itself and needs no external reference data. Auto-loaders developed for use in conventional turrets have the problem of being required to compensate for the changes in both the vertical position of the breech and the angle it makes to the 'horizontal' datum brought about by the gun tube (and hence the breech) being elevated or depressed. Since the auto-loader normally takes the place of a crewman, the oscillating turret can be made smaller and lighter, although that was not the case with the T54E1, which employed a full four-man crew. Just two examples of the T54E1 were produced. The oscillating turret of one was eventually scrapped and the (standard) hull put to another use; the other T54E1 was sent complete to the Ordnance Museum at the US Army's Aberdeen Proving Grounds. The other T54 types, both with conventional turrets, fared no better, while the heavier T57 and T77,

which were produced at around the same time and mounted a much more powerful 120mm gun in their oscillating turrets, were cancelled before the hardware was even ready for testing.

THE M67 FLAMETHROWER

Other combat vehicles derived from the M48 include the M67 flamethrower tank, developed specifically for the US Marine Corps and used by them in combat in Vietnam. The flame tube, disguised to resemble a 90mm gun, employed 'thickened gasoline' (otherwise known as napalm) put under pressure, and ignited by a 24,000-volt electrical spark. The total burn time was around a minute, depending on the size of the nozzle employed. Nozzles of 19mm (.75in) and 22mm (.88in) were the most common. Maximum range was several hundreds of metres. The M53 155mm SP gun and the M55 8in SP howitzer were also based on the M48, as was the projected T162 175mm SP gun, although the last-mentioned had enough in common with the M60 to be regarded as a derivative of that tank rather than of the M48. In any event, the T162 never got beyond the prototype stage before it was cancelled, a victim of changing circumstances.

While the early marks of the M48

Patton 2 were certainly the best tanks, all round, that the US Army had ever had, they had limitations. As has been observed, their fuel consumption gave very serious cause for concern, but the penetrating power of their 90mm guns was found to be deficient, too, especially when set against the protection standards achieved by the new Soviet vehicles then coming into service. By 1956, it was clear that a new design for what was now unofficially known as the main battle tank had to be finalised as a matter of urgency. The new vehicle was required to combine the across-the-ground performance of a medium tank with the firepower and protection of a heavy tank – still no simple matter to achieve. To judge by its date of introduction, 1960, the tank that resulted might seem to belong to a later era, but it relied so heavily on earlier tank designs that it deserves to be classified with them despite the high standard of performance its later versions achieved.

UPGRADING THE M48

The first step towards finalising this new vehicle's specification was to make the simple decision that the hull and running gear of the existing M48 should be retained in almost exactly its original

form. This step had been made possible, as much as anything, by the enlightened decision to adopt a 2160mm (85in) turret ring for the earlier tank. The decision had not been strictly necessary at the time but had allowed the M48 to be upgunned

to the M48A5 specification and now permitted the hull of the old tank to form the basis for a new vehicle. The next step was to decide on the powerplant. Recent changes in regulations pertaining to the types of fuel that could be used by

different families of US Army vehicles now permitted the consideration of a diesel engine, and a modified version of the existing AV-1790, the AVDS-1790, was selected. As has been noted, this engine was first fitted to the M48A2. The engine turned the M48A2 into a much more capable tank in the process, and also enabled the vehicle to serve as a test-bed for the powerplant for a new generation of main battle tanks.

The third task was to select a gun, which clearly had to be a 105mm weapon or larger. The choice came down to the British X15E8/L7A1 or the American T254, both of which fired identical ammunition. The choice was a compromise – the barrel of the British gun was married to the breech from the American weapon, the result being known as the T254E3 and standardised as the 105mm M68. There was a move to have a lightweight version adopted of the 120mm M58, as fitted to the Heavy Tank M103, but since this gun fired separated-charge ammunition and thus needed two

■LEFT: A US M60A3 tank on exercise in the Middle East in June 1988. The range-finding and fire-control systems of the M60A3 were a considerable improvement on the basic M60.

loaders (and was still very much slower in operation), it was soon eliminated from the competition. The new tank inherited the M48's .50in AA machine gun, but in a revised form – the M58 – and in a revised cupola. The co-axial machine gun specified was the 7.62mm M73. By the end of 1958, it remained only to decide on the turret. A new form with a long nose, known as the T95E7, and originally designed for the long-running but ultimately ill-fated T95 'light' medium tank development programme, was a clear favourite. It offered considerably improved ballistic protection, but would not be available until 1960. Thus, the M48A2's turret was selected for initial production, with the expectation that it would soon be superseded. Siliceous cored armour was to have been used on the turret and the front glacis plate, but cost and the low manufacturing capacity of the few plants able to produce it led to conventional homogenous cast steel armour being specified instead.

THE M60

A development contract for the new tank was awarded to the Chrysler Corporation in September 1958 and called for four pilot tanks to be constructed. The vehicle was designated XM-60 in its prestandardisation form, the 'X' (for 'experimental') sub-designator being adopted right across the board by the US armed forces at around that time. The vehicle was standardised as the 105mm Gun Full Tracked Combat Tank M60 on 16 March 1959. The main difference between its hull and that of the M48 was the profile of the nose – the M60's was wedge-shaped instead of elliptical. The hull could be cast as a single unit or fabricated by welding cast sub-sections. The turret was invariably cast of a piece. The running gear was identical to that of the M48 except that the roadwheels were now of forged aluminium, and the hydraulic shock absorbers were deleted, bumpers being substituted to limit the travel of the first and last roadwheels.

The M60 entered US service in December 1960 and remained in production until mid-1985, by which time some 15,000 had been delivered to the US Army and US Marine Corps and to many export customers. As late as the

M60A3

Armament: one 105mm gun, one .5in machine gun, one 7.62mm machine gun
Crew: four
Length: (gun forward) 9.3m (30.5ft)
Width: 3.63m (11.9ft)
Height: 3.27m (10.7ft)
Armour: 25–127mm (.98–5in)
Engine: 750bhp diesel
Range: 480km (298 miles)
Speed: 48km/h (30mph)
Country of origin: USA

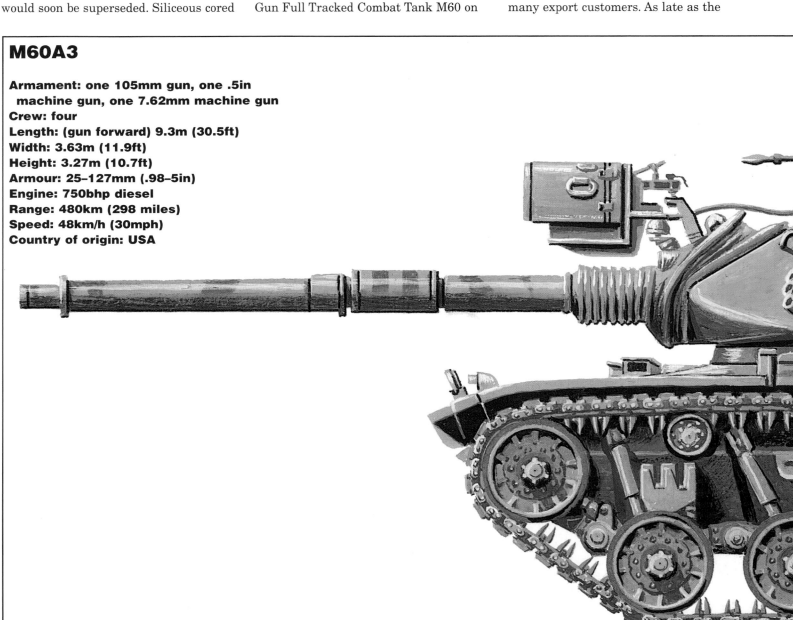

mid-1990s, the M60 was still the most numerous tank in US service. The base-model tank, with the turret from the M48A2, was superseded by the M60A1 in October 1961, and the former went out of production a year later after a total of 2200 had been manufactured. As well as the elongated turret, the new variant had detail changes to the running gear, and a steering T-bar in place of the original wheel. Adequate electronic ballistic computers were still not available, although provision had been made for

■LEFT: Many US armoured units still operate the M60. This Marine Corps vehicle, fitted with extra turret armour and a plough, is pictured breaching Iraqi defences in the 1991 Gulf War.

M551 Sheridan

Armament: one 152mm
  gun/missile launcher,
  one .5in machine gun,
  one 7.62mm machine gun
Crew: four
Length: 6.29m (20.6ft)
Width: 2.82m (9.25ft)
Height: 2.27m (7.5ft)
Armour: 40–50mm (1.57–1.97in)
Engine: 300bhp diesel
Range: 575km (357 miles)
Speed: 70km/h (43mph)
Country of origin: USA

one when the new turret was designed. Hull-front armour was increased in thickness in the M60A1 to 110mm (4.33in), and comparable upgrading was applied to the hull sides. The tank's all-up weight increased from 46.25 tonnes to very nearly 49 tonnes in consequence of these changes, but no modifications were made to the powerplant. The tank's maximum road speed stayed at 48km/h (30mph), the original vehicles having been governed to that anyway.

The committee that had originally decided on the M60's specification in 1957, which had been chaired by Chief of Staff General Maxwell Taylor himself, had been at pains to further specify that by 1965, the US Army armoured divisions should have been provided with an alternative to conventional tube artillery. The alternative was specified as an infra-red, line-of-sight guided missile capable of subduing tanks that were so well armoured as to be invulnerable to conventional ammunition of the time. By January 1964, such a missile, the Philco-Ford MGM-51 Shillelagh, was available, and four different turrets capable of

mounting a short-barrelled XM81 gun/launcher for it were available for study. The XM81 was called a gun/launcher because it could fire conventional 152mm ammunition as well as the Shillelagh. Two of the available turrets were compact designs with semi-remote operation that placed the gunner and loader down in the hull; the other two turrets were more conventional. One of the slimline turrets was chosen, and work commenced on adapting the new weapon to the M60 tank. The M60A2, as the missile-armed tank was designated,

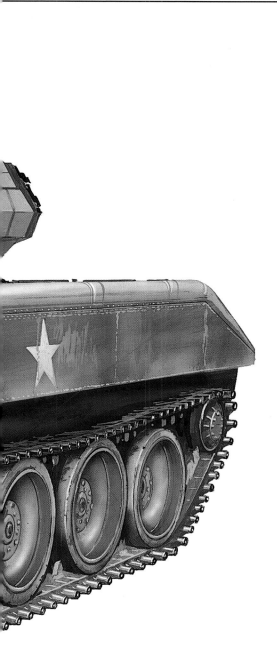

the aborted US–West German MBT70. The XM150 gun/launcher was a more capable weapon all round than the XM81 and could fire conventional sub-calibre armour-piercing fin-stabilised discarding sabot (APFSDS) ammunition as well as launch the Shillelagh missile. However, just in case XM150's merits were lost on the reviewing committee, Chrysler also made provision to equip the K tank with the smooth-bore 120mm Delta gun, which fired a similar sub-calibre round and was very much the shape of things to come. At a time when the US Army (and virtually all of its funding) was absorbed in the Vietnam War, it did not much matter anyway. The K tank design exercise stood very little chance of success, even though it also had a certain innovative value in areas other than its armament. The disappearance without further trace of the K tank meant that the Shillelagh already had three strikes against it. The weapon's installation into the ill-fated M551 Sheridan light tank was to make it a straight four in a row.

By the time the 1960s drew to a close, the M60 main battle tank was beginning to look a little jaded. In January 1970, the Chief of Staff approved a programme

■BELOW: Although the M551 Sheridan has not been a wholehearted success, the type served with some distinction in the Gulf in its role as a fast reconnaissance vehicle.

to substantially update it by means of what was known as product improvement. Proposals came thick and fast. Some were relatively straightforward, like the top-loading air cleaner cartridges, which extracted much more dirt from the air going into the engine and henced prolonged the mean time between replacements, and the add-on stabilisation system, which worked with the existing hydraulic turret actuation hardware.

UPDATING THE M60

Other straightforward modifications included the adoption of a new type of track with longer life and replaceable rubber pads. A new and much more reliable co-axial machine gun was also fitted, as were passive infra-red sensors, a laser range-finder and solid-state digital ballistics computer, and a thermal jacket for the gun barrel to minimise distortion caused by uneven heating or cooling. What became known as the RISE (reliability improved selected equipment) engine, on the other hand, required considerably more work, but proved well worth the expenditure.

Not all the proposed modifications were accepted by any means. One element developed for the K tank, the innovative tube-over-bar (TOB) suspension system, found its way into the M60A1E3 test vehicle but did not make the production model. The system

was never much of a success. It was 1972 before it entered service, and just 525 examples were constructed. All of them were fairly rapidly withdrawn and converted into, among other things, bridgelayers and Combat Engineering Vehicles with A-frames and bulldozer blades as well as a 165mm short-barrelled demolition gun.

Chrysler incorporated a not dissimilar turret to that employed on the M60A2 into its K tank design study, although it mounted a much more powerful gun/launcher, which was developed for

replaced simple torsion bars with components mounted in tubes, thereby doubling their effective length and increasing roadwheel travel by 45 per cent. It was a considerable improvement over the original system, which dated from the M26. However, before the improved tank went into production, two further systems were presented. One was a simpler, and hence cheaper, method, using ordinary torsion bars forged from H-11 electroslag refined steel; the other a more complicated but even better method, using hydropneumatic units. A hybrid of the latter two seemed set to be chosen, but in the end, the designers opted to revert to the original M60 system, even though all the improvements would have given both a better ride and enhanced cross-country performance.

M60 AT SPEED

In tactical terms, the replacement of the mechanical, analogue ballistics computer with the new XM21 electronic, digital ballistics computer system developed by Hughes was probably the most important improvement in the revised tank's equipment. The computer took into account such factors as altitude, ammunition characteristics, cross wind (measured by a mast-mounted sensor on the turret top), cant, drift, gun jump, gun tube wear, sight parallax and target motion when laying the gun, while the tank's laser range-finder was accurate to within 10m (33ft) at any range between 200 and 5000m (660 and 16,400ft). All this almost guaranteed a first shot hit in trained hands. The revised M60 was standardised as the 105mm Gun Full Tracked Combat Tank M60A3 on 10 May 1979, and the first unit to receive them, the 1st Battalion, 32d Armor Brigade, got 54 of them just 16 days later.

And development of the M60 series, at least unofficially, did not stop there. The engine came in for renewed scrutiny, this time vis-à-vis its performance rather than its reliability. Two straightforward variants of the AVDS-1790 were proposed – the AVDS-1790-5A developing 910hp and the AVDS-1790-7A, which developed 950hp. Consideration was also given to a technically innovative derivative, the

M103

**Armament: one 120mm gun,
 one 7.62mm machine gun,
 one .5in machine gun
Crew: five
Length (gun forward): 11.4m (37.4ft)
Width: 3.76m (12.3ft)
Height: 3.56m (11.67ft) (to cupola)
Armour: 12.7–178mm (.5-7in)
Engine: 810bhp petrol
Range: 128km (80 miles)
Speed: 34km/h (21mph)
Country of origin: USA**

AVCR-1790, which developed no less than 1200hp from the same basic unit, largely thanks to its variable compression ratio pistons. A gas turbine unit from Avco-Lycoming was also looked at, and although it was not accepted for the M60 series, it went on to become the powerplant for the all-new M1 Abrams, the MBT with which the US Army would go into the 21st century. Each and every one of these powerplants would have needed a new transmission package,

since the CD-850 was close to the top of its performance envelope in dealing with the 750hp that the standard engine put out. A variety of improved transmissions were offered, both from Allison, the original suppliers, and from other sources. In the event, the US armed forces did not adopt a new power unit, although Teledyne-Continental later offered the M60AX as a private venture, with the AVCR-1790 engine and the Renk RK-340 transmission, together with

■RIGHT: The Centurion gained universal popularity with all those who used it. This early version mounts the 17pdr gun that proved itself in action against Panthers and Tigers in World War II.

National Waterlift hydropneumatic suspension. Even with 4 tonnes of additional armour, the M60AX was 50 per cent faster on the road than the other variants, and almost three times faster across rough ground, managing 38km/h (24mph) to the 14.5km/h (9mph) of the tanks with torsion bar suspension.

ISRAELI M60S

Israel was one of the most enthusiastic M60 users, having graduated through M47 and M48 Pattons – and M4 Shermans in a variety of guises, too, come to that. Along with improved Centurions of British origin and the locally produced Merkava, M60s were the mainstay of Israel's armoured divisions during the 1973 Yom Kippur War and in the fighting in Lebanon in 1982. It is clear from users' reports that the tanks performed as expected, the M60A3s proving themselves more than a match for the Soviet-supplied T-62 tanks with which the opposing Egyptian and Syrian forces were largely equipped. M60A3s proved largely equal to the few T-72s they encountered, too, although that may have been due to inept handling rather than any particular weakness in the T-72s

themselves. Meanwhile, the Israeli M60A1s scored well against the T-54/55s, despite the latter's heavy armour. The Israeli Defence Forces have a solid history of improving the weapons with which they are supplied, and the M60 has been no exception. The best-known Israeli M60 'accessory' is the Blazer explosive reactive armour system, which employs plates of explosive sandwiched between thin sheets of steel armour. The purpose of this explosive armour is to defeat HEAT rounds by detonating the incoming warheads prematurely on the outer armour, setting off the explosive 'filling', which in turn disrupts the destructive super-hot jet of gas from the warhead. Reactive armour can be defeated (in theory, at least) by tandem HEAT projectiles with multiple warheads, and it serves no purpose whatsoever against kinetic energy AP rounds, which just go straight through. However, it is certainly effective against infantry armed with AT guided weapons – a source of considerable danger to a modern armoured vehicle.

In addition to going to form gun tanks, M60 chassis were also used as the basis for the M728 Combat Engineering

Vehicle (as has been noted, many of the unsuccessful M60A2s were thus converted), and some gun tanks also received simplified bulldozer blade installations so that they could construct hull-down firing positions for themselves. Mine ploughs similar to those fitted to earlier generations of tank, although rather more effective on the whole, were routinely available to M60s, and mine detonating rollers have also been fitted.

ENGINEER VARIANTS

More than 400 Armoured Vehicle Launched Bridges (AVLBs) have been constructed on M60 chassis. Such AVLBs can span a gap of more than 20m (66ft) and can support the weight of a fully loaded tank. They can be positioned in three minutes and recovered, from either end, in 10–20 minutes, depending on conditions. Many of the improvements brought into the M60 programme also found their way into the M88 Armoured Recovery Vehicle, including the AVDS-1790 engine. By the time the M60 appeared, it had ceased to be truly feasible to construct SP guns on tank chassis, although the M48/M60 chassis did form the basis for the M998 'Sergeant

York', the DIVAD (Division Air Defense) AA tank projected to replace the M42 'Duster'. The M998 had a radar fire-control system based on that found in the F-16 fighter-bomber and twin 40mm Bofors cannon capable of a combined rate of fire of 600 rounds per minute. The tank took a long time and cost many hundreds of millions of dollars to develop. When it was apparently ready to be issued, belated testing under more realistic conditions than had been previously applied revealed it as entirely inadequate, and the M998 was withdrawn before it ever entered service.

AMERICAN HEAVY TANKS

The T43 project, initiated in 1947, was aimed at developing a 55-tonne tank that was armoured to a maximum thickness of 127mm (5in), carried a 120mm main gun and was equipped with an 800hp engine for a maximum road speed in the region of 32km/h (20mph). When the project got under way, there was some doubt as to the tactical necessity for such a vehicle, but the Berlin Blockade of 1948–49 seemed to make it essential to develop a tank capable of taking on the IS-3 in a level contest. When the prototype T43 appeared, its running gear, while uprated and lengthened to take account of the bigger overall dimensions, clearly owed a lot to the M-26. The tank's hull and turret, however, were quite different in form, having a much better ballistic profile. The turret, in particular, was bigger than any seen on a tank before, with room for four men – the commander, the gunner and two loaders, the extra loader being made necessary by the choice of the 120mm M58 gun, which used separated ammunition. The crew was kept down to five by the tank's having no hull machine gun. Nonetheless, the finished T43 weighed 57 tonnes, since it had been progressively uparmoured to a maximum on the hull front of 178mm (7in). It achieved its design speed, but only at the cost of a very poor reliability record, and not surprisingly, its fuel consumption was heavy. A full fuel load of 1015 litres (268 US gallons) gave the T43 a range of just 130km (80 miles), although it could be said that that was not a particularly

■RIGHT: A Mk 3 Centurion of the 8th Hussars crossing the Imjin river in the Korean War. It mounted a powerful 20pdr main gun in an effort to combat the well-armoured North Korean T-34s.

serious disadvantage, given the vehicle's role.

The new heavy tank was standardised in 1953 as the 120mm Gun Tank M103, but it was really still not ready for service, and many small modifications remained to be made before it could be reckoned combat ready. It finally entered service as the M103A1 in 1957 with the US Army and – somewhat surprisingly, given their amphibious assault role – the US Marine Corps. The tank never saw combat and was not supplied to any of the United States' client states. It was soon replaced by the M60 and withdrawn.

CENTURION AND CONQUEROR

As early as July or August 1943, the British War Office prepared an outline specification – A41 – for a new heavy cruiser tank, and another – A45 – for a much heavier infantry/assault tank, both to be powered by the Rolls-Royce Meteor engine. The assault tank was to be a non-starter, but the cruiser tank was to become a resounding success. It was designed 'in house' by the Department of Tank Design, the first time that body had had sole responsibility for a vehicle since it had been inaugurated, having previously always shared it with the prime contractor. Development was entrusted to AEC, which produced some of the best heavy trucks the British Army had, but whose experience with armoured

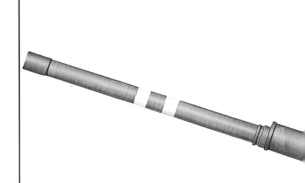

Sho't (Israeli Centurion)

Armament: one 105mm gun, one .5in AA machine gun, one 7.62mm machine gun
Crew: four
Length (gun forward): 9.85m (32.3ft)
Width: 3.4m (11.2ft)
Height: 2.94m (9.65ft) (to turret)
Armour: 17–118mm (.66–4.64in)
Engine: 750bhp diesel
Range: 205km (127 miles)
Speed: 43km/h (27mph)
Country of origin: Israel

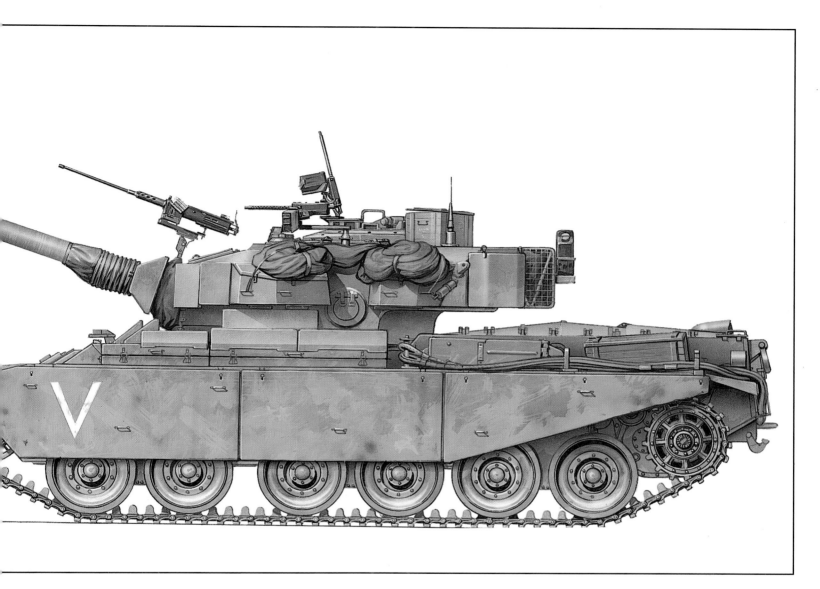

vehicles was limited to producing armoured cars and command vehicles and to development work on mine flails for the Valentine and Sherman. That comparative lack of experience notwithstanding, a full-scale mock-up of the A41 was under construction by the end of the year and was finished the following May, whereupon the almost inevitable wrangling over armament commenced.

The 17-pounder, as fitted to the Sherman Firefly and the A30 Challenger, was clearly the best high-velocity gun available, but was deficient firing anything but armour-piercing ammunition. The 95mm howitzer was equally superior with high explosive ammunition, but such rounds could not disable enemy armour at anything like stand-off range. Then there was the shorter-barrelled 17-pounder known as the 77mm gun, developed for the Comet, which was inferior to either in their optimum role, but could at least fulfil

both to a reasonable degree. The decision was a compromise – 15 of the 20 A41 pilot tanks would be completed with 17-pounder guns and the rest with 77mm dual-purpose cannon. There was some talk of mounting the 93mm howitzer – and indeed, a version of the tank was designated to receive it – but the project came to nothing.

CANNON OR MACHINE GUN?
Arguments continued over secondary armament. On the one hand was the Polsten 20mm cannon; on the other, the tried-and-tested 7.92mm Besa machine gun. The dispute was centred on the former's considerably greater destructive power versus the latter's greater flexibility, greater sustained fire capability and reduced ammunition storage requirements. There was even argument as to whether a second machine gun should be mounted in the rear of the turret. The A41 had no hull machine gun; indeed, it had no room for

one, nor for a fifth man to operate it. And since the tank was likely to travel gun back for much of the time, because of the length of the 17-pounder's barrel, it was argued that a machine gun sited in the rear of the turret would at least provide a measure of forward-facing protection from infantry attack in confined spaces. The matter was settled only when it was pointed out that the installation of a Besa there would leave no room for an internally mounted smoke bomb discharger, which was a rather more important requirement. As in the case of the main armament, the cannon-versus-machine gun debate was settled by compromise. The first five 17-pounder pilots would have a co-axial Besa, and the remaining 10 would have either a Besa machine gun or a Polsten cannon in a flexible mount to the left of the turret face. In the event, the Polsten was invariably unpopular with the men who tested the pilot vehicles and consequently was soon deleted, as was the separate

Sho't
(for specifications see page 114)

mounting. The Besa, in its turn, eventually gave way to a .30in Browning, and the same gun was also adopted as anti-aircraft armament.

THE CHRISTIE SYSTEM
About the only element of British tank design over the previous decade that had proved satisfactory to designers, manufacturers and users alike was the Christie suspension system. It is somewhat ironic that it should now be discarded, but there were serious doubts raised as to its potential for development

in a tank that was to start out at almost 45 tonnes and would inevitably get heavier still as it was developed. Instead, the designer in charge at AEC came up with a suspension system on the Horstmann principle, as first used in the Vickers Light Tank Mk I of 1929, with paired medium-diameter roadwheels linked by horizontal concentric coiled springs, along with six track-return rollers. Departing from the Christie system meant the loss of the second layer of armour protecting much of the suspension, and to make up for this it

was proposed to fit the new tank with removable and easy-to-replace armour skirts to help defeat infantry anti-tank weapons firing hollow-charge warheads.

When the finished mock-up was shown to the Director of the Royal Armoured Corps and to the Tank Board, it was greeted with a certain degree of awe and was accepted with only minor modifications. At 43 tonnes in weight and more than 9.75m (32ft) long with its gun forward, the new tank dwarfed the Cromwell and the other cruiser tanks and made even the Churchill look

decidedly skimpy. In addition, it looked right, with its well-angled frontal glacis and its boat-shaped hull. Christened the Centurion, the tank was ordered into pilot production at the Royal Ordnance Factories in Woolwich and Nottingham, although series production was to go to Vickers-Armstrong and Leyland Motors, as well as to the Royal Ordnance Factory at Leeds. By April 1945, four prototypes had been delivered, and two more were ready to leave the factories. Rather than follow the normal routine of submitting the new vehicles to a lengthy test programme at proving grounds, it was decided to ship them out to a composite unit of the Guards Armoured Division, then fighting its way towards Berlin, and test them under combat conditions instead. Operation Sentry, as the attempt to get the tanks into action prematurely was known, came to nothing, for by the time the six Centurions left Southampton for Belgium on 14 May 1945, the war had already been over for almost a fortnight.

The first task facing the six new tanks when they left Antwerp five days later, was a 650km (400-mile) road march to the 7th Armoured Division's HQ at Gribbohm. From then until the end of July, the tanks visited virtually every British armoured unit in Germany and the Low Countries. They received a unanimously warm welcome and came closer than anything in the Allied armoury to being the 'universal tank'. Virtually all the crews who tried the vehicles for themselves agreed that they were the best they had ever worked with. If there was dissent at all, it came from the drivers. The Centurion was a heavy vehicle, with nothing in the way of power assistance for steering or gear changing, which was often a two-handed job.

THE SUPERB CENTURION

When it finally entered service four years later, in 1949, the Centurion was certainly a contender for best tank in the world. But had its designers suggested that the Centurion would still be in operation, albeit in a much modified form, past its 50th birthday, they would probably have been ridiculed. As late as the 1990s, Denmark, Jordan, Singapore and Sweden were still using Centurions, while Israel still had around 1000 modified Centurions in its order of battle. In combat in 1973, Israel's Centurions had beaten a superior force of considerably more modern tanks into the ground on the Golan Heights. It is a tribute to the integrity of the original concept that the tank was able to stand

■ABOVE: The Centurion was adopted as the main battle tank of the British Army in 1949. The Mk 10 variant, mounting the 105mm L7 main gun, is seen here landing in Aden in the 1960s.

progressive uparmouring, uprating and upgunning and still remain firmly in contention. It is not surprising, that being the case, that the Centurion was to appear in a host of different forms and guises, some of them originated by its makers, and some instigated by users in development programmes of their own. The tank had faults, of course, but these were mostly to do with mobility – a top speed of no more than 35km/h (22mph) and a range of only 160km (100 miles), thanks to a 650hp engine and a 460-litre (120 US gallon) fuel tank, respectively. While those two components remained unchanged, and the tank's all-up weight increased, speed and range could only get worse. In the end, in desperation, a 910-litre (240 US gallon) monowheel trailer unit was developed that could be towed behind the tank.

Thirteen marks of Centurion were produced, with each from Mk 5 onwards being manufactured in two variants. During the course of this development, the Centurion went through two changes

Centurion AVRE 105

Armament: one 105mm gun, one .5in AA machine gun, one 7.62mm machine gun
Crew: four
Length (gun forward): 9.85m (32.3ft)
Width: 3.4m (11.12ft)
Height: 2.94m (9.64ft)
Armour: 17–118mm (.66–4.64in)
Engine: 650bhp petrol
Range: 105km (65 miles)
Speed: 35km/h (22mph)
Country of origin: United Kingdom

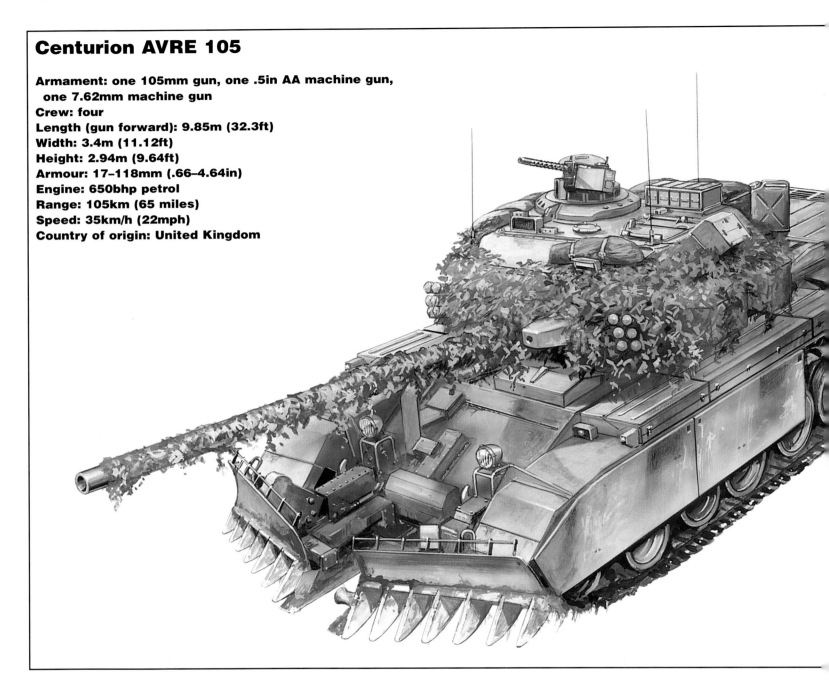

of gun. The 83mm L/64 20-pounder succeeded the 17-pounder and was superseded in its turn by the 105mm L7 gun. The tank was uparmoured twice as well and received infra-red driving and fighting systems, including a 'black'/white searchlight. It was also equipped with a .50in ranging machine gun, ballistically matched to the main armament, which was later replaced with a laser range-finder. Other modifications included a redesigned commander's cupola, extra fuel tanks and added external stowage. In its final form, as the Mk 13, the Centurion weighed just under 52 tonnes combat ready on its 610mm-wide (24in) tracks. By the time Mk 13 appeared, internal fuel capacity had risen to over 1000 litres (265 US gallons), but total

range was still no better than 190km (120 miles). A diesel engine made a considerable difference and improved the tank's overall viability considerably. The Israeli Defence Forces installed the 750hp Continental diesel in the Centurions that they renamed 'Sho't', and Vickers fitted the General Motors V-12 diesel to the tanks they refurbished.

ENDLESS CENTURION VARIANTS
As was mentioned earlier, besides serving as gun tanks, Centurions were also used as the basis for the widest possible range of battlefield support vehicles. There were two types of Centurion AVLB, and there were Centurion AVREs, with bulldozer blades and 165mm demolition guns. Centurions also went to make up ARVs

and ARKs, which could also function as bridges or ramps spanning up to 23m (70ft) individually or more if used in tandem. Centurions were also tested as flamethrower tanks and as the chassis for self-propelled guns and tank destroyers. Although popular with all who used it, the Centurion never achieved the production levels of its rivals in the United States or the Soviet Union. Something over 4000 were produced in all, of which around 1500 were supplied in one guise or another to the British Army. The Centurion, in all its multitude of forms, lasted long enough in British Army service to span two systems of designation. It was conceived as a tank under the old 'A' specification system and then became a 'fighting

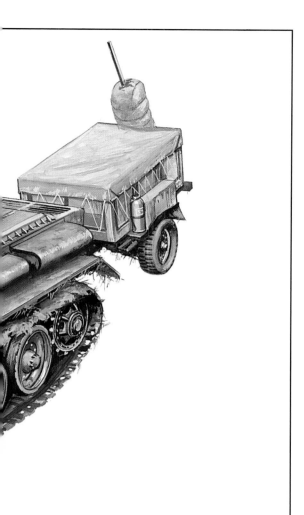

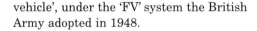
ABOVE: The Centurion Mk 3 has been in service with Israeli forces since 1960. The Israelis have made a series of improvements to their Centurions, which they call the Sho't.

vehicle', under the 'FV' system the British Army adopted in 1948.

THE UNHAPPY CONQUEROR

The A45 heavy tank conceived in parallel with the Centurion saw the light of day in prototype form in 1948. It had running gear similar to that of the Centurion, although uprated and with four pairs of smaller roadwheels per side. The A45 also had the same Meteor engine and a 17-pounder gun in the same electrically operated, stabilised turret that the lighter tank used. However, it soon became clear that the A45 could not outperform the Centurion in any particular and was promptly abandoned. It chassis, meanwhile, survived to become the basis of another heavy tank, planned,

like the American M103, to be able to take on the Soviet IS-3. This became the FV214, known as the 'Conqueror', although the first pilot was known as the FV221 'Caernarvon'. The Conqueror was standardised in 1950 but was only ever produced in small numbers and was never operated by anyone but the British Army. A total of 180 of these 66-tonne monsters were produced up until 1959. They were protected by frontal armour 178mm (7in) thick and armed with a 120mm L11 gun, which was probably their best feature. The gun was mounted in a cast turret that had positively spacious accommodation for the three men who worked there. Even though it was a much heavier machine, the Conqueror was capable of keeping up with the Centurions it was there to support, thanks to its 810hp uprated Meteor engine. Despite this the Conqueror was still tactically obsolescent and mechanically unreliable, and it was taken out of service in 1966, as soon as the Chieftain had been issued in significant numbers.

The first tank to be produced in France after World War II was based on a

design completed before the German invasion of 1940. The original design was basically a Char B1's hull with a full-traverse turret to carry the 1898-vintage 75mm gun. Under Nazi occupation (and therefore clandestinely) the plans were largely redrawn but not changed significantly in principle.

FRENCH TANKS

The new concept retained the B1's running gear and tracks, but had a turret capable of accommodating a 90mm gun. Work started on a prototype soon after the liberation of France, and the finished vehicle, known as the ARL-44, after the Ateliers de Construction de Rueil, where it had been built, was rolled out in 1946. With 120mm (4.72in) of frontal armour, the ARL-44 weighed in at 48 tonnes, and the tank's 700hp Maybach petrol engine gave it a top speed of 37km/h (23mph). The plan was to build some 300 examples, but work stopped after just 60 had been completed, because of changes in tactical thinking in the French Army. A heavy tank was planned to replace the ARL-44 and the many captured PzKpfw V Panthers that the French Army operated. The result was the AMX-50, built by Ateliers de Construction d'Issy-les-Moulineaux, which had an oscillating turret mounting first a 90mm, then a 100mm and finally a 120mm gun. The AMX-50 weighed 56 tonnes and was

located behind. The tank had a decidedly low profile, the height of the vehicle to the top of the commander's hatch – there was no cupola fitted – being just 2.3m (7ft 6in). This made concealment that much easier. Since the prototype was first wheeled out in 1948, a variety of main guns have been fitted to the AMX-13. Variants have had the manually loaded 75mm gun in the FL-11 turret, the auto-loader 75mm or 90mm gun in the FL-10 turret and the auto-loader 105mm gun in the FL-12 turret, the use of an automatic loader reducing the turret crew to just the commander and gunner. Those variants with the 75mm gun were often equipped with wire-guided and later HOT (High-subsonic Optically guided Tube-launched) AT missiles. The FL-12 turret, together with its GIAT 105mm gun, was also supplied to Austria to equip the Steyr Kurassier tank destroyer. The combination of light weight, high speed and considerable firepower – not to mention a low price tag – made the AMX-13 very popular with smaller nations

■**ABOVE: The Swiss-built Pz68 was closely modelled on the US M48, although all components apart from the British 105mm L7 main gun were produced domestically.**

powered by a 1000hp petrol engine, but was eventually cancelled in favour of American M47 Patton 1s, which had the advantage of being available free under the US Military Aid Program.

The first French tank to be wholly designed and built after World War II was the 15-tonne AMX-13, which was to prove to be a considerable success. It sold in relatively large numbers abroad, despite being quite different in character from anything that had gone before in that it was the first production tank in the world to be fitted with an oscillating turret. With a hull just 4.9m (16ft) long, armoured to a maximum of 25mm (1in) and powered by a 250hp petrol engine to a maximum speed of 60km/h (38mph), the AMX-13 was clearly intended for a revamped cavalry role with the newly created French airborne forces. They had a requirement for an air-portable armoured vehicle that was capable of giving fire support as well as acting as a tank destroyer.

The AMX-13 also differed from most other postwar designs in having its engine located at the front of the vehicle, alongside the driver, while the turret was

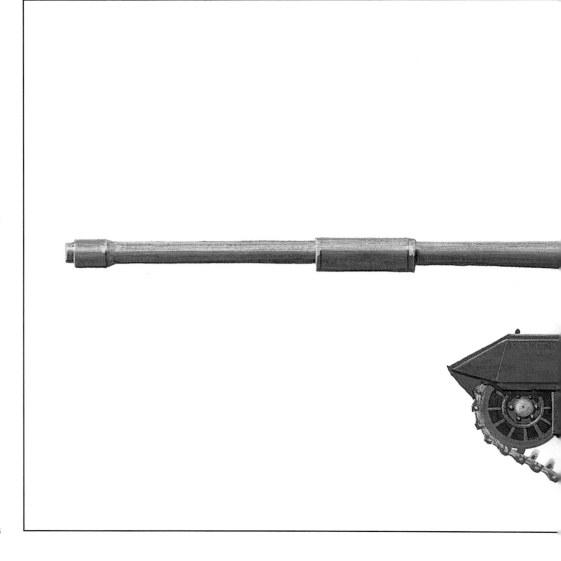

right from the time of its introduction into service in 1953. Over a score of countries bought it, and many use it still, getting on for half a century later. During the Six-Day War of 1967, it became apparent that although the 75mm gun's HEAT round would pierce the side armour of a T54/55 tank quite easily, it would not penetrate the frontal armour. As a result, most of the AMX-13s that continued in service through the 1970s and 1980s were fitted with one of the bigger-calibre guns. The 90mm gun was the most common, its 8.9kg (20lb) HEAT projectile being able to penetrate 320mm (12.6in) of vertical armour or 120mm (4.72in) of armour set at an angle of 65 degrees. Unlike the kinetic energy AP round, a HEAT round's penetrating power does not diminish with range. In fact, no KE/AP ammunition is supplied for any of the AMX-13's three cannon, the choice being limited to HE, HEAT and smoke only.

As well as forming the basis of the original light tank/tank destroyer, the AMX-13 chassis was subsequently used for a very wide variety of purposes. Bridgelayers and armoured recovery vehicles based on the AMX-13's chassis were designed to operate alongside the gun tanks, while 105mm and 155mm SP guns were also produced, along with anti-aircraft tanks with twin 30mm Hispano-Suiza cannon. There was also a range of APCs and armoured infantry fighting vehicles (AIFVs), including missile launchers, mortar carriers, cargo carriers, ambulances, mine layers and combat engineering tractors. In all, around 4000 AMX-13 tanks were produced, and perhaps half that number of the support variants.

SWISS EXPERIMENTS

Somewhat considering the mountainous nature of the terrain that covers most of the country, the only other non-Iron Curtain country to produce a tank of its own during the 1940s and 1950s was Switzerland. Having procured Jagdpanzer 38(t) Hetzer tank destroyers from Czechoslovakia, AMX-13s from France and Centurion Mk 5s and Mk 7s from Britain, the Swiss embarked on a development programme of their own that resulted, in 1958, in the prototype KW 30, with a locally designed 90mm gun. Ten preproduction Pz58s, as the tank became known, were manufactured with the British 20-pounder gun, while the tank that finally went into production, the Pz61, had the well proven British 105mm L7 gun. The Pz61 entered service in 1965. Thanks to relatively light levels of protection – just 60mm (2.4in) of armour on the hull front – the tank weighed some 37 tonnes ready for combat. A 630hp diesel engine gave it a handy top speed of 50km/h (30mph), and 750 litres (200 US gallons) of fuel was enough for a range of 300km (185 miles). Some 150 Pz61s were manufactured in all before production switched over to the rather better Pz68, which had a stabiliser system for its gun and a more powerful engine, as well as other refinements in later sub-variants. A number of 400 Pz68

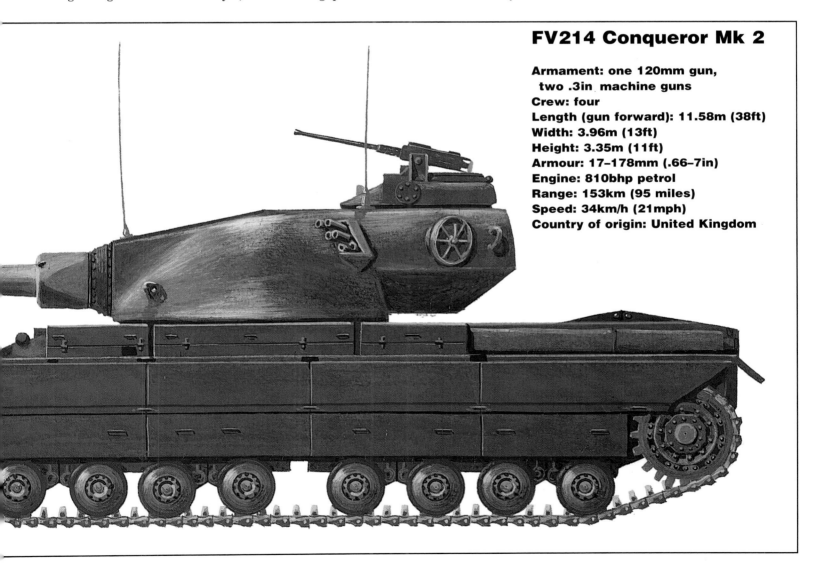

FV214 Conqueror Mk 2

**Armament: one 120mm gun,
  two .3in machine guns**
Crew: four
Length (gun forward): 11.58m (38ft)
Width: 3.96m (13ft)
Height: 3.35m (11ft)
Armour: 17–178mm (.66–7in)
Engine: 810bhp petrol
Range: 153km (95 miles)
Speed: 34km/h (21mph)
Country of origin: United Kingdom

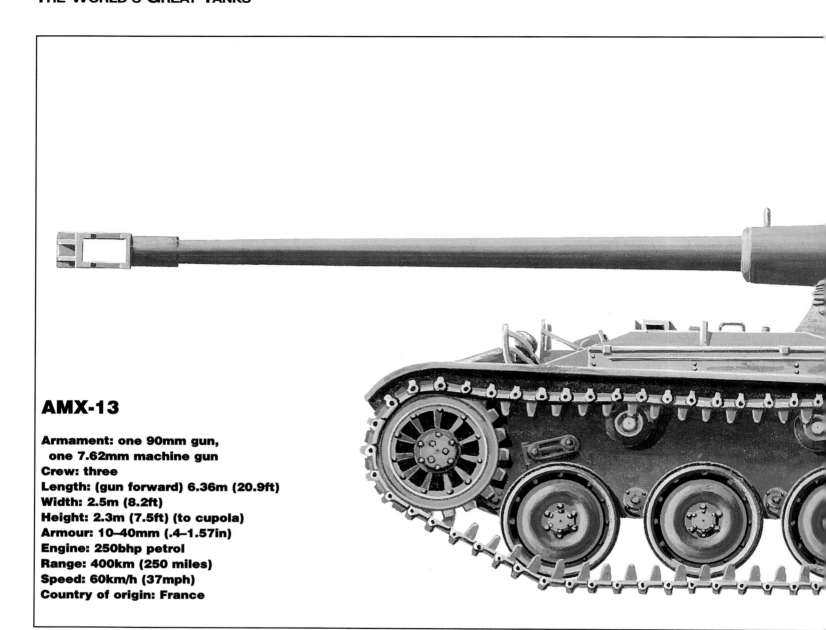

AMX-13

Armament: one 90mm gun,
  one 7.62mm machine gun
Crew: three
Length: (gun forward) 6.36m (20.9ft)
Width: 2.5m (8.2ft)
Height: 2.3m (7.5ft) (to cupola)
Armour: 10–40mm (.4–1.57in)
Engine: 250bhp petrol
Range: 400km (250 miles)
Speed: 60km/h (37mph)
Country of origin: France

gun tanks were produced, and AVLBs and ARVs were also constructed on the same chassis.

SOVIET MEDIUMS

The frontline tanks with which the Soviet Union finished World War II, the T-34/85 and the IS-3, may not have been the best there were, but a combination of sheer weight of numbers and cunning tactical employment had made them unbeatable overall. However, by the time the USSR had shrugged off any pretence that its wartime alliance with the western powers had been anything more than a temporary expedient to defeat Hitler, these vehicles, particularly the T-34/85, were starting to look a little jaded. A replacement medium tank, the T-44, had already been produced in small numbers in 1945 and 1946. It was based on the T-34, with the same 85mm gun and

angular turret, but incorporating many new features, including a transversely mounted engine. The T-44 proved unreliable, and a much improved version was on the way that took in many of the lessons learned from the advanced IS-3. The prototype of this tank appeared in 1946, went into production at Kharkov the following year and was issued to the elite of the Red Army's armoured divisions in either 1949 or 1950. The tank became known as the T-54, and together with the derivative T-55 was to become the most important tank of the period that followed, not only because it was produced in staggering peacetime numbers, but also because it represented the state of the art in tank design at the time of its introduction and for many years thereafter. The T-54/55 stayed in production continuously from 1948 to 1981, and an estimated total of at least

50,000 were built. Used over the years by any number of Warsaw Pact and other communist states and their clients, the T-54/55 was initially manufactured at Kharkov and Omsk, then later in Poland and Czechoslovakia and in the People's Republic of China, where it was designated the Type 59.

The most obvious feature the T-54 inherited from the IS-3 was the 'skillet' turret, the oblate inverted bowl that had proved so good at shrugging off anti-tank projectiles during World War II. Being an altogether lighter vehicle than the IS-3, at 36 rather than 46 tonnes, it did not have the heavy tank's formidable 122mm gun, but a 100mm L/54 D-10T. This weapon was developed from a naval QF gun and was capable of launching a 16kg (35lb) capped AP projectile at a muzzle velocity of 1000 metres per second (3280 feet per second) to penetrate 185mm

conditions in the turret, a small ammunition storage capacity (just 34 rounds for the main gun) and the inability of the gun itself to depress through more than four degrees. This last-mentioned shortcoming was to become increasingly important as the use of prepared hull-down firing positions became more common. In these positions, the tank is inclined on a bulldozed ramp on the edge of dead ground, its hull protected by the earth bank thus formed. To be effective, the gun must be capable of being depressed through the same angle the ramp makes, and four degrees is not enough.

THE T-54 BECOMES THE T-55

In terms of armour, the T-54 was adequately protected, with 100mm (3.93in) of armour on the glacis plate and turret front and 170mm (6.7in) on the gun mantlet. Its tried-and-tested Christie running gear had five large, unevenly spaced roadwheels, which were suspended on torsion bars and also acted as track-return rollers. This system was well up to the top speed of 52km/h (32mph) that the tank's 570hp V-2-54 diesel engine somewhat surprisingly provided. Internal fuel tanks with a capacity of 812 litres (215 US gallons) gave a maximum range of around 400km

■BELOW: The AMX-13 was phased out by the French Army in the mid-1970s, but it continues in service throughout Southeast Asia with countries who appreciate its low maintenance costs.

(7.28in) of vertical armour at a range of 1000m (3280ft). A HEAT round was later developed for this gun that could penetrate 380mm (15in) of armour anywhere within its 2500m (8200ft) effective range. More recently still, a high-velocity armour piercing discarding sabot (HVAPDS) sub-calibre round was developed. Fired at 1420 metres per second (4660 feet per second), it could defeat 200mm (7.9in) of vertical armour at the same 2500m (8200ft) range and was not put off by reactive armour plates.

THE T-54 FIRE-CONTROL SYSTEM

The fire-control system of the early T-54s depended on simple optical sights with offset reticules, which may have been adequate in 1948 but was soon outdated and was not updated until the mid-1950s. The fire-control system was one of the T-54's weaknesses, along with cramped

T-54

Armament: one 100mm gun, two 7.62mm machine guns, one 12.7mm AA machine gun
Crew: four
Length (gun forward): 9m (29.5ft)
Width: 3.27m (10.72ft)
Height: 2.4m (7.87ft) (to cupola)
Armour: 20–100mm (.78-4in)
Engine: 520bhp diesel
Range: 400km (250 miles)
Speed: 48km/h (30mph)
Country of origin: Soviet Union

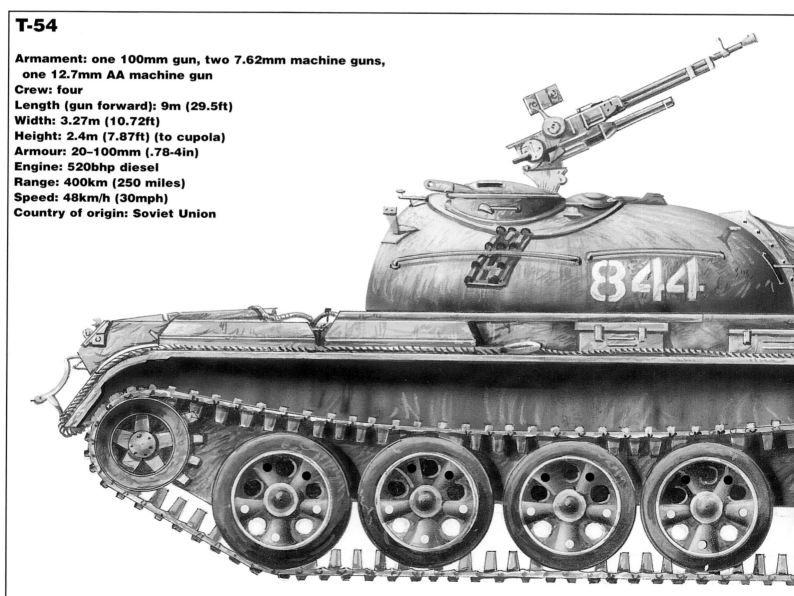

(250 miles) and were supplemented by jettisonable external tanks for transit purposes.

Among the modifications made to the T-54 over the years was the addition of a second cupola for the loader, although this feature, and the 12.7mm AA machine gun it mounted, was later deleted. The tank's D-10TG or D-10T2S main gun was fitted with a bore evacuator and also received a one-axis, and eventually a two-axis, stabiliser and power elevation system. Infra-red driving lights and searchlights were also added, along with NBC protection and a deep-fording system. Eventually the T-54 was

■LEFT: The T-54 became a potent symbol of Soviet expansion in Eastern Europe after World War II. Tens of thousands were built, and the type has seen service with 55 countries.

reclassified as the T-55, with an uprated engine and increased internal fuel capacity. The driver-operated bow machine gun remained in place initially but was later deleted to give space for the storage of nine extra rounds of main gun ammunition.

The T-55 made its first appearance at the 1961 Moscow parade to mark the anniversary of the October Revolution. During the whole of its life, the T-54/55 was not uparmoured at any time and never had any but the 100mm gun, albeit in increasingly more effective forms. That it was to be reckoned a match for the American M60 and even the M60A1, which were standardised a full decade and more after the T-54 first appeared, says a great deal for the Soviet tank's basic design, and much for the Soviet Union's 'no-frills' tank warfare philosophy as a whole. Over the years, T-54/55s have

seen combat all over the globe – in the Middle East conflicts of the 1960s and 1970s, in Afghanistan, along the Chinese border (where they were used by both the Soviets and the Chinese), in the Iran–Iraq war and during Desert Storm, in Angola and in many of the other conflicts that sprang up all over Africa during the latter third of the 20th century.

THE ENDURING T-55

The tanks even saw action in Europe during the suppression of the Hungarian uprising in 1956 and during the wars that followed the dissolution of Yugoslavia and the Soviet Union itself. And that list is not exhaustive. In addition, more than 30 separate wars and conflicts were reckoned to be under way during the latter part of 1996, and it is reasonable to suggest that given the

T-55
(for specifications see page 128)

■ ABOVE: An Egyptian Army T-55 fitted with mine-clearing equipment on the Golan Heights during the Yom Kippur War. The T-55 is limited by an inability to fire accurately 'on the move'.

pattern of their distribution, T-54/55 tanks were involved in the majority of them.

As well as serving as gun tanks, T-54/55s have been found in the usual run of supporting roles. They have been fitted with flamethrowers, bulldozer blades and snowploughs, as well as with mine clearing rollers and ploughs. There have also been four types of ARV and three types of AVLB based on the T54/55. Users have made modifications of their own as well. India, for example, has refitted many of its T-54/55s with later Soviet-made 115mm guns or with the British 105mm L7, while many of the tanks the Israelis have captured have been recycled, often after having been fitted with L7 cannon, much-needed new fire-control systems and air conditioning.

SOVIET HEAVIES

The IS-series of heavy tanks continued in production after the end of World War II, with the general run of minor improvements being made to their armament, powerplants and protection. After Stalin's death in 1953, the Soviet authorities saw no reason to attach his

T-55

Armament: one 100mm gun, one 7.62mm machine gun, one 12.7mm machine gun
Crew: four
Length: 6.45m (21.15ft)
Width: 3.27m (10.72ft)
Height: 2.4m (7.87ft)
Armour: 20–203mm (.79–8in)
Engine: 580hp
Range: 500km (310 miles)
Speed: 50km/h (31.07mph)
Country of origin: Soviet Union

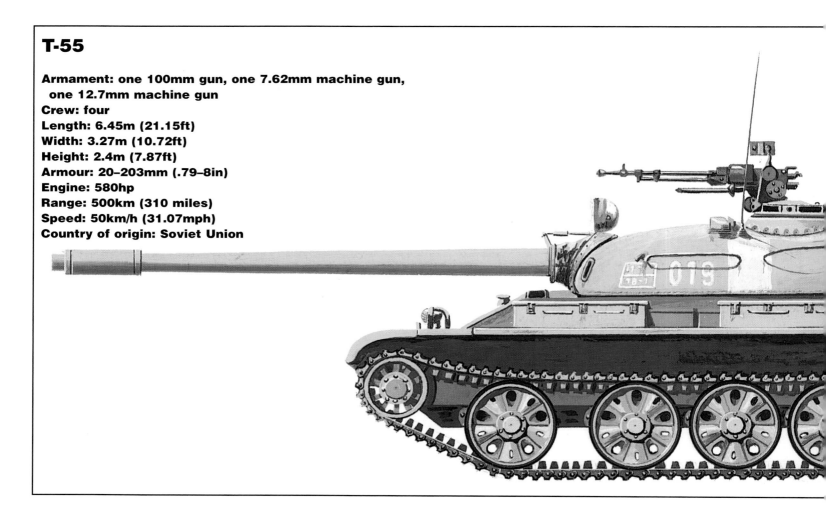

name to a tank any longer, and the next new version to come off the Kharkov production line was called the T-10. It was a very similar-looking tank to the IS-3, but it had been lengthened somewhat and had had a seventh roadwheel added to its running gear. It was somewhat heavier than the IS-3, too, at 50 tonnes all up. The T-10 was shown in public for the first time at the Moscow parade on 7 November 1957, the 40th anniversary of the revolution. Just as the M103 was to provide fire support for the M48, and the Conqueror was to supply the same for the Centurion, so the T-10 was to back up the T-54/55s. The T-10's modified 122mm D-74 gun fired a massive 25kg (55lb) armour-piercing round at a muzzle velocity of 885 metres per second (2900 feet per second) and could penetrate 185mm (7.28in) of vertical armour at 1000m (3280ft). In other words, it could blow holes in anything it might meet. Like all guns employing separate projectile and charge, the D-74 was relatively slow to load, and two to three rounds per minute was the practical limit to the T-10's rate of fire. As in the case of the T-54/55, the small angle of depression of the gun – just three

degrees in the T-10 – posed problems in firing from hull-down positions. The angle of depression was limited by the low profile of the turret: there simply was not room to get the breech any higher. The danger to the tank was minimised, however, by its 120mm (4.75in) of sharply angled frontal armour, and by the good all-round ballistic shape of the hull and turret. And despite the T-10's considerable weight, its 700hp V-2-IS V-12 diesel engine, a development of that originally produced for the A-20 tank in the mid-1930s, produced a top speed of 42km/h (26mph). Nine hundred litres (238 US gallons) of fuel gave the tank a range of only 250km (155 miles), which was low by Soviet standards but was perfectly adequate for a support tank such as this. The T-10 had 710mm-wide (28in) tracks in order to keep the ground pressure within reasonable bounds.

The T-10 was updated in the mid-1960s. It was uparmoured and the main gun was given a two-axis stabiliser in addition to a new fin-stabilised HEAT round whose 14kg (31lb) warhead could penetrate almost 500mm (19.7in) of armour plate anywhere within its effective range. The T-10's DShK 12.7mm

co-axial and anti-aircraft machine guns were replaced with the 14.5mm KPV, an infra-red fighting system was fitted, with both co-axial and flexibly mounted searchlights as on the later T-54s, and provision was made for a snorkel and an NBC protection system. The improved variant was known as the T-10M. Although T-10s were withdrawn from frontline Soviet service during the late 1970s, and many were placed in storage, they were still to be found with the armies of Soviet clients, including Syria, for a further decade.

SOVIET LIGHTS
The Soviet Union's tank designers also developed a light tank during the years immediately after World War II, using a light cross-country vehicle named the 'Pinguin' as a point of departure and incorporating some of the lessons learned from the light tanks produced in small quantities over the previous decade. From the start, it was decided that the new light tank should be a fully amphibious vehicle. A twin water jet propulsion system was specified to push the tank through the water, and the internal volume of the vehicle was

■RIGHT: Tank strategists in the former Warsaw Pact placed great emphasis on amphibious capabilities. All East German T-55s were equipped as standard with a snorkel.

adjusted to give the required buoyancy without the use of flotation screens, although a trim board was fitted. Inevitably, the requirement that the tank should be amphibious resulted in a rather bigger vehicle than was strictly necessary for the purposes of reconnaissance. But that drawback was to be turned into a positive feature in many of the support vehicles which sprang from the original.

THE AMPHIBIOUS PT-76

The PT-76, as the tank was designated, was first seen in 1952. It had a welded hull that was armoured to a maximum of just 14mm (.5in) on the sides and 11mm (.4in) on the glacis plate and the turret front, which meant that it would always be vulnerable to light cannon fire and even to heavy machine guns. The tank had a crew of three and was armed with the 76.2mm D-56 gun first developed for the T-34/76. The PT-76

44km/h (27mph) on land and 10km/h (6mph) through the water. Just as the French AMX-13 was to prove popular with the smaller nations, who could not justify maintaining an armoured force based on bigger, more expensive vehicles, so the PT-76 proved popular with the minor Soviet client states. It was the only tank US forces encountered in any quantity in Vietnam, and it proved highly vulnerable, not only to superior vehicles but also to infantry AT weapons.

Like that of the AMX-13, the PT-76's chassis was put to many uses, both on the infantry battlefield and in support. It formed the basis of the BTR-50 armoured personnel carrier and the BMP infantry fighting vehicle; it was used as a vehicle for the ASU-85 airborne anti-tank gun and for the much respected ZSU-23-4 SP air-defence system, with its quadruple 23mm cannon; it served as a transporter/launcher for 'Frog' surface-to-surface and SA-6 'Gainful' surface-to-air missiles; and it was the foundation of the 122mm SP gun and of a wide variety of load carriers. Modifications over the years to PT-76 gun tanks were limited to the main armament. The improved DT-56TM gun, stabilised in both azimuth and elevation and with a bore evacuator, was retrofitted to all Red Army PT-76s and to those of other Warsaw Pact members.

■BELOW: By the time of the 1991 Gulf conflict, the T-55 was hopelessly outdated. This Iraqi vehicle was destroyed on 2 March by the French 6th Light Armoured Division.

PT-76

Armament: one 76.2mm gun, one 7.62mm machine gun (plus one 12.7mm AA ma
Crew: three
Length (gun forward): 7.63m (25ft)
Width: 3.14m (10.3ft)
Height: 2.26m (7.4ft) (to turret)
Armour: 5–17mm (.19–.66in)
Engine: 240bhp diesel
Range: 450km (280 miles)
Speed: 44km/h (27.5mph)
Country of origin: Soviet Union

e gun)

CHAPTER 5
THE MODERN TANK

Modern tanks are sophisticated fighting machines, armed with powerful main guns and containing state-of-the-art fire-control systems. And tanks such as the American Abrams and British Challenger represent the apogee of armoured fighting vehicle design.

The year 1966 was the 50th anniversary of the tank's going into battle. In the preceding half century more technological innovation had taken place than in all the rest of previously recorded time put together, and the development of the tank reflected that. What had started off as a lumbering metal box in 1916 had by 1966 become a hyper-sophisticated weapons system. The tank was as at home in the dark as in daylight; it was able to hit a target more than 2000m (6560ft) away with its first shot; and it was invulnerable to all but the most powerful or most sophisticated weapons. The sheer strength of the tank's defences had made it necessary for would-be opponents to expend precious time and resources in developing elaborate measures to neutralise it.

By the 1960s, the days of trial-and-error experimentation in tank design were long gone, and with them the tendency to produce an armoured fighting vehicle almost, it sometimes seemed, in the hope that it would somehow come out right. Now, with the lessons of combat in all sorts of terrain and climate well learned, and with few technological limitations or barriers between conception and realisation, the situation was different. Tank designers could settle down to defining vehicles capable of giving their crews a solid chance of winning through if they fought

■LEFT: Significant developments in protective armour have ensured that main battle tanks, such as these General Dynamics M1A1 Abrams, will remain in service into the next century.

them competently, taking into account, as always, the firepower and protection levels, the agility, the flexibility and the all-round preparedness of the forces they were likely to come up against.

ARMOUR IN THE MIDDLE EAST
The cockpit of armoured warfare during the 1960s and 1970s was without a doubt the Middle East, where the state of Israel, carved out after World War II very much against the wishes of its neighbours, was fighting for its life against what appeared to be much stronger, better-equipped and implacable enemies. Since the war, Syria and Egypt had veered away from longstanding British and French influence and been seduced into the Soviet sphere. As a token of the esteem in which they were held, Syria and Egypt had received almost state-of-the-art hardware from the USSR, particularly armour and aircraft, and in the attempt to combat what could well have been a geo-political disaster for the United States, Washington adopted a preferential policy towards Israeli weapons procurement needs. The result was almost America versus Russia by proxy and in miniature. On the Israeli side, M47s and M48s (and later M60s) from the United States fought alongside some French-built AMX-13s and a large fleet of British-manufactured Centurion tanks against numerically superior Arab forces comprising T-54/55s, T-62s and eventually T-72s. The Israelis usually fought on two fronts at once, but always emerged victorious, although sometimes severely battered. Then, in 1979, after a very long gestation period indeed, came a

■ABOVE: Israel probably has more experience of armoured warfare than any other nation. The indigenously produced Merkava MBT is a direct result of that experience

main battle tank designed and manufactured in Israel – the 'Merkava', or 'Chariot'.

There were many stimuli for the development of an indigenous Israeli tank. The uncertainty of continuing supply in sufficient quantity from traditional sources was certainly the strongest, but there was also the suitability of foreign tanks to be considered, given that NATO and Israeli combat strategies differed. In 1967, right after the Six-Day War, Israeli planning for a locally developed main battle tank began, although it was a further three years before the design team got down to details. From the start, it was decided to utilise as many components from the existing tank fleet of M48s, M60s and Centurions as possible, and this resulted in the choice of the AVDS-1790 engine and Allison cross-drive transmission. Unusually, in the Merkava the powerplant/transmission package was to be located in the front of the tank, where it would serve the secondary purpose of providing extra protection from head-on fire. The remainder of the running gear was a hybrid, the six Centurion-style roadwheels per side being suspended – paired – on helical springs, with the track

supported during its return run by four rollers. Because of the location of the powerplant and transmission at the front of the tank, the Merkava had its turret set towards the rear, which was another unusual feature. As a result, the Merkava alone of the later generation of MBTs was normally operated gun forward, even in transit.

THE ISRAELI MERKAVA
At a combat weight of 60 tonnes, the Merkava was 8 tonnes heavier than the M60A1 with the same powerplant and was hard pushed to maintain the same sort of performance levels as the American import. That was clearly a reasoned decision on the part of the tank's designers, who were surely instructed that protection was more important than performance. The actual protection was never specified, but it was unlikely to have been less than 150mm (5.9in) on the frontal surfaces, and the armour was set at a very flat angle indeed on both hull and turret. The tank's range of 400km (250 miles) was well suited to – and indeed, was predicated on – the Israeli doctrine of deep penetration. The Merkava's ammunition storage capacity also reflected the requirement to be able to operate in isolation for longer periods than normal, if necessary – 92 rounds could be carried in the vehicle and there was room for a further 45 in a unique rear compartment accessible only from outside the tank. As an alternative,

Merkava

Armament: one 105mm gun, two or three 7.62mm machine guns, plus one .5in AA machine gun and one 60mm mortar:
Crew: four
Length (gun forward): 8.63m (28.3ft)
Width: 3.7m (12.13ft)
Height: 2.64m (8.66ft) (to turret)
Armour: not available
Engine : 900bhp diesel
Range : 400km (250 miles)
Speed: 46km/h (28.5mph)
Country of origin: Israel

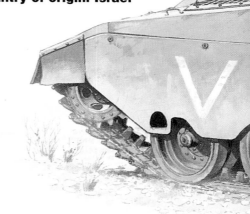

this secure rear area could be used to transport an entire 10-man infantry squad over short distances, should the need arise, but it was normally occupied by a 60mm mortar and 30 rounds of ammunition. The choice of main gun, too, was dictated by compatibility with the remainder of the Israeli fleet, although here there was less flexibility since the Israeli Centurions, M48A5s and M60s all had what was essentially the same 105mm gun, whether it was actually called the L7 or the M68. Fire control was provided by an Elbit Matador system, also locally produced, which incorporated a laser range-finder and a digital computer, together with the same range of sensors employed by the M60A3 and all other MBTs since.

THE MERKAVA MK 2

In 1983, an improved Merkava Mk 2 began to appear, with an upgraded fire-control system, appliqué armour on the hull front and the front and sides of the turret, and with the mortar now located to the left of the turret so that it could be operated from within the vehicle. All remaining Mk 1s were later upgraded to this standard. Some Merkava Mk 2s and all the later Mk 3s, which entered service in 1987, were equipped with an uprated engine and an improved transmission system, while the Mk 3 also had a completely new main weapon, in the shape of a 120mm smooth-bore cannon, and a new fire-control system to go with it. The 120mm smooth-bore was compatible with those fitted to most other second-generation MBTs. The British Chieftain and Challenger were exceptions here, in that they had rifled guns.

INDIGENOUS ADVANTAGE

The Merkava's auxiliary weapons fit remained unchanged right through to the Mk 3. It comprised a 7.62mm co-axial machine gun and either one or two similar weapons mounted on the turret top and operating under remote control. One of these machine guns was sometimes replaced by a .50in Browning M2. The Merkava Mk 3 also had a hydropneumatic suspension system similar to that fitted to the private venture M60AX, which significantly improved the Mk 3's cross-country performance. The Mk 3 also had a provision for a modular system of fitting extra armour as required, particularly to the turret sides and front – a system likely to be adopted for other types of MBT in the future.

All in all, the Merkava was a rather better tank than the M60, even compared with the latter in its ultimate form – at least for Israeli purposes. The Merkava's designers had two factors working in their favour throughout: they had a fairly clear idea of the sort of terrain in which their tank would be called upon to operate and a very clear understanding

T-62

Armament: one 115mm gun,
  one 7.62mm machine gun,
  plus one 12.7mm AA machine gun
Crew: four
Length (gun forward): 9.33m (30.6ft)
Width: 3.3m (10.8ft)
Height: 2.4m (7.9ft)
Armour: 15–242mm (.59–9.52in)
Engine: 580bhp diesel
Range: 450km (280 miles)
Speed: 50km/h (31mph)
Country of origin: Soviet Union

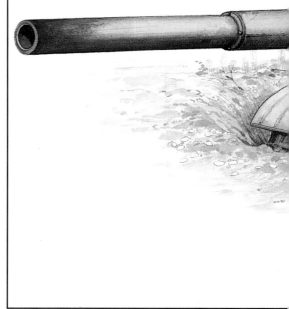

■ **LEFT: Israeli tank commanders' main adversary during the Yom Kippur War was the Soviet-built T-62. Despite its 115mm main gun and additional armour plating it performed poorly.**

of the tactical doctrine that would control that operation. The same was not the case for the men who specified and developed the tanks the Israelis had to fight. The Soviet-supplied main battle tanks, like their NATO counterparts, were expected to function quite literally anywhere on Earth, from the polar ice to the equatorial jungle and everywhere in between, and also to fulfil all manner of different tactical requirements.

The poor performance that the Syrian and Egyptian T-54s put up during the 1967 Six-Day War came as a considerable, and very unwelcome, surprise – no less in Moscow than in

Damascus and Cairo. It was clear that if the Arab regimes were to be further supported, they would have to have better hardware – not to mention better training. And better hardware was available and soon forthcoming, in the form of the T-62.

SOVIET TANKS

The T-62 programme started in the late 1950s. The tank entered production in 1961 and was first seen in public at the May Day parade in 1965, which means that it had probably been issued to frontline units in 1963 or 1964. In overall appearance, it was clearly derived from the T-54/55, with the same squat, low-profile dome turret without a mantlet and with Christie running gear, although the wheels were spaced differently than those of the earlier design. The new tank had slightly thicker frontal armour – to a maximum of 240mm (9.5in) on the face of

the turret – which helped to increase its weight by 4 tonnes. Despite the extra weight, the T-62's performance still matched that of the T-54 by virtue of a slightly uprated V-2-62 engine having been specified, and like both its predecessor and its successors, the new vehicle made use of external fuel tanks to increase its range. And not all the T-62's extra weight was due to heavier armour. Some of it was taken up by the type's most radical improvement over its predecessors: an entirely new and much more powerful main gun.

THE T-62

The T-62 was the first main battle tank to be equipped with a smooth-bore gun, in this case a 115mm U-5TS, for which a range of fin-stabilised ammunition was developed, including anti-personnel HE/fragmentation, HEAT and APFSDS rounds. The HEAT warhead was effective

against up to 430mm (17in) of armour anywhere inside its operating envelope, while the sub-calibre kinetic energy round, which left the muzzle at a scorching 1680 metres per second (5510 feet per second), could penetrate 330mm (13in) of armour at a range of 1000m (3280ft). The new gun was physically larger than the old 100mm cannon, of course, and that made conditions in the small turret even more cramped than before. The gun's size also limited the ready ammunition supply to just four rounds, with 36 more stowed within the hull, and meant as well that the new tank shared the T-54's limited capacity to depress its main gun below the horizontal, with all the tactical penalties thus incurred. The tank's tactical capability was further restricted by a fire-control system that was nowhere near as reliable as its American counterpart, although that shortcoming was later redressed when a system incorporating a laser range-finder and a digital ballistics computer was introduced. NBC protection was provided in the T-62 as standard, and a snorkel could be fitted for deep-fording operations to a maximum depth of 5.5m (18ft). Both active and passive IR systems were also fitted.

T-62 UPGRADES

The T-62 went through a number of evolutions. The T-62A had better fire-control and IR systems than the base-model tank, as well as a reprofiled turret, which improved the conditions inside. The T-62M had improved tracks with a

■LEFT: Although the fording capability is an undoubted bonus, thus removing the need for specialised bridge laying vehicles, it takes nearly eight hours to prepare the T-64 for a river crossing.

considerably longer life expectancy. Variants included a command tank, with upgraded communications and a navigation system. There was a flamethrower tank in which the flame gun did not replace the main cannon but

T-72M

Armament: one 125mm gun,
one 12.7mm AA machine gun,
one 7.62mm machine gun
Crew: three
Length (gun forward): 9.24m (30.3ft)
Width: 4.75m (15.6ft)
Height: 2.37m (7.8ft) (to cupola)
Armour: 35–280mm (1.37–11.02in)
Engine : 780bhp diesel
Range : 480km (298 miles)
Speed: 60km/h (37mph)
Country of origin: Soviet Union

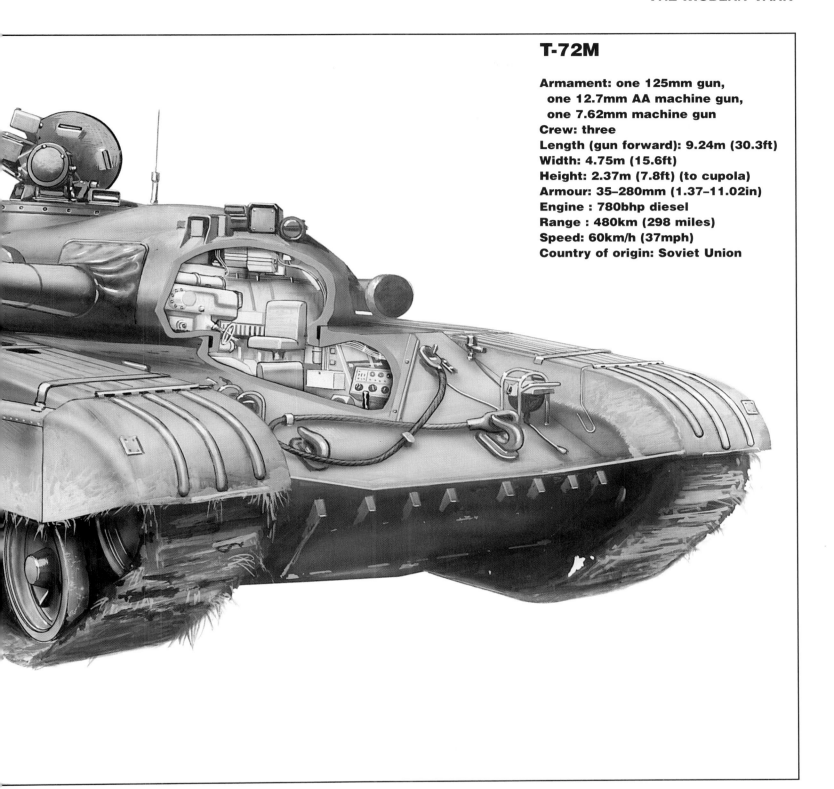

was fitted in lieu of the co-axial 7.62mm machine gun. And an armoured recovery vehicle was also developed. Like the T-54/55, the T-62 stayed in production over a considerable period. It was manufactured in the Soviet Union up until 1975, in which time some 20,000 examples were produced, and a further 1500 were made in Czechoslovakia from 1973 to 1978. The type also went into production in North Korea, which has produced an unknown number both for

itself and for communist client states within its sphere of influence. Coming up for a quarter of a century after its introduction, the T-62 was still in frontline service with the Soviet Union and many of its clients.

No sooner had the T-62 been put into production than Soviet designers started on its successor. Feeling that they had a short breathing space this time, thanks to the superiority of the U-5TS gun, the designers were able to spend longer over

their work and come up with a rather different design. In fact, a variety of different designs were drawn up, the best of which was selected by trial. The United States had been following this procedure for some time, but this was the first occasion on which the Soviet Union adopted the same competitive method.

The most obvious difference between what was to become the T-64 and its predecessors was in the running gear. The T-64 had six smaller roadwheels,

T-80

Armament: one 125mm gun, one 12.7mm AA machine gun,
  one 7.62mm machine gun
Crew: three
Length (gun forward): 9.9m (32.5ft)
Width: 3.4m (11.16ft)
Height: 2.3m (7.54ft) (to cupola)
Armour: composite
Engine: 985shp gas turbine
Range: 400km (248 miles)
Speed: 75km/h (46.6mph)
Country of origin: Soviet Union

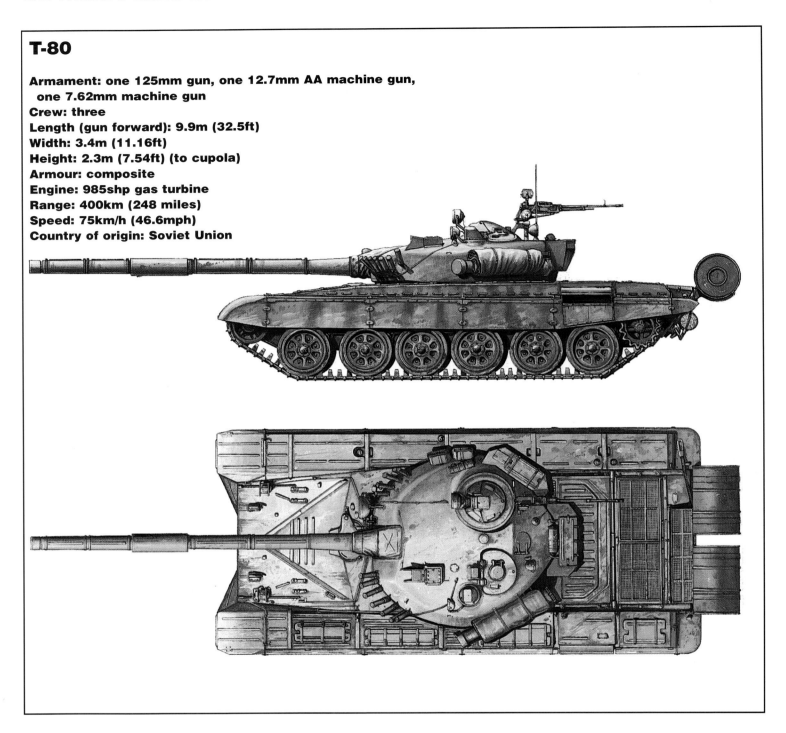

each with its own hydropneumatic suspension unit, and four track-return rollers. This meant that for the first time since the 1930s, a Soviet medium tank had something other than Christie suspension. The turret, on the other hand, seemed little different from the outside from that which Petrov had designed for the IS-3 and which then turned up unchanged on the T-54 and T-62. Inside the turret, though, significant things had been going on, for the new tank not only mounted a still bigger 125mm D-81TM main gun but had its turret crew reduced to two, an auto-loader having taken over from the tank's

fourth crewman. The retention of the low-profile turret meant that depression was still inadequate, although at five degrees it was something of an improvement over previous types.

THE AT-8 MISSILE
The T-64's powerplant was completely new, too. It was a five-cylinder diesel with two crankshafts, each cylinder having a pair of opposed pistons. In its original form, it produced some 750hp, and subsequently considerably more. The new engine was not entirely trouble free, but when it performed as intended it was very good indeed, and gave the 42-tonne

T-64 a top road speed of 75km/h (47mph). The new suspension system, although not without its faults, allowed this speed to be sustained over long periods and also permitted much higher cross-country speeds. The T-64 also received an all-new fire-control system, based on a laser range-finder and stabilised optical sights, along with the now standard IR searchlights and driving lights, NBC protection and a deep-fording snorkel. A variant was produced with removable skirt armour, and a second, which the US Army designated the T-64B, had the improved 125mm gun as fitted to the later T-80. This weapon could fire the

■LEFT: T-72s on exercise. The autoloader system for the tank's 125mm main gun has been widely criticised for being impossible to fire manually and difficult to reload.

64, at 80km/h (50mph), and the retention of the hydropneumatic suspension system meant that this speed was sustainable too. In the meantime, a reduction in length of almost 500mm (19.68in) over the T-64 combined with a slight increase in width gave greater stability and improved control. The auto-loader and improved fire-control system for the conventional 125mm gun made for superior firepower and a much increased chance of a first-shot kill. The T-72 soon proved to be a very potent and attractive package indeed. A number of variants were produced, with skirt armour being retrofitted, the better to protect the upper track run and the engine compartment. The first major upgrade was redesignated the T-74/T-74M, in which modifications included the fitting of thicker frontal protection and panels of appliqué armour elsewhere, together with anti-radiation cladding. The T-72 chassis was also used as the basis for an armoured recovery vehicle and a combat engineering tractor, as well as for the ZSU-30-2 anti-aircraft tank, which was armed with twin radar-controlled 30mm cannon. All T-72s were fitted with retractable dozer blades so that they could prepare firing positions for themselves.

AT-8 anti-tank/anti-helicopter missile as well as conventional ammunition. The AT-8 missile, with a two-stage solid-fuel rocket motor and a hollow-charge HEAT warhead, was believed to be capable of penetrating up to 600mm (23.5in) of conventional tank armour at up to 4000m (13,125ft). The missile was guided by a semi-active laser system, the designator being mounted on the tank's turret front. The effective range against helicopters was said to be twice that for a tank, but since the missile's top speed was no more than 500 metres per second (1640 feet per second), and that was not achieved immediately on launch, the real effective range also depended on the type of helicopter and its course relative to the tank. The T-64B, which was operated exclusively by the Red Army, also received reactive armour – a total of 111 plates, which were hung all over the turret, on the frontal glacis and on the hull sides as far back as the engine bay. A total of some 8000 T-64s are thought to have been produced, but how many of those were to the more capable T-64B specification – and how many, if any, earlier tanks were converted to that specification later – is a matter of pure conjecture.

Some commentators hold that the relatively small number of T-64s produced indicates that there were serious problems with the type, and it certainly seems to be true that a simplified version was rushed into production. This version had a less complicated, more conventional V-12 engine and was shorn of the missile firing capacity, but retained the new suspension system and had a very similar form of both hull and turret. But whether this move was intended to take up any slack caused by failings in the original T-64 or whether the new tank was in fact an interim design with some experimental features is open to speculation. The new tank was eventually designated the T-72. It became the mainstay of Warsaw Pact and communist client states' armoured divisions from fairly soon after it appeared in 1971 and looked set to hold that position in the new order for some time to come, if only for reasons of economy.

THE T-72

The T-72 was clearly much better value for money than was the T-64, even though the latter seemed to have more advanced features. The T-72 was mechanically much simpler – which was always an important consideration for the Soviets, their allies and clients – and actually had a better power-to-weight ratio than the T-64, thanks both to the power having been increased and the weight having been reduced. The T-72's top speed was higher than that of the T-

THE T-72 IN ACTION

From its introduction in 1971 to the break-up of the Soviet Union in the early 1990s, the T-72 stayed in continuous production. It was even manufactured after the USSR's collapse – despite considerable difficulty and albeit in very much smaller numbers – such was the demand from ex-Soviet clients such as Finland who could afford to pay to increase the size of their T-72 fleets. Manufacture in plants in the Czech Republic, Poland and Serbia, however, ceased. Nonetheless, in the mid-1990s, T-72 tanks were to be found in large numbers around the world. In most cases, these tanks were the best the armies in question had, and so it could be expected that they had been kept in relatively good order wherever possible. The T-72 saw action in the Middle East during the Israeli invasion of Lebanon in 1982, in Afghanistan, in the Persian Gulf and in the war in the former Yugoslavia,

■**RIGHT: Some T-80 models are fitted with a main gun that is capable of firing conventional ammunition and the AT-8 Kobra laser-guided anti-tank and anti-helicopter missile.**

as well as in the former Soviet Union itself. It must be said that it was never really a match for the 'product improved' M60, the Merkava, the M1 Abrams, the Chieftain, the Challenger or even the AMX-30, although it was mostly in the hands of second-rate fighting forces when it went into battle against these tanks, so there is room for some speculation as to the real cause of its poor performance.

THE T-80

The last tank produced in the Soviet Union was also a derivative of the T-64, but this time a very much more sophisticated vehicle, which had been up-engineered rather than simplified. Its 985hp gas turbine engine and new transmission produced a top road speed of 75km/h (47mph), and the tank had a range of 400km (250 miles) on 1000 litres (265 US gallons) of fuel. The main armament saw a return to the 125mm gun/launcher discarded for the T-72, the weapon being controlled by a digital computer receiving basic data from optical sights coupled to a laser range-finder, but with low-light television (LLTV) and active/passive IR thermal imaging to provide a sight picture in poor visibility. The three-man crew had improved protection in the form of laminated armour for the front glacis plate and the option to fit plates of reactive armour elsewhere to counteract HEAT rounds. Somewhat curiously, since the hydropneumatic system seemed to have worked so well in previous vehicles, the T-80, as the new tank was known, saw a return to torsion bar suspension. The tank's roadwheels were of a revised pattern, but otherwise the running gear was the same as that of the T-72, with skirt armour to protect the upper track run. The T-80 was first issued in 1984, and just how many were produced is a matter for speculation. By the time of the break-up of the Soviet Union, somewhere between 4000 and 8000 were probably in service. None were ever issued to the armed forces of even the USSR's closest allies. Clearly, the T-80 was capable of considerable further development, although where that process could lead – if indeed it were to lead anywhere – is equally a matter for speculation.

EE-T1 Osorio

Armament: one 120mm gun or one 105mm gun, two 7.62mm machine guns
Crew: four
Length (gun forward): 9.36m (30.7ft)
Width: 3.26m (10.7ft)
Height: 2.37m (7.77ft) (to turret)
Armour: not available
Engine : 1040bhp diesel
Range : 550km (342 miles)
Speed: 70km/h (43.5mph)
Country of origin: Brazil

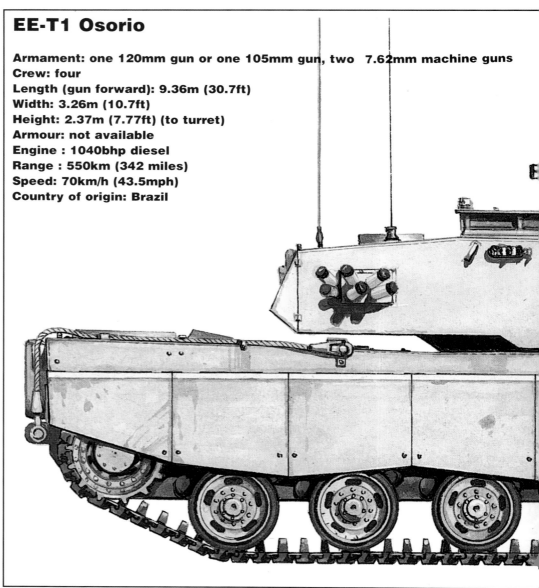

After the revolution in China brought the communists to power there in 1949, the Soviet Union supplied its neighbour to the east with large numbers of obsolete tanks, as well as all sorts of other weapons and vehicles. Even when industry in the People's Republic reached a level where it was possible to contemplate the local manufacture of a main battle tank, it was to the Soviet Union that the Chinese Government turned, obtaining a licence to produce T-54s of its own.

CHINESE COPIES
Designated the Type 59, the resultant tank was crude in comparison even with the original, which had little enough in the way of refinement, and lacked IR systems and NBC protection. Nonetheless, the Type 59 was produced in large numbers, both for China's People's Liberation Army and for supply to client states. As time wore on, and the original model's deficiencies became more and more obvious, a variety of upgrade packages became available, all of them based more or less on the re-engining and regunning process the Israelis carried out on the T-54/55s they captured from the Syrians and Egyptians. One package, from the Chinese national armaments manufacturer, NORINCO, saw a 730hp diesel engine replace the original 525hp unit, with a considerable effect on overall performance. Another upgrade replaced the original 100mm gun with a British 105mm L7 married to a relatively sophisticated fire-control system that included a laser range-finder and IR thermal imaging system. This package brought a relatively enormous improvement in the tank's tactical capability.

Its obsolescence notwithstanding, the Type 59 – and its original, the Soviet T-54, of course – continued to provide the main armoured component of a good many of the world's smaller armies in the mid-1990s, and the tanks looked set, in many cases, to continue in that role until they literally fell to pieces. It is arguable that their outright worth hardly merited their upkeep, but against that it can be said that in general they were never likely to encounter anything more potent than themselves, and in the absence of a better tank, even a T-54 or a Type 59 could be very formidable indeed.

Not surprisingly, when a locally developed tank did appear in the People's Republic of China, it was modelled very closely on the earlier Soviet design. Somewhat confusingly, the Type 69, which appeared for the first time in the early 1980s, was manufactured in two variants. It was produced as the Type 69-I, with a smooth-bore 100mm gun, and as the Type 69-II, with a rifled 100mm gun.

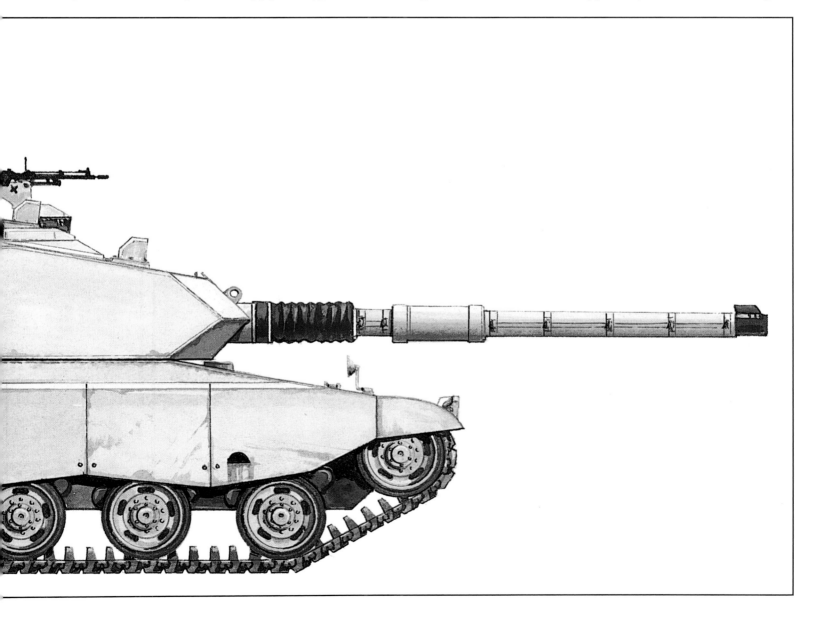

Stridsvagn (Strv) 103

Armament: one 105mm gun, three 7.62mm machine guns
Crew: three
Length: 7.04m (23.09ft)
Width: 3.63m (11.9ft)
Height: 2.14m (7.02ft)
Armour: 90–100mm (3.54–3.93in)
Engine : 240hp and 490hp
Range : 390km (242 miles)
Speed: 50km/h (31mph)
Country of origin: Sweden

Both tanks were a good deal better than their common predecessor. They were fitted with bore evacuators, fire-control systems linked to their weapons' characteristics, and their guns were stabilised in both elevation and azimuth. Otherwise, externally the tanks were very similar to the original in appearance, with the addition of skirt armour and IR searchlights. The Type 69s were powered by a slightly refined version of the Type 59's powerplant that gave only around 50hp more, and the new tanks had similar overall performance to that of the Type 59 as a result.

TYPE 69-III

In about 1985 a new Chinese tank, the Type 69-III, was first seen in public. It was clearly a very different vehicle from the other Type 69s, with a redesigned hull and new running gear with six smaller roadwheels and three track-return rollers along with the torsion bar

suspension of the original. The Type 69-III also had improved armour, including a glacis plate composed of laminated material, and a much better 105mm rifled gun under the control of a digital computer. The new tank was later renamed the Type 80. All-up weight was a little higher than that of previous models, at around 38 tonnes, but a turbo-charged version of the engine that powered the Type 69s, with its output thus boosted to about 725hp, gave considerably better performance, including a 20 per cent increase in top speed to 60km/h (38mph). There was no sign of an auto-loader, so the crew level was maintained at four, with the driver in the hull and the commander, gunner and loader in the turret. Like the Type 69, the Type 80's secondary armament included a co-axial 7.62mm machine gun and a 12.7mm anti-aircraft machine gun in the commander's hatch, but the remotely controlled 7.62mm machine gun in the hull of the Type 69 was deleted in

the Type 80 in favour of more ammunition storage space. Even a decade after the type's appearance, there were no reliable estimates of the total number produced or in service. There were reports that the Chinese T-80 had also gone into production in Pakistan in 1991–92 to supply that nation's armed forces.

CHINESE AMPHIBIANS

As mentioned previously, the People's Republic of China also produced PT-76 amphibious light tanks under licence from the USSR. Building on the overall success of this relatively cheap armoured vehicle, and on its suitability for operation in areas inaccessible to conventional main battle tanks, the Chinese later produced two light tanks of their own, the Types 62 and 63. The Type 63, which weighed around 18 tonnes, had a welded hull based on that of the successful Type 77 APC and a turret very much akin to that of the Type 59 MBT,

but somewhat reduced in size and armed with an 85mm gun. Like the PT-76, the Type 63 was fully amphibious, although with a 400hp diesel engine it was somewhat faster than the Soviet vehicle, both on land and in the water. A similar vehicle was said to be in production in North Korea. The Type 62, on the other hand, was a conventional light tank, and capable of wading only. It was somewhat heavier than the Type 63, at 21 tonnes, but shared the turret and main gun of the amphibian.

ASIAN TANK MANUFACTURE

As noted earlier, the Soviet T-62 tank was produced in North Korea. Later, not far away across the 38th parallel, the South Korean industrial conglomerate Hyundai, with interests in everything from family cars to warships, also turned its attention to the possibilities of producing a main battle tank. In Hyundai's case, though, the approach was very different from that of the North Koreans. The company did not seek out an existing design and apply for a licence to manufacturer it, but rather took a very detailed specification to one of the world's best tank design houses – General Dynamics Land

■BELOW: Switzerland continues to operate a total of 372 Pz68 tanks alongside the more modern Leopard 2. The type has proved highly capable in the country's mountainous terrain.

Systems Division, formerly Chrysler – and commissioned a wholly new vehicle. The resulting tank, known as the K-1, used composite armour to provide adequate protection at the lowest possible weight. Powered by Hyundai's own version of the Mercedes-Benz 871 diesel engine, which produced 1200hp, the 52-tonne tank had a top speed of 65km/h (40mph) and a range of 500km (310 miles). Not surprisingly, the main armament chosen was the 105mm M68/L7 rifled gun used in so many other successful modern tank designs, and the fire-control system, designed by Hughes, complemented it in every way. The K-1's suspension was something of an innovation – a hybrid system using six medium-sized roadwheels and track-return rollers, with the four central roadwheels on each side sprung on torsion bars and the front and rear wheels given hydropneumatic units. The ride height of the front and rear wheel pairs could be controlled manually so that a nose-up or nose-down attitude of three degrees could be achieved. This added almost 50 per cent to the maximum depression angle of the main gun, thus permitting the tank to operate effectively from a hull-down position while still reaping the tactical benefits of having a low-profile turret.

Further to the east, Japan had been manufacturing tanks of its own since the early 1960s for use by its Self-Defence

Leopard 1A4

Armament: one 105mm gun, two 7.62mm machine guns
Crew: four
Length (gun forward): 9.54m (31.3ft)
Width: 3.37m (11ft)
Height: 2.76m (9ft) (to periscope)
Armour: spaced, multi-layer composite
Engine : 830bhp multi-fuel
Range : 600km (373 miles)
Speed: 65km/h (40mph)
Country of origin: Germany

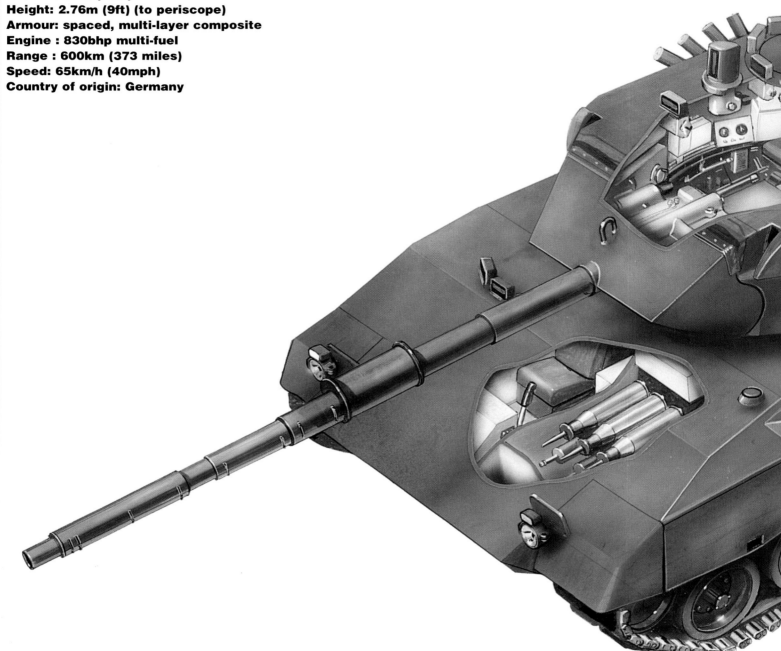

Forces, so named because the country's post-World War II constitution prohibits the holding of offensive weapons. Work on the Type 61, as the first postwar Japanese tank was known, started as far back as 1954. Over the remainder of the decade four prototypes and then a dozen preproduction tanks were manufactured before the type was standardised in 1961. Production proper came to an end in

1970, by which time some 550 Type 61 tanks had been built. In every way, the Type 61 resembled an American tank developed during the same period. It had armour up to 65mm (2.5in) thick and a 90mm unstabilised gun with a simple mechanical fire-control system and optical sights, and its running gear comprised six medium-sized roadwheels sprung by torsion bars with the track

running on three return rollers. All-up weight of the Type 61 was 35 tonnes, and the tank's 600hp Mitsubishi diesel engine gave it a top speed of 45km/h (28mph).

MITSUBISHI'S TYPE 74
As the Type 61 was going into series production, a design team at Mitsubishi began work on a successor in collaboration with military experts. After

reduced the frontal area of the turret to no more than the size of the mantlet. Stabilised in both axes, the gun was laid onto the target by a modern fire-control system with laser range-finder and the full range of environmental sensors. A scant 3 tonnes heavier than the Type 61, the Type 74 was powered by a 750hp engine and therefore showed a slightly higher top speed. Perhaps the most important innovation was in the suspension system. All five pairs of large roadwheels were hung on individually controllable hydropneumatic units with no less than 450mm (17.75in) of vertical travel. By applying differential adjustment, the tank could be given a six-degree tilt front to back or back to front, while invoking the suspension rise on one side or the other could impart nine degrees of artificial list. Alternatively, all the units could be operated together to vary the ground clearance between 200 and 650mm (7.9 and 25.59in). Altogether, some 850 Type 74 tanks were produced between 1974 and 1988, and the type had largely replaced the Type 61 by the early 1990s, although some of the older tanks were retained for training purposes.

■ BELOW: A fine study of German Army Leopard 1s on exercise in the Black Forest. The first Leopards were equipped with the excellent British Royal Ordnance L7A3 105mm main gun.

a false start or two, and a longish development process, a design study known as STB-3 was adopted and standardised for production as the Type 74. The overall design was quite conventional, the fine angle of the glacis plate, behind which the driver sat, leading right up to the face of the turret. The latter housed a 105mm L7A1 gun with a redesigned recoil mechanism that

Leopard 2

Armament: one 120mm gun, two 7.62mm machine guns
Crew: four
Length (gun forward): 9.67m (31.7ft)
Width: 3.7m (12.1ft)
Height: 2.48m (8.13ft) (to turret)
Armour: spaced, multi-layer composite
Engine: 1500bhp diesel
Range: 550km (342 miles)
Speed: 72km/h (45mph)
Country of origin: Germany

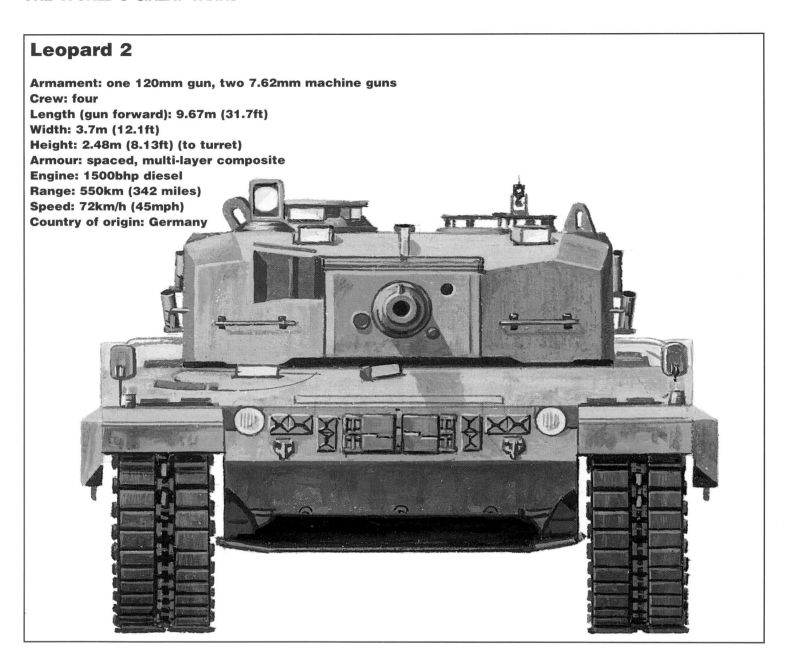

The replacement for the Type 74, in its turn, was to be a very much bigger tank. Constructed of multi-layer laminated armour with ceramic reinforcing, the vehicle weighed some 50 tonnes and was powered by a 1500hp engine. The tank was armed with the same smooth-bore 120mm gun supplied by Rheinmetall that was selected for the M1A1 'Abrams', which was fitted with an auto-loader system to reduce the crew to three men and with a state-of-the-art fire-control system. Developed over a period of some 12 years, once again by Mitsubishi in conjunction with the Japanese Self-Defence Agency, the TK-X appeared in prototype form in 1986, went into limited production as the Type 90 in 1990 and was first issued to troops two years later. With this tank, Japan displayed very convincingly its ability to manufacture a

heavy armoured fighting vehicle capable of standing alongside any other in the world. And Japan has managed this despite being unable to access a wide market and thus recoup development costs or benefit from economies of scale, since besides forbidding the country to hold offensive weapons, the Japanese constitution also prohibits the sale of arms, though this may change in the future.

THE MINOR LEAGUES

The smaller tank-producing nations – among them Britain, France and Germany – usually have to find export markets for their vehicles to help defray the development costs. Although for the three countries mentioned, such sales are not the reason they build tanks, for some they are. Brazil, for example, probably has no need of main battle tanks for its

army, which, indeed, has no heavy armour formations. Yet not one but two MBTs were designed for production there, the Engesa EE-T1 'Osorio' and the somewhat lighter and smaller Bernardini MB-3 'Tamoyo'. In fact, only the hull and running gear of the 44-tonne Osorio, which is powered by a 1000hp diesel engine and capable of up to 70km/h (43mph), was of local design. The turret, complete with gun and tactical hardware, came from the British firm Vickers. Two different units were available, with either the 105mm L7A3 rifled gun or the GIAT 120mm smooth-bore gun. Different levels of target acquisition and gunlaying hardware were available too – either a simple system with unstabilised optical sights and a laser range-finder or a more complex system with stabilised optics, thermal imaging and environmental sensors.

The Bernardini Tamoyo, which some would say is a throwback to the old medium tank concept, is a rather simpler vehicle all round, but effective enough for all that, with spaced, laminated armour to offer a reasonable level of protection while keeping the all-up weight of the vehicle down to 30 tonnes. The Tamoyo is somewhat unusual in that its Saab-Scania powerplant is a commercial vehicle engine, although its 500hp gives the tank a respectable top speed of over 65km/h (40mph) together with a maximum range of 550km (340 miles) on 700 litres (185 US gallons) of fuel. When it first appeared in 1983, the Tamoyo was equipped with a 90mm main gun, but four years later, an uprated version of the tank was introduced, with a 740hp Detroit Diesel engine and a 105mm L7 gun. Neither the Osorio nor the Tamoyo ever got into series production, despite considerable interest both at home and abroad, and both Bernardini and Engesa were forced to fall back on the main core of their respective businesses. For the former, this was the remanufacture of M3 Stuarts as the X1A1 and X1A2, while for Engesa it was producing a very useful and popular range of light armoured vehicles, such as the Cascaval armoured reconnaissance car and the Urutu APC.

THE TAM

Further south, in Argentina, there was a perceived need for a medium tank, but rather than attempt to work up a design locally, the Argentinians called in a German consortium of Thyssen and Henschel. The result was the TAM, a 30-tonne tank based on the Marder mechanised infantry combat vehicle (MICV), but armed with a 105mm gun in a specially conceived turret set back on the hull. A 720hp Mercedes diesel engine – the same as that fitted to the original Marder and all its many variants – drove the front sprocket for a top speed on the road of 75km/h (47mph), and the simple swinging arm/torsion bar suspension gave a good cross-country ride. Some 250 TAMs went into service with the Argentine Army, alongside the best of the World War II-vintage M4 Shermans already serving in its two armoured brigades. Thyssen-Henschel also produced a version for export, known as the TH 301, which had the rather better Rheinmetall Rh-105-30 cannon in place of the locally produced version fitted to the TAM. The weapon was controlled by a

much more sophisticated system, which included low-light television and IR thermal imaging as well as environmental sensor input to its digital ballistic computer.

ITALY'S OF-40

In the early 1970s, the Italian heavy armaments manufacturer OTO Melara and the state-owned vehicle maker, FIAT (through its commercial vehicle arm, Iveco), were granted a limited licence to manufacture around 1000 German Leopard 1 tanks for the Italian Army. The licence forbade the consortium from manufacturing the tanks for third parties, and so a design for a similar – although rather heavier – tank was worked up in-house for the export market. The resulting tank first appeared, as the OF-40, in 1977. It was 45 tonnes in weight, was powered by an 830hp diesel, was armed with OTO Melara's own successful 105mm rifled gun and had a crew of four. The OF-40 was a conventional second-generation main battle tank with adequate protection against guns similar to its own and with a respectable first-round hit capability, thanks to a digital ballistic computer linked to a laser range-finder, stabilised optical sights and a range of sensors. Oddly, a turret stabilisation system was offered only as an afterthought, although it became standard on the improved Mk 2 version

of the tank. With a top speed of just 60km/h (38mph), the OF-40 was never particularly fast, but it made up for that, to some degree at least, by having a range of 600km (370 miles) on the 1000 litres (265 US gallons) of fuel it could hold in its internal tanks. Sales of the OF-40 were never encouraging, the 36 bought by the United Arab Emirates being the most significant order.

THE RADICAL S-TANK

Even less successful, at least in business terms, was a distinctly odd turretless main battle tank designed by Sven Berge of the Swedish Army's Ordnance Department in 1956–57 and manufactured by Bofors between 1966 and 1971. Only 300 examples of the tank were ever built, and the rest of the world's armed forces showed no more than a certain intellectual curiosity in it, although the British Army, for one, borrowed a number for extended testing. Nonetheless, the Stridsvagn (Strv) 103B – or S-Tank, as it was sometimes known – deserves inclusion in any history of the tank for its unorthodox peculiarity alone, despite the fact that many hold that it was actually a tank destroyer of a type

■ BELOW: In keeping with NATO policy, the ammunition for the 120mm Rheinmetall main gun on the Leopard 2 is interchangeable with that of the American M1 Abrams MBT.

of the British 105mm L7 gun with a 62-calibre barrel – was fixed within the hull, recoil being the only movement allowed it. It was pointed in azimuth by aligning the entire vehicle, fine tuning being achieved by slewing the tracks slightly. It was adjusted in the vertical plane by differential movement of the hydropneumatic suspension system, which gave 10 degrees of depression and 12 degrees of elevation – a range not much less than that of many tanks with conventional turrets, and hardly inferior at all to that of the AMX-13 with its oscillating turret, which is said to have been the inspiration for the Swedish tank in the first place. Naturally enough, the complete lack of a turret made for a very low profile indeed – the entire vehicle was just 2.1m (7ft) tall – and thus for ease of concealment.

BOEING'S POWERPLANT

The unorthodoxy of the S-Tank did not stop there, however. The powerplant consisted of two entirely different types of engine: a 240hp multi-fuel piston engine from Rolls-Royce and a 490hp gas turbine unit from Boeing, never widely considered as an engine maker. The two units were linked to a common shaft and drove the tracks via a Volvo torque converter and the front sprockets, the turbine being brought in only when extra power was required. Together they gave the 39-tonne tank a top speed of 50km/h (30mph), while range on the smaller engine alone was 400km (250 miles). There were just four roadwheels and two track-return rollers per side, and suspension was by independent hydropneumatic units that were locked solid when the main gun was to be fired, providing a platform more rigid than most.

The tank's overall layout was rather unusual too, the powerplant and transmission being located in the front of the vehicle. The driver was in the centre on the left-hand side. He was also the gunner, a situation that presented no conflict of roles, since it was never the intention that the tank should fight on the move. Across from the driver sat the radio operator, facing aft. He could drive the tank in reverse, if necessary, as well

■RIGHT: The latest model in the Leopard class is the 2A5. The most obvious difference to earlier variants is the upgraded armour package fitted to the front of the turret.

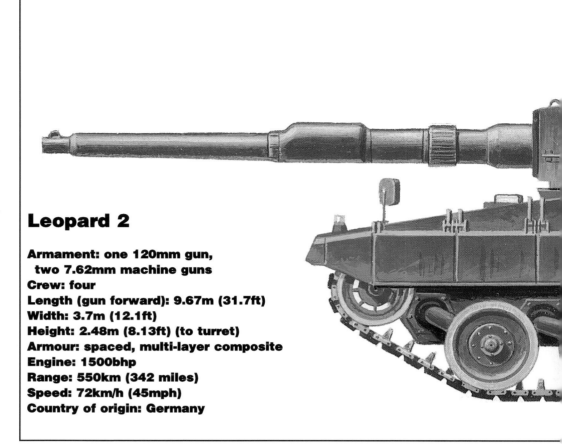

Leopard 2

Armament: one 120mm gun, two 7.62mm machine guns
Crew: four
Length (gun forward): 9.67m (31.7ft)
Width: 3.7m (12.1ft)
Height: 2.48m (8.13ft) (to turret)
Armour: spaced, multi-layer composite
Engine: 1500bhp
Range: 550km (342 miles)
Speed: 72km/h (45mph)
Country of origin: Germany

as operate the loading mechanism manually in an emergency. The commander, who could also lay and fire the gun, was positioned beneath a stabilised, rotating cupola to the radio operator's rear. The hydraulically operated auto-loader was capable of supplying main gun ammunition at a rate of up to 15 rounds per minute.

In the prototype Strv 103s, there were no fewer than five 7.62mm machine guns, all of them remotely controlled – two on

either side of the hull, fixed in armoured pods, and one on the roof, which the commander could manipulate from within the tank and which doubled as an anti-aircraft gun. Production models had the right-hand guns deleted and replaced by a 12.7mm ranging machine gun, which was itself deleted later when a laser range-finder was developed. Early

models also lacked the flotation screens that turned the vehicle into an amphibian driven by the action of its tracks – an important consideration in a country strewn with lakes. Neither did they have the upwardly retractable bulldozer blade, these two items, however, being retrofitted to all tanks. Infra-red driving lights were provided as original equipment, but no searchlight was fitted. Also, there was no system of NBC protection, and in such circumstances as required it, the crew were expected to fight in individual NBC suits.

THE OUTDATED STRV 103

By the late 1980s, the Strv 103s were looking a little tired. A refurbishment project saw the Rolls-Royce piston engines swapped for 290hp Detroit Diesels, while an improved fire-control system, including IR thermal imaging, and an integrated NBC protection system were also developed. Quite whether the Swedish experiment would have proved workable in action will probably never be known. However, with the emphasis in the tactical use of armoured vehicles being fairly firmly on manoeuvrability,

the limitations of a tank such as the Strv 103 must militate against it. The tank had what is essentially a fixed forward-facing gun, despite the hydropneumatic system, and was virtually incapable of fighting on the move. Sweden also produced an amphibious light tank/tank destroyer, the Infanterikanonvagn (Ikv) 91, a conventional tank with its 90mm gun in a centre-mounted turret. Weighing 15.5 tonnes, powered by a six-cylinder Volvo diesel producing 295hp and utilising standard Christie suspension, the Ikv 91 entered service with the Swedish Army in 1975. Plans for a new indigenous main battle tank to be produced towards the end of the century were developed and then cancelled.

AUSTRIA'S KURASSIER

If the Swedish Army was impressed by the French AMX-13 to the extent of allowing its features to affect its strategic planning, the Austrians went one better and commissioned armaments and vehicle manufacturer Steyr-Daimler-Puch to copy the AMX-13, even using the original FL-12 turret and GIAT 105mm gun, onto the chassis of an APC produced by Saurer. The result was a light

tank/tank destroyer that was essentially similar to the AMX-13 but more lightly armoured. It was christened the Panzerjäger K, also known as the Kurassier. Its most unusual feature was perhaps its transmission, which used hydraulic drive, a similar system to that tested in both Britain and the United States during the transitional period between the two world wars. The Kurassier's tactical performance was virtually the same as that of the AMX-13, and a total of 120 vehicles were constructed for the Austrian Army.

GERMAN REBIRTH

In some senses, Germany in the aftermath of World War II was an even more desolate place than it had been in 1919. Divided in two, with the Soviet Union occupying the eastern part of the country, and the Allies the rest, it was coming to terms with a new identity as well as recovering from losing the most devastating war in the history of mankind. The importance of the Federal German Republic in the west as a buffer against the Iron Curtain was not lost on the NATO powers, and at the end of 1955 the West German Army was created, being largely equipped by the United States, which sent first M47 and then M48 tanks. That same year, West reliant on US tanks at the time, laid down outline plans to jointly develop a main battle tank in the 30-tonne class, with the emphasis on mobility, rather than on protection. The venture was soon abandoned, and the two nations went their own separate ways. In West Germany, appropriate manufacturers with experience of building tanks during the preceding quarter century were grouped into two consortia and evolved competing designs, completing prototype vehicles in 1960. 'Group B' soon withdrew, largely because their product was more advanced and would therefore have taken considerably longer to get into production. This action left the field clear for the consortium led by Porsche, which produced a total of no fewer than 26 prototypes and 50 preproduction models of their new tank in the three years that followed. Production was then handed over to Krauss-Maffei in Munich, and a licence to build the tank for the Italian Army was granted to OTO Melara of La Spezia. The first Leopards, as the new tank became officially known, rolled out in September 1965. Over the following decade, over 4200 Leopard MBTs were completed, together with almost 1500 more chassis that were used in ARVs, armoured engineering vehicles and AVLBs, as well as in the Gepard anti-aircraft tank. The German Leopard went through a series of evolutions during this period, and Leopards were sold to a variety of NATO partners, as well as to Australia.

THE GERMAN LEOPARD

The Leopard 1 was rather more substantial than the original concept had envisaged, its combat-ready weight up to 40 tonnes despite the tank's primary armour being just 70mm (2.75in) thick on the glacis and 60mm (2.4in) thick on the turret front and sides. The Leopard 1's hull was of welded construction, while its turret, from Rheinmetall, was cast as a single piece. The running gear was based on seven medium-sized dual roadwheels, with their axes offset to accommodate the

■ **RIGHT: Modern MBTs guzzle fuel at an alarming rate. Renault engineers have tried to remedy this by designing the AMX-30's HS110 engine to run on oil, petrol or paraffin.**

AMX-30

Armament: one 105mm gun, one 20mm cannon or one .5in machine gun one 7.62mm AA machine gun
Crew: four
Length (gun forward): 9.48m (31.1ft)
Width: 3.1m (10.17ft)
Height: 2.29m (7.51ft) (to turret)
Armour: 15-80mm (.6–3.1in)
Engine : 700bhp multi-fuel
Range : 600km (373 miles)
Speed: 65km/h (40mph)
Country of origin: France

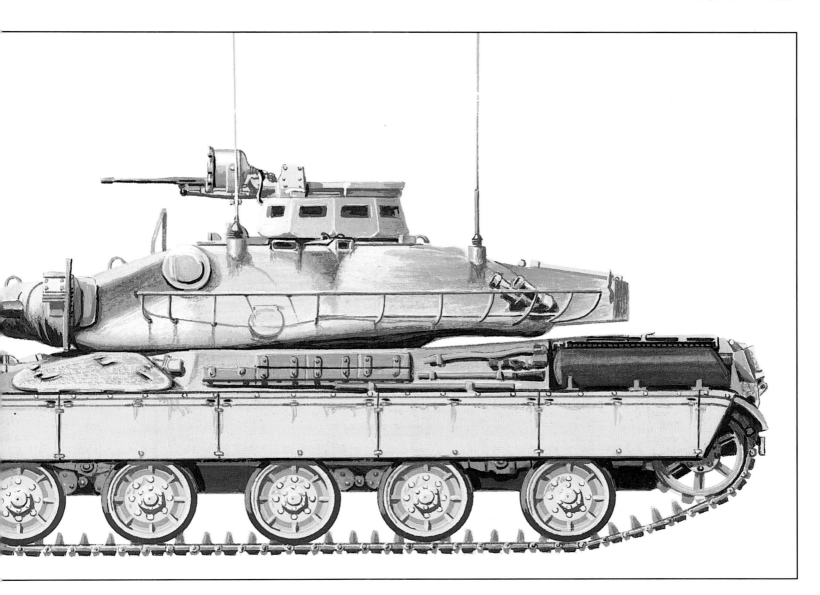

bell-cranks that connected them to the torsion bars on which they were suspended. There were four track-return rollers, and the rear sprockets were driven via a ZF torque convertor gearbox by a 10-cylinder, 830hp multi-fuel engine from Mercedes-Benz. The engine gave the tank a maximum speed of 65km/h (40mph), and the entire powerplant/transmission package was designed to be replaceable in 30 minutes, even in the field, with the right equipment. The main armament consisted of the British 105mm L7A3 rifled gun, which somewhat surprisingly was neither stabilised nor precisely controlled in the original Leopards, although stabilisation in both axes and a fire-control computer were provided from the Leopard 1A1 variant onwards. The tank had co-axial and AA machine guns, in both cases 7.62mm MG3s. The basic ammunition load was 60 rounds of main gun ammunition (three in the turret, 57 in the hull) and 5500 rounds for the

machine guns, the proportion of rounds of different types for the main gun being a matter for local decision. NBC and fire-suppression systems were fitted as standard, and a snorkel that mated with the commander's hatch was available for deep-fording operations to a maximum depth of 4m (13ft). When the snorkel was brought into use, the tank's apertures, in particular the turret ring, were rapidly sealed by means of inflatable rubber rings.

The Leopard 1's upgrade path followed a typical formula. The Leopard 1A1 gained not only the stabilisation system and fire-control computer but also a thermal sleeve for the gun tube, new design tracks, along with reinforced rubber skirts and modifications to the hatches and fording equipment. The Leopard 1A2 received a turret of higher specification steel, a better NBC protection system and image intensifiers for the commander and driver, while the Leopard 1A3 gained a new turret

altogether, which had spaced armour and better ballistic contouring, including a wedge-shaped mantlet in place of the bulbous original. The Leopard 1A4 was fitted with spaced armour on the hull front as well. The Leopard 1A4 was more than 2 tonnes heavier than the original, but there was no noticeable degradation of performance.

THE LEOPARD 2

Even before evaluation of the prototype Leopard 1 was complete, work had already started on the development of a successor, although it took a back seat to the West German–US MBT-70 joint project. When that was cancelled in January 1970, attention switched to the Leopard 2, and over the next five years, 16 prototypes were built to varying specifications. At around 55 tonnes, the Leopard 2 was considerably heavier than the Leopard 1, but not that much bigger. The extra weight went to improve the tank's level of protection and bring it into

AMX-40

Armament: one 120mm gun, one 20mm cannon,
 one 7.62mm AA machine gun
Crew: four
Length (gun forward): 10.1m (33ft)
Width: 3.36m (11ft)
Height: 2.38m (7.8ft) (to turret)
Armour: laminated
Engine : 1300bhp diesel
Range : 600km (373 miles)
Speed: 70km/h (43.5mph)
Country of origin: France

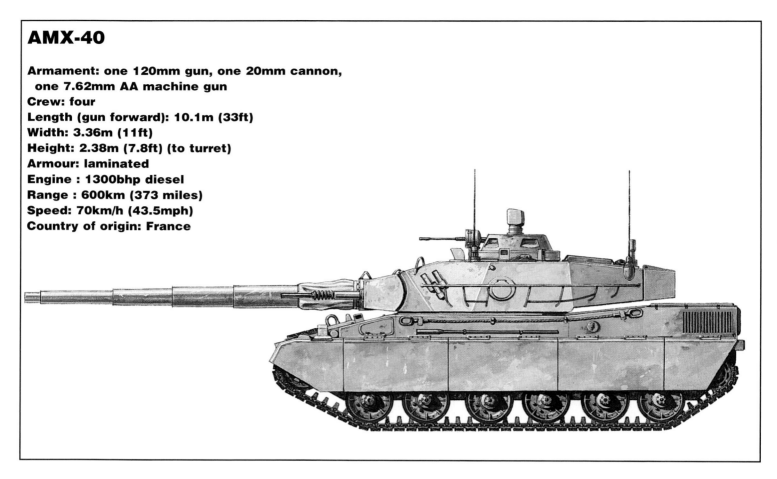

line with the British Chieftain, which would clearly be the Leopard 2's chief rival in the export market. The exact nature of the Leopard 2's armour was kept secret for some time, and it was assumed to be a spaced laminate. But it eventually emerged that it was British Chobham armour on a steel frame, which accounts to some degree for the tank's rather angular form. The other significant improvement over the Leopard 1 was in the main armament. A 120mm smooth-bore gun developed by Rheinmetall was chosen, for the reason that both fin-stabilised sub-calibre AP rounds and HEAT warheads function better if they do not rotate around their axis in flight. The Americans were to reach the same conclusion when the time came to select a gun for their own new MBT, and so did the French for the AMX-30 replacement. But the British, who also increased the size of their MBT's main armament to 120mm, kept faith with the rifled barrel.

A number of the Leopard 2 prototypes were fitted with hydropneumatic suspension, but in the end a torsion bar system with friction damping was chosen for the production tank, the rest of the running gear being identical to that of the Leopard 1. An improved multi-fuel

engine, as originally developed for the MBT-70, was specified, its 1500hp providing the tank with a top speed of around 70km/h (43mph), which gave it a slight edge in that department over its predecessor. An order for 1800 Leopard 2s for the West German Army was placed in 1977, and the first vehicles were delivered the following year. Holland also acquired Leopard 2s, as did Sweden and also Switzerland, where they were known as Pz 87s and manufactured locally under licence. Spain also looked likely to acquire an improved version of the tank before the end of the 1990s.

LEOPARD UPGRADES
Like the Leopard 1, the Leopard 2 was to undergo successive upgradings as refinements were developed. A number of improvements became available in 1995, including a new tube for the main gun, extra armour and an improved fire-control system. But by that time, a much more major revision, involving a 140mm smooth-bore gun complete with auto-loader, had become practicable. This revision would allow the crew to be reduced to three and the turret to be downsized somewhat, while at the same time ammunition capacity would be increased and the tank's firepower

considerably enhanced. An improvement programme to incorporate this modification was put in train, but the first vehicles were not expected to emerge from it until towards the end of the first decade of the new century. A still more radical proposal called for the replacement of the traditional turret by an unmanned, fully automatic gun installation, remotely controlled by the commander/gunner who would be seated alongside the driver down in the hull. Although the technology to realise this certainly existed by 1995 – indeed naval guns of a very similar nature to the main gun of an MBT had been remotely controlled for many years – it was probably too radical a move to be implemented before 2010, even in prototype form. But even that could well mean that an improved Leopard 2 will be among the first of what will undoubtedly be the basic MBTs of the first quarter of the 21st century.

FRANCE'S LIGHT AND FAST MBT
With the collapse in the mid-1950s of the proposal for a 30-tonne tank to be developed jointly with the Germans, the French initiated a project to create a similar vehicle of their own. The prototype AMX-30 was completed in

1960, and series production commenced six years later. From the outset, the new French MBT – the first 'universal' tank ever constructed in France – was to be fast and light to accord with the offensive doctrine of the army of the day, swopping for agility the high levels of protection that come with heavy armour. As a result, the AMX-30 was underprotected and vulnerable by the standards set by contemporary American and, in particular, British and German tanks, let alone by the Soviet tanks of the period. Therefore, in that sense at least, the AMX-30 was technically obsolescent from the time of its introduction – and it had an unstabilised gun and a very simple fire-control system into the bargain. Nonetheless, the AMX-30 was still in service in the late 1990s, and many smaller nations found that it was good value for money, both in terms of the original purchase price and of ongoing maintenance and upkeep costs, and it sold well abroad as a result. Saudi Arabia was the most important customer, taking delivery of around 300 'desertised' AMX-30S tanks with skirt-like sand shields and lowered gear ratios.

By the time the AMX-30 was ready to go into production, it was seven tonnes heavier than the 30 tonnes originally

specified. Nonetheless, the choice of an Hispano-Suiza HS-110 multi-fuel engine, which developed 700hp, meant that the design speed of 65km/h (40mph) could be maintained quite comfortably. The running gear, driven via the rear sprocket, comprised five mid-sized roadwheels (the first four bogied into pairs) sprung on torsion bars, with five track-return rollers. The 105mm gun had become almost mandatory by that time, but the French, already considering their position in NATO, opted for a gun of that calibre of their own – the GIAT CN-105-F1 – which was not compatible in terms of ammunition with the British L7, the American M68 derivative or the later Rheinmetall Rh-105. It did, though, offer a wider range of ammunition types, including an illuminating round.

FRENCH AMMUNITION

The favoured type of anti-tank ammunition in France was the HEAT hollow charge round (indeed, no AP round was available for the GIAT gun until 1981), yet the GIAT gun had a rifled barrel. As has been mentioned, HEAT rounds perform better if they do not spin in flight, so in order to neutralise the spin imparted by the rifling, a complicated sabot incorporating a ball-

ABOVE: The AMX-40 was designed to operate at temperatures up to 50 degrees Centigrade – an attempt to capture the Middle East export market. It never entered full-scale production.

bearing race was developed. Despite being thus hampered, the 11kg (24lb) charge was still capable of blowing a hole in 400mm (16in) of armour at a range of anything up to 3000m (9840ft). When a sub-calibre kinetic energy round was finally developed, its 26mm-diameter (1in), 3.8kg (8lb 8oz) penetrator, fired at a muzzle velocity of 1525 metres per second (5000 feet per second), was capable of penetrating 150mm (5.9in) of armour at an angle of 60 degrees at a range of 1000m (3280ft). As secondary armament, the original AMX-30 had a conventional 12.7mm machine gun in a co-axial mount, but this was later changed to a 20mm GIAT M693 cannon with dual ammunition feed, which was also fitted to the AMX-40. The weapon could fire high explosive incendiary (HEI) or armour-piercing incendiary (API), and belts of both types of ammunition were loaded from different sides of the breech, according to which was required. To deal with helicopters and other airborne threats, the cannon could be delinked

Centurion AVRE 165 FV 4003

Armament: one 165mm demolition gun, two 7.62mm machine guns
Crew: five
Length: 7.55m (24.77ft)
Width: 3.4m (11.2ft)
Height: 2.94m (9.65ft)
Armour: 17–152mm (.66–5.98in)
Engine: 650bhp petrol
Range: 102km (63 miles)
Speed: 35km/h (22mph)
Country of origin: United Kingdom

from the main gun and elevated independently to 40 degrees.

Over the years, the AMX-30 has been improved by the addition of an integrated fire-control system, incorporating a laser range-finder and LLTV, and the provision of armoured skirts and appliqué armour for the turret, as well as an explosive reactive armour system to combat HEAT rounds. The tank's chassis has been used as the basis for the normal range of battlefield support vehicles and as a mobile launcher for 'Roland' and 'Shahine' anti-aircraft missiles, 'Pluton' tactical nuclear SSMs, the ACRA anti-tank missile and the Javelot anti-aircraft

rocket system. It has also been the vehicle for the GCT 155mm SP howitzer and for radar-controlled twin 30mm anti-aircraft guns. In an attempt to make the tank a serious contender for export orders that would logically have gone to more heavily armed and armoured vehicles, a derivative known as the AMX-32 was produced, with better protection and a 120mm smooth-bore GIAT gun, but only in prototype form. At 43 tonnes, it weighed much the same as a rather better alternative, the all-new (but basically similar) AMX-40, with its laminated frontal armour and 1300hp diesel engine. Neither tank achieved any

real measure of success except in terms of design experience. AMX-30B2s (44 in all) saw active service as part of Operation Daguet, the French contribution to the war to liberate Kuwait in 1991. Despite the fact that they never encountered anything more formidable than infantry, there was considerable criticism of their overall performance.

THE LECLERC
Rather better, and considerably more modern, was the tank whose design programme started in 1983, after a second Franco-German joint MBT venture collapsed. Prototypes of what has

■**ABOVE: The Leclerc MBT is built by French manufacturer GIAT. In the Leclerc, the French Army finally has a vehicle comparable in performance to those of France's NATO partners.**

Even with an all-up weight of 54 tonnes, the Leclerc was capable of well over 70km/h (43mph) and, according to the manufacturer's, could go from rest to 32km/h (20mph) in five and a half seconds. The Leclerc was physically comparatively small – 1m (39in) shorter in the hull than the Leopard 2 and a whole 2m (6ft 6in) shorter than the British Challenger, although all three were roughly the same width. The Leclerc's length-to-breadth ratio made for better stability and manoeuvrability, although its small size was a drawback for the crew, for there was very little in the way of internal stowage, and no provision for carrying gear externally.

120MM AUTO-LOADER
The main innovation in the new French tank came in its armament. For the first time, a 120mm gun was provided with an auto-loader, reducing the turret crew to two men. The auto-loader was located in the turret bustle, along with 22 ready rounds, behind an armoured bulkhead and with a blow-out panel in the roof to direct the resulting explosion up and away from the crew and powerplant

should it take a direct hit. The gun was a smooth-bore, like that fitted to the AMX-32 and AMX-40, and provision was made for up to six different ammunition types to be held. The rounds were selected by the gunner when the tank was loaded up, and the contents of each of the 22 ammunition positions in the auto-loader was entered into the computer system as the device was charged. The system allowed a rate of fire of 10 rounds per minute, and storage space for further ammunition was provided in the hull. The turret was designed with a future upgrade to a 140mm gun in mind, although such a modification would certainly reduce the already limited internal space even further.

THE LECLERC'S COMPUTERS
Another aspect of the Leclerc's design that qualified the tank for its third-generation status was its level of data processing technology. Even the driver's controls were operated via the computer system, in a form of 'drive by wire' similar to that used in modern combat aircraft. All data pertinent to the tank's operation were held in the computer, accessible to the three-man crew via VDUs and custom-designed displays, options being selected from a menu using edge-of-screen buttons. Despite a considerable degree of redundancy (three levels is common), manual back-up

been hailed – somewhat grandiosely perhaps – as the first third-generation tank were tested in the late 1980s, and production of the 'Leclerc', which was named after the French general who received the surrender of Paris in 1944, commenced in 1990, the first vehicles being issued to units of the French Army in 1992. In one very important respect, the designers of the Leclerc stuck to the doctrine that produced the AMX-30. They gave the tank a turbo-charged 1500hp diesel engine to provide a high power-to-weight ratio, together with a torque converter transmission and suspension system capable of making the most of it.

■ABOVE: The Cheiftain chassis provides the basis for a number of support vehicles, including the Mk 6 Armoured Vehicle Launched Bridge (right), which can span 12m (39.37ft).

systems were provided all round. More conventional was the tank's armour, although as is the case with all modern tanks, its actual make-up was shrouded in secrecy. The armour was assumed to be of spaced, laminated, composite construction, probably with the provision to add plates of ERA at will. Modules of additional 'conventional' armour could also be added to the 'basic' tank, after the fashion of the Merkava Mk 3, and the powerplant probably had sufficient in reserve so that this superloading would hardly affect overall performance. The French state-owned armaments maker GIAT, which manufactured the Leclerc at Roanne, had high hopes of the vehicle's sales potential. Despite the Leclerc's being an unsuccessful contender as the British Army's new MBT (it lost to Challenger 2, as did the M1A2 and the Leopard 2), GIAT's expectations seemed likely to be fulfilled when an order for 435 units was received from the United Arab Emirates to complement that for 765 from the French Army. Such is the sophistication of the Leclerc as a fighting vehicle that at the time of writing it seemed unlikely that it would replace the

highly effective AMX-30 derivatives in the range of battlefield support roles, at least in the short term. However, if that were the case, the AMX-30D ARV would almost certainly need uprating to cope with the Leclerc's greater weight.

BRITAIN'S CHIEFTAIN

The first British postwar MBT initially saw the light of day as the result of a War Office statement on the 'likely' desirable characteristics for a tank to replace the Centurion. The statement was issued in 1958 and reflected the lessons learned in the Korean War. Top of the list of desirable characteristics was a more powerful gun with a higher rate of fire, ideally 10 rounds in the first minute and then six rounds per minute for four minutes thereafter. The next requirement was for a better fire-control system in order to improve the chances of a first-shot hit. The third item on the list was maximised armoured protection, particularly over the frontal arc. Fourthly, the tank was to be within a (dry) weight

limit of 52 tonnes and, finally, was to have a top speed of over 42km/h (26mph). In line with these requirements, Leyland started work on the design for a hull for the new vehicle that same year, while Vickers took responsibility for the turret, which was to mount the 120mm L11 rifled gun then newly developed by the Royal Ordnance Factory. The tank that was born of these efforts appeared in 1961, was ordered for the British Army in 1962 and entered service five years later as the FV4201 Chieftain main battle tank.

From the outset, it was clear that the new tank was designed to stand and fight it out, probably head-to-head – its nose was a single-piece casting, as was its mantletless turret. The angle of the glacis and the turret face, too, were clearly devised to throw off solid shot, and the entire tank had very few traps for incoming projectiles. Horstmann suspension, similar to that employed on the Centurion, was specified, with three pairs of roadwheels and three track-

return rollers, the whole arrangement protected by deeper than normal armoured skirts. The engine was a Leyland L60 multi-fuel unit mated to a semi-automatic gearbox, the package located conventionally in the rear and driving the rear sprockets. Steering was by means of a Merritt-Brown regenerative system. Actual performance was a little better than specified, although not sparkling, with a top road speed of 50km/h (30mph) available in later marks. A fuel capacity of 955 litres (252 US gallons) gave a maximum range on the road of something over 500km (310miles).

CHIEFTAIN EXPORTS

Early Chieftains had ranging machine guns like the later Centurions, but later marks acquired laser range-finders that were integrated with a digital fire-control computer. Altogether, some dozen variants of the Chieftain were produced, the main improvements being in the powerplant and in the fire-control

Chieftain Mk 3, FV 4201

Armament: one 120mm gun, two 7.62mm machine guns
Crew: four
Length (gun forward): 10.8m (35.4ft)
Width: 3.5m (11.5ft)
Height: 2.9m (9.5ft)
Armour: cast, welded steel plus 'stilbrew' appliqué armour system
Engine : 750bhp multi-fuel
Range : 500km (310 miles)
Speed: 50km/h (30mph)
Country of origin: United Kingdom

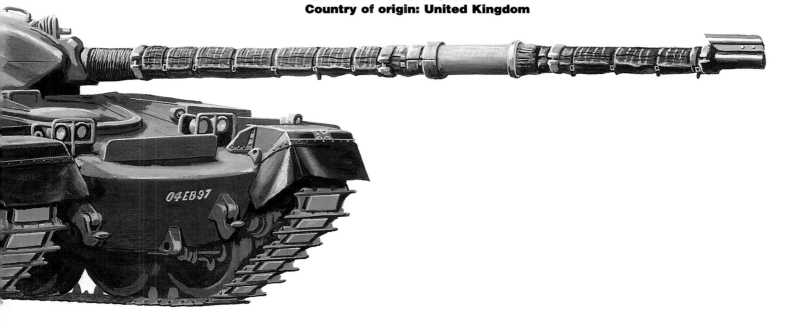

Challenger 1, FV 4030

Armament: one 120mm gun, two 7.62mm machine guns
Crew: four
Length (gun forward): 11.55m (37.9ft)
Width: 3.52m (11.5ft)
Height: 2.5m (8.2ft) (to turret)
Armour: Chobham composite laminate
Engine: 1200bhp diesel
Range : 500km (310 miles)
Speed: 56km/h (34.8mph)
Country of origin: United Kingdom

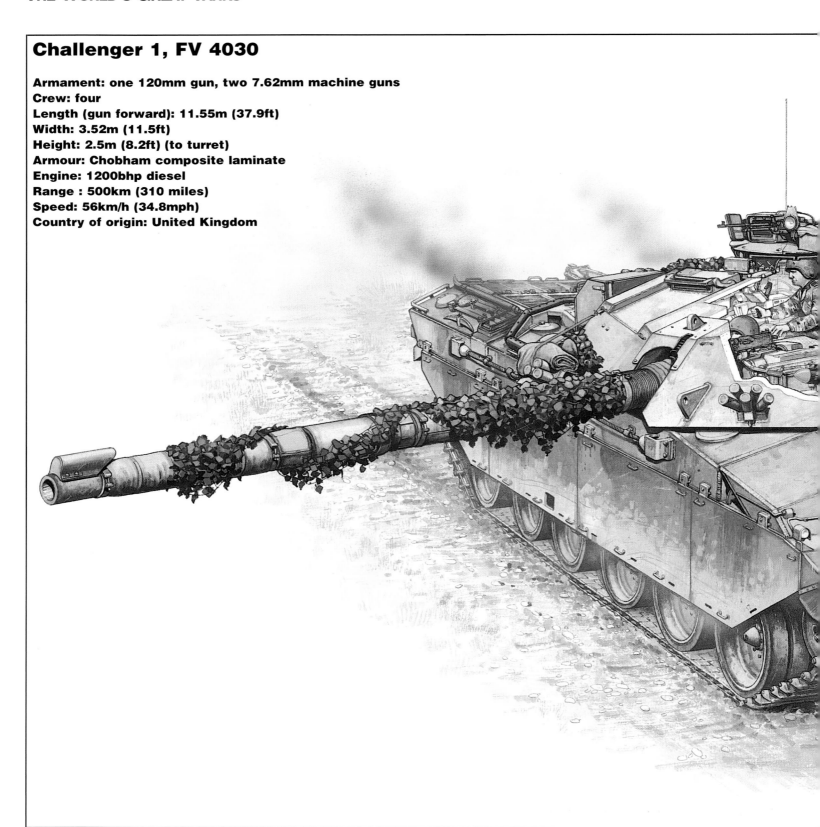

mechanisms. The British Army acquired some 900 Chieftains, and the tank sold well overseas. Prerevolutionary Iran bought more than 1000, many of which were later lost (and not a few captured) during the long war with Iraq. Jordan, Kuwait and Oman bought Chieftains, too. Many of the British Army's Chieftains, most of which were still in service or in

storage in the mid-1990s, were upgraded by the addition of 'Stillbrew' composite laminate armour and by the adoption of the Barr & Stroud Thermal Observation and Gunnery Sight (TOGS) system developed for the Challenger. A whole range of Chieftain-based armoured recovery vehicles and bridgelayers were developed for the British Army to

supersede the older Centurion-based support vehicles.

THE SHIR 1
The enthusiasm with which the shah's pro-Western Iran took to the Chieftain gave a much needed boost to the British tank industry and set in train a programme to develop a new MBT,

development initiative in 1977 and the cancellation of the so-called MBT-80 project.

CHIEFTAIN TO CHALLENGER
The obvious main difference between the Chieftain and the Challenger lay in the new tank's much more angular shape. This was a clear indication that the Challenger was fabricated from flat plates of Chobham armour – a composite of different types of metal, ceramics and other materials – laid on a frame, in the same manner as in the Leopard 2. Not quite so evident was the replacement of the Horstmann suspension system with one using hydropneumatic units, which gave the new tank much better cross-country performance. The powerplant was the same Perkins/Rolls-Royce Condor engine fitted to the Khalid, which gave the Challenger a top road speed of 57km/h (35mph) despite an increase in all-up weight to 62 tonnes. The same L11 gun fitted to the Chieftain was retained, as were the two 7.62mm machine guns, one in a co-axial mount and the other in the commander's cupola. The Challenger entered service with the British Army in Britain and Germany in 1983, alongside the Chieftain, and by the end of the decade, some 450 were in use.

known as the 'Shir'. The Shir 1 version was designated the FV4030/2, but it was actually a late-model Chieftain with a rather better Perkins/Rolls-Royce Condor 1200hp engine and a fully automatic gearbox. Shir 1s were ordered by Iran under the shah, but when he was driven into exile in the revolution of 1979, the order was cancelled, although some 275

tanks based on the Shir 1 were later supplied to Jordan as the 'Khalid'. The Shir 2, on the other hand, 1225 of which had been ordered by prerevolutionary Iran, was to have a different future. It went on, after further revision, to become the new British MBT, the FV4030/3 Challenger, after the collapse of an Anglo-German joint

Challengers of the British Army's 4th and 7th Armoured Divisions (with 43 and 114 vehicles respectively) saw action during Operation Granby, the United Kingdom's contribution to the war to liberate Kuwait in 1991. The tanks acquitted themselves well, despite some prewar reservations.

CHALLENGER 2

By the late 1980s, it was clear that the Chieftains, at least, were badly in need of replacement. And although the Challenger was widely regarded as adequate in terms of firepower and protection, its fire-control system had

■LEFT: The Challenger can fire High Explosive Squash Head (HESH) rounds. HESH is one of six different types of ammunition that can be fired from its 120mm main gun.

come in for a certain amount of criticism, and there is no doubt that its performance was deficient. The British Army wanted a lighter vehicle – although no less well protected, thanks to advances in armour technology – with more sophisticated 'vetronics' and a more powerful engine. In fact, the Army was asking for the American M1A1 'Abrams' and making few bones about it. What appeared to be a fair evaluation contest ensued between the American tank, the Leopard 2, the Leclerc and an updated (although not uprated) Challenger from Vickers. However, from the outset, the British Army stood very little chance of getting what it wanted and did not have long to wait for a decision. In mid-1991 it was announced that the Army would adopt Challenger 2, little changed from the original save for its main armament and a new integrated fire-control system.

The new weapon was to be the XL30 high-pressure 120mm rifled gun, as originally developed for the MBT-80. The XL30 had greater life expectancy than the L11 and superior performance from the same ammunition. The gun also had a considerably shorter barrel, which improved the tank's manoeuvrability in towns and villages and on twisty country roads. It was also announced that Challenger 1s would go through a midlife improvement programme in order to bring them closer to, but not up to, Challenger 2 specification.

INDIAN CHIEFTAINS
The decision to adopt the upgraded Challenger should, perhaps, be viewed against the distinct possibility that Vickers would have been forced to close its tank manufacturing plant had the order gone elsewhere. Such an

eventuality would have meant the end of tank production in the United Kingdom, quite possibly for ever, with all the loss of expertise and experience that implied – a scenario that was undesirable and unacceptable, not just for Britain, but for NATO (or any future substitute) as a whole. As it was, with the Government order to fall back on, Vickers was able to continue development work on private ventures such as had produced the MBT Mk 1 as a low-cost Centurion replacement during the 1960s. MBT Mk 1s were sold to a number of users, and India opted for the tank as the basis for its 'Vijayanta', about 1500 of which were built, mostly under licence in India. Vickers later produced prototypes of other, more advanced, light and main battle tanks, and the company remains an important independent force in AFV development, with major partners in

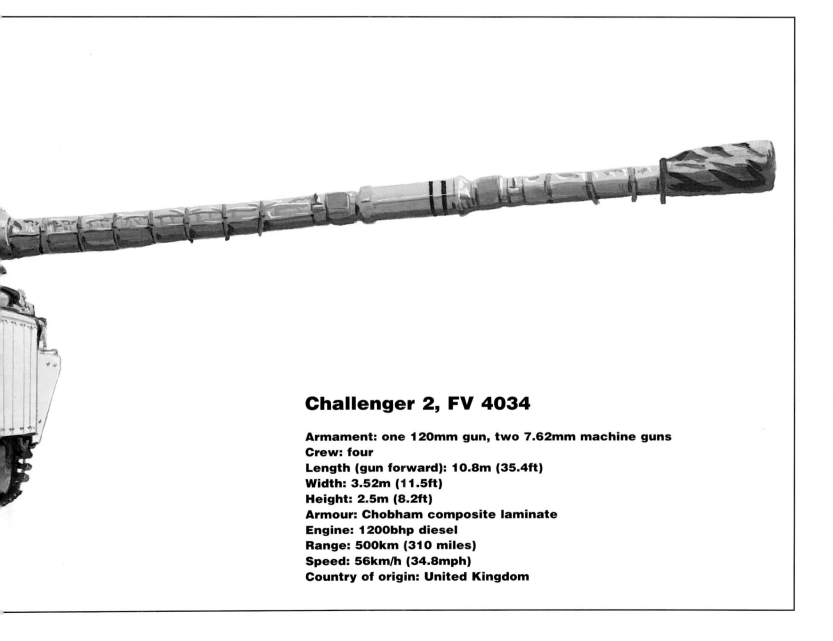

Challenger 2, FV 4034

Armament: one 120mm gun, two 7.62mm machine guns
Crew: four
Length (gun forward): 10.8m (35.4ft)
Width: 3.52m (11.5ft)
Height: 2.5m (8.2ft)
Armour: Chobham composite laminate
Engine: 1200bhp diesel
Range: 500km (310 miles)
Speed: 56km/h (34.8mph)
Country of origin: United Kingdom

Europe and the United States. At the other end of the scale, in the early 1960s the British Ministry of Defence formulated a requirement for a light tank/reconnaissance vehicle, which resulted in a tracked light tank, the FV101 Scorpion. Besides the Scorpion itself, there were six variants: Striker had 'Swingfire' AT guided weapons, Spartan was a special-purpose APC, Samaritan

was an armoured ambulance, Sultan was an armoured command vehicle, Sampson was an ARV, and Scimitar was a variation on the light tank theme, with a 30mm Rarden cannon in place of the Scorpion's 76mm gun in the same 360-degree-traversing turret. The FV100-series 'family' entered service with the British Army during the mid-1970s, and members of the group were sold widely

abroad. All ran on five roadwheels with torsion bar suspension and were powered by a 4.2 litre/195hp version of the Jaguar XK engine, better known as the powerplant of that company's early sports cars, sports saloons and limousines. The engine was located in the front of the vehicle alongside the driver, from where it drove the front sprocket through a cross-drive

Scimitar, FV 107

Armament: one 30mm Rarden cannon, one 7.62mm machine gun
Crew: three
Length: 4.8m (15.74ft)
Width: 2.1m (6.9ft)
Height: 2.1m (6.9ft)
Armour: 12.7mm (.5in)
Engine: 190bhp petrol
Range: 644km (400 miles)
Speed: 90km/h (56mph)
Country of origin: United Kingdom

transmission system as developed for the Chieftain. The Scorpion and its variants were capable of 90km/h (56mph) on the road and at around 8 tonnes all-up weight, the tanks trod very lightly, which made them viable for use in the Falkland Islands. Scorpions and Scimitars, plus one Sampson ARV, saw combat for the first time during Operation Corporate in the Falklands, providing fire support for

British infantrymen. Light tanks were also deployed alongside Challengers in Iraq and in peacekeeping operations in the Balkans. The FV100-series vehicles had an NBC protection system as standard, and vehicles supplied to customers in the Middle East and Africa frequently had air conditioning. A folding flotation screen could be fitted, and in the water the vehicles could be driven by their tracks, although an optional propeller kit was available to those users that had a regular requirement for amphibious working. Naturally, the creation of a set of armoured vehicles all on one chassis – as was also the case with the French AMX-13, for example – paid large dividends in terms of driver training and maintenance and logistics.

THE NEW US MBT

It is a little difficult to believe that the United States entered the 1980s with a main battle tank, the M60, that was effectively a World War II design, albeit extensively upgraded – but it is true. As early as 1963, a decision in principle was taken to develop an entirely new MBT to

■ BELOW: The first Vijayanta tanks entered Indian Army service in 1965. By the 1971 Indo-Pakistan War six regiments were equipped with the model. Some 1700 are still in service.

replace the M60, which had then been in service for three years, and on 1 August of that year the United States signed an agreement with West Germany to cooperate in such a venture. The MBT-70, as the project was known, never came to fruition, thanks to a German decision to pull out. The US Army proceeded alone towards a development vehicle called the XM803. This too was cancelled in late 1971 as being overly complex and far too expensive. By that time, many people in the US military establishment were becoming decidedly uneasy at the lack of real progress being made. Nonetheless, the two cancelled projects had gone a considerable distance down their respective paths, and had provided a wealth of data, both negative and positive, about the sort of vehicle it was possible to construct and operate at a reasonable cost. In essence, leaving aside the nature of the new tank's protection, there were 12 different viable possibilities within the five other main areas of armament, fire control, powerplant, suspension and track type, and that gave rise to a wealth of possible combinations. This number was soon considerably reduced when two main guns – a rifled 110mm gun of British origin and a 120mm smooth-bore gun from Rheinmetall – and one powerplant – a 1500hp gas turbine from Avco Lycoming – were eliminated from the list. Also

initially taken into consideration were
plans for 'product improved' M60A1s,
but those, too, were soon knocked out
of contention.

CHRYSLER AND GM DESIGNS

At that time, there were two private
sector centres of expertise in heavy tank
design and construction in the United
States – Chrysler, which got into the
business via the Medium Tank M3 and
was currently in the process of further
upgrading the M60, and Detroit Diesel, a
division of the rival General Motors
Corporation, which built the ill-fated
M551 Sheridan light tank and had been
heavily involved in the MBT-70/XM803
programme. Both were now asked to
submit proposals for a project to be
known as XM1, and both produced
concepts for tanks in the 50-tonne class,
with torsion bar suspension, and armed
with the 105mm M68 gun and the
Bushmaster 20mm cannon in a co-axial
mount. The proposals from General
Motors were for a tank powered by one or
two diesel engines, while that from
Chrysler kept the powerplant option
open, suggesting that either a diesel or a
gas turbine engine could be fitted, despite
the latter type being out of favour. One
thing was obvious from the submissions:
it was not possible to meet the protection
levels required and stay within the
prescribed weight limit.

SPIRALLING COSTS

Meanwhile, the engineers of the US
Army's Tank Automotive Command
(TACOM) were working on the problems
of protection levels versus all-up weight.
By March 1973, it had become evident
that spaced composite laminated armour,
set at appropriate angles, offered the best
possibilities. Even so, it would be
necessary to increase the tank's all-up
weight limit. It was apparent that the
original cost-per-unit limit, set at
$400,000, was also in need of upward
revision – to more than $500,000. This
compared with estimates of $611,000 per
unit for the cancelled XM803. On 28 June
1973, contracts to design, develop, build
and test prototype tanks to the XM1

specification were awarded to Chrysler
and General Motors. The former was
allocated $68,999,000, the latter
$87,969,000, the fees being calculated on
a cost-plus-incentive basis.

GAS TURBINE POWERPLANT

When the two companies finalised their
designs, there was one big surprise.
Despite the US Army's MBT Task Force
having come down firmly against the use
of a gas turbine engine, Dr Philip Lett,
the head of Chrysler's design team, opted
to specify it anyway. Lett cited growth
potential, smaller physical size and
reduced power losses as his reasons,
combined with the turbine's lower noise
level, smokeless operation and easier
starting in cold conditions. It was to
prove a crucial decision, and the Avco
Lycoming AG-1500 turned out to be a
very good engine indeed. Although it was
more expensive to produce than the
variable compression ratio AVCR-1360
specified by General Motors, which was
an upgraded version of that offered for
the M60A3 and fitted to the private
venture M60AX, the gas turbine would
prove to be cheaper to maintain. In fact,
over the projected life of a powerplant,

there was to be very little difference in cost between the two propulsion units. Other new factors affecting both prototypes were the availability of Chobham armour – the new type of composite protection developed in the United Kingdom – and the decision to delete the Bushmaster cannon from the specification as a result of after-action analyses from the 1973 Arab–Israeli War. The Bushmaster had been specified for its ability to destroy light armour and soft-skinned vehicles, but it soon became clear that tank crews invariably used their main guns against such targets anyway. Deleting the Bushmaster also allowed more storage space for main gun ammunition.

ABRAMS PRODUCTION BEGINS

The two prototypes, together with automotive test rigs, were delivered to the Aberdeen Proving Grounds at the end of 1975. Combined development and operational testing ran from 31 January to 7 May of the following year, and both tanks met the specified requirements. At this late stage, a third contender entered the arena – the German Leopard 2, modified to meet American requirements and armed with the 105mm gun. The

Leopard 2 was to be tested on an equal footing with the two indigenous prototypes despite its much higher price tag. In the end, it was this higher price that lost the German tank the job, for it too met or exceeded all the requirements. The choice was made between the two XM1s in July 1976, but was never made public officially. However, reports indicated that General Motors won with a bid of $208 million, against one of $221 million from Chrysler, to produce 110 tanks in 1979 and 352 more in 1980. By this time, the US Army had decided it wanted the gas turbine engine, but in the General Motors tank, and proposed simply switching powerplants without going through a complicated selection process all over again. The Secretary of Defense would have none of that. But there was a further complication too. It was now decided that there would be a need to upgun the tank in the foreseeable future, and that meant a redesign of the turret. The decision to award the initial contract was thus put back until November 1976. Both contenders took the opportunity to expand their engine options and resubmitted designs with both engine types. At a news conference on 12 November, it was announced that

Chrysler had won the contract with a bid of $196 million dollars, against the $232 million bid by General Motors. The latter's price had gone up dramatically as a result of the higher installation cost of the gas turbine engine. Chrysler's had gone down as the result of a cost-cutting exercise based on better estimates. The first pilot tank rolled out in February 1978. Production of the first 110 units commenced at the Lima Army Tank Plant, and on 28 February 1980 the first two were delivered to the US Army. The new tank was named in honour of General Creighton Abrams, a former armour commander and later Army Chief of Staff. Two years later, a second production line came on stream at the Detroit Tank Plant, at just about the same time that Chrysler sold its tank construction operation to the General Dynamics Corporation and retired from a business that it had influenced considerably over 40 years. In all, almost 7500 M1 Abrams tanks were ordered for

■BELOW: Challenger has provision for the external stowage of two 200-litre fuel drums, as well as a number of turret 'bins' containing ammunition, camouflage netting and crew kit.

Abrams M1A1

Armament: one 120mm gun, one 12.7mm machine gun,
  two 7.62mm machine guns
Crew: four
Length (gun forward): 8.48m (27.82ft)
Width: 3.65m (12ft)
Height: 2.43m (7.97ft) (to hatch)
Armour: rolled homogenous steel with composite arrays
Engine: 1500shp gas turbine
Range: 465km (288 miles)
Speed: 67km/h (42mph)
Country of origin: USA

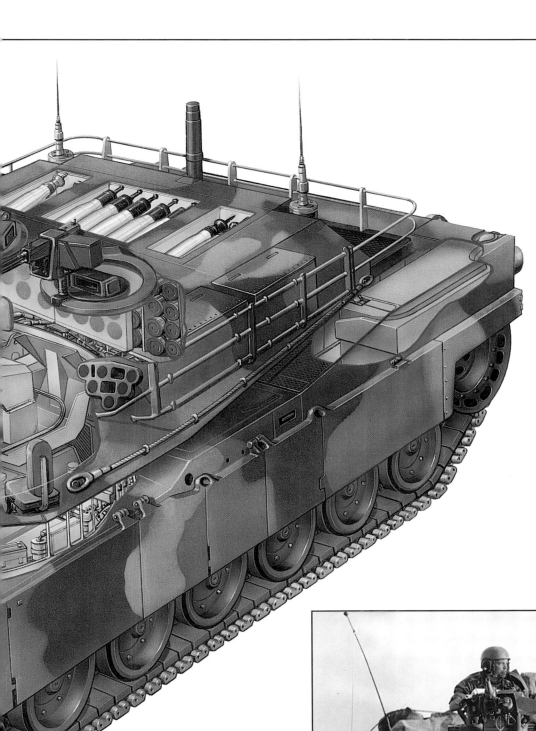

delivery before the end of the 1980s, production reaching 70 per month at the end of 1983. Ten years and $400 million dollars (at 1972 values) after the development process began in earnest, the US Army had a new main battle tank.

THE MIGHTY ABRAMS

The M1 Abrams was a four-man tank with an all-up weight of just under 55 tonnes. It carried 55 rounds of 105mm ammunition for its main gun, 12,400 rounds of 7.62mm ammunition for its co-axial and loader's-hatch machine guns and 1000 rounds of 12.7mm ammunition for the AA machine gun in the commander's cupola. Most of the main gun ammunition was stowed in the turret bustle, which was separated from the fighting compartment by armoured bulkheads and had blow-off panels in its top surface. The tank was powered by a 1500hp AGT-1500 engine, which would run on diesel fuel, kerosene or petrol. It gave the Abrams a top speed of 72km/h (45mph) but its very high rate of fuel consumption meant that the tank's range was only around 500km (310 miles) on a full load of 1908 litres (504 US gallons) of fuel. Transmission to the driven rear

■BELOW: The Abrams is well protected. During the 1991 Gulf War, for example, one was hit by two anti-armour rounds fired from only 500m (1640ft), which simply bounced of its armour.

sprockets was by means of an X-1100 cross-drive unit, a derivative of the unit originally developed for the M60, which included variable hydrostatic/regenerative steering. The tank's seven dual, offset roadwheels were suspended on 'advanced' titanium-steel torsion bars that allowed each wheel pair 380mm (15in) of vertical movement. The fire-control system was similar in its complexity to that fitted to the M60A3, with environmental and gun-condition sensors incorporated to improve the chances of making a first-round kill.

THE M1A2

Not entirely surprisingly, the M1 Abrams was hailed on its appearance as the best tank in the world, with the most effective armour for its weight, the best performance, the best fire-control system and so on. For all that, very soon after it appeared it was obsolescent in one particular – its main armament. This was upgraded to 120mm – fairly painlessly, thanks to earlier foresight – with the choice of the smooth-bore gun developed in Germany. The M1A1 Abrams, as the improved tank was known, entered service in the summer of 1985, and was superseded in turn in 1992 by the M1A2, which had better thermal imaging hardware for both driver and commander, improved vetronics and a global

■ **BELOW: The two British Scorpion tanks that fought in the 1982 Falklands War performed extremely well in the boggy terrain. One even withstood running over an Argentine mine.**

Commando Stingray

Armament: one 105mm gun, one 7.62mm machine gun, one .5in AA machine gun
Crew: four
Length (gun forward): 9.35m (30.7ft)
Width: 2.71m (8.9ft)
Height: 2.55m (8.3ft) (to turret)
Armour: welded steel
Engine: 535bhp diesel
Range: 483km (300 miles)
Speed: 67km/h (42mph)
Country of origin: USA

positioning system (GPS) satellite navigation system. Further improvements under what was known as the Block III programme, scheduled to commence before the end of the 1990s, included the provision of either an improved 120mm gun or one of a larger calibre (probably 140mm), either of which would have an auto-loader to reduce the crew to three men. Block III improvements also called for the realignment of the engine into a transverse position in order to free more internal space. The extra space could provide either greater ammunition storage capacity or – more likely, perhaps – capacity for extra fuel tanks and an internal auxiliary diesel engine to supply power to the electronics and tactical systems. Such an arrangement would allow the turbine to be powered down

when the vehicle was in 'resting' mode without costing the tank its ability to fight and survive.

After such a long and costly development programme, it might seem a little surprising just how 'conventional' the resulting tank was. Many suggestions were made for deviation from the accepted norms during the earlier MBT-70/XM803 projects, but all were rejected as being either too costly or of limited increased effectiveness – and all too often both. As a result there was very little real innovation to be found in the M1, save for its powerplant, and even that was not the first time a gas turbine had found its way into a tank. So how good was the Abrams?

The Abrams had the same sort of armour as the British Challenger and the German Leopard 2, and thus had roughly equivalent protection levels to these two tanks. The Abrams was faster and more agile than the Challenger, but no better in this respect than the German tank and distinctly worse than the French Leclerc.

THE COMPETITORS LINE UP
The M1A1, with a reduced final drive ratio, had slightly better acceleration than the French tank, but was some 6.5km/h (4mph) slower as a result. It was the characteristics of the turbine engine that gave the Abrams its good acceleration, but the engine's high running temperature made for a considerably more obvious heat signature – a very important factor in modern armoured combat, where thermal imaging is as important as any other recognition system. The Abrams' profile height was exactly the same as that of

the Challenger, and both were a whole 400mm (16in) taller than the Leopard 2 and the Leclerc – another important factor now that tanks regularly sat not hull down but turret-down. The M1A2's fire-control system was accepted as being the best in the business, but frankly, the difference between the best and the second-best in the mid-1990s was much less than the difference between the best and second-best gunners. There was nothing much to choose in terms of firepower between the American, French and German tanks, and the British 120mm gun was only slightly inferior, and that because of the different characteristics of rifled and smooth-bore guns when firing APFSDS or HEAT rounds. The Soviet T-80, with its combined gun/missile launcher, could not be compared in real terms with this quartet except in its destructive power, which was probably considerably greater if – and it was a big 'if' – the tank operated to specification. As it was so much lighter than the NATO tanks, there was every reason to suppose that the T-80's protection levels did not meet theirs, with everything that meant for survivability. Also, there had to be serious doubts about the capabilities of the post-Soviet Russian Army – and the armies of other former Soviet states – to maintain its vehicles to the required standard. Former Soviet client states, who never received anything better than late-model

T-72s anyway, certainly did not have anything capable of standing up to the Abrams – or any of the other NATO MBTs, come to that, with the possible exception of the French AMX-30. This situation was very effectively demonstrated during Operation Desert Storm, the American component of the war to free Kuwait in 1991. Well over 1000 M1A1s were committed to the battles of late February, when they faced perhaps 700 or 800 Iraqi tanks, mostly T-62s and T-72s but with a sprinkling of T-54/55s. The results were very spectacular. The M1A1s destroyed every

Iraqi tank they caught, at almost no loss to themselves.

THE WIDENING GAP
This apparently huge gap between the capabilities of succeeding generations of tanks has been true right through the armoured fighting vehicle's brief history, and is no more so, really, at the end of the 20th century than it was in World War I, when armoured vehicles fought for the first time on the Western Front. This is the case largely, and paradoxically, because the real gap is actually very narrow. That armour is just slightly

Vickers/FMC Mk 5

Armament: one 105mm gun, one .5in machine gun,
  one 7.62mm machine gun
Crew: four
Length (gun forward): 8.61m (28.25ft)
Width: 2.7m (8.85ft)
Height: 2.62m (8.6ft)
Armour: not available
Engine: 552bhp diesel
Range: 480km (298 miles)
Speed: 70km/h (43.5mph)
Country of origin: USA/UK

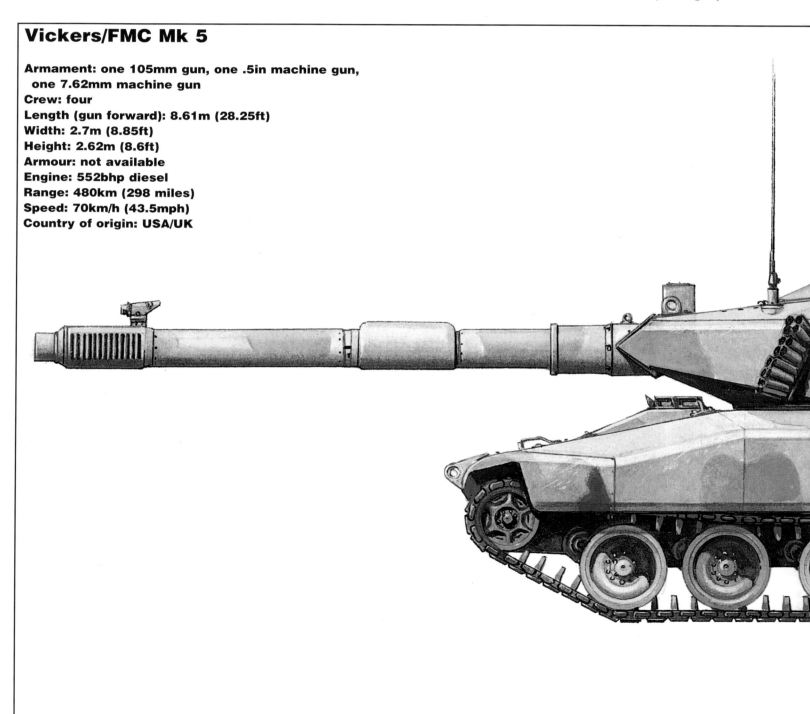

thicker or a projectile just marginally more capable is all that was or is required for one tank to annihilate another, even before tactics and training are taken into account, something which tank designers are all too aware of.

It is fitting that the human side of armoured warfare should take a back seat to the vehicles themselves in this sense, for technology has written the history of the tank, with all that implies for the future. The entire purpose of the armoured fighting vehicle has always been to reduce the vulnerability of human beings on the battlefield, and it is

■ABOVE: The Vickers FMC Mk.5 is an Anglo-American project designed to meet the requirements for a light tank for export markets, and can be dropped from a large transport aircraft.

quite conceivable that it will be robot AFVs that eventually remove people from the battlefield altogether (although there is still the old adage to be considered that the battle is finally won only when a lone infantryman is left standing upon the objective). Be that as it may, although remote-controlled unmanned tanks probably remain the ultimate goal of the men who decide the form new vehicles will take, the immediate objective is the same as it has always been: to improve the survivability of the men who have to crew the vehicles of today and thus allow them to win the battle at hand. To this end, the search for better armour and the means to fight the vehicle from a place of comparative safety (from a hull-down position in pitch darkness, for example) goes on. Hand in hand with this research go efforts to produce more powerful guns firing more capable ammunition that is guided and controlled more precisely by better computers with a greater capacity to eliminate any chance of not hitting the target with the all-important first round. Throw in the quest for greater mechanical reliability and better performance coupled with the need to keep the overall package as small and compact as possible while still giving the

■ABOVE: This T-62 was just one of the 3500 Iraqi tanks lost during the 1991 Gulf War, testimony to the power of Western MBTs, as well as modern anti-tank weaponry.

crew reasonable working conditions and providing the space to store enough fuel to maximise the vehicle's operating range and enough ammunition to give it a fighting chance of winning through an engagement and you have a rough agenda for the design of a modern armoured fighting vehicle. It has become clear that these factors are what defines a 'great' tank. A deficiency in any one of them will be enough to reduce a tank to a lower status, if only in the broadest of relative terms.

HISTORY'S GREATEST TANKS
By these criteria, there have been comparatively few truly great tanks. The Panther and the Tiger qualify, although the latter's range limitations could be held against it. The Sherman in its regunned form, as the Firefly, probably

qualified too, despite its comparative vulnerability to the German tanks just mentioned, as well as an uncomfortable tendency to catch fire, thanks to its petrol engine. Another qualifier was the Soviet T-34 as were the heavier Iosef Stalin tanks, particularly the Mk 3, which was certainly the most powerful tank of its day. Did any of the British tanks of World War II qualify as great? The Comet came closest, perhaps, but on balance, armoured vehicle design was an area in which the British were singularly deficient, although with the Centurion, which was as good as anything of its time and significantly better than most, they caught up decisively during the 1950s.

THE UNANSWERED QUESTION
In the post-World War II period, assessing the comparative strengths and weaknesses of individual tanks becomes more difficult. There have been few enough truly poor tanks produced, and the capabilities and characteristics of most have met the basic criteria for

survivability on the battlefield well enough, at least against other vehicles of their own generation. Put a new design up against one 20 or 30 years old, however, and the result is likely to be decisive enough (even if the Israeli armoured divisions did sometimes manage to defeat superior tanks in battle) – but the same is true in all fields of military technology.

As the 20th century draws to a close, the tank is threatened by a bewildering array of battlefield anti-armour weapons, as sure an indication as can be that it is still perceived as a highly significant threat. Periodically, the question arises of whether future armoured vehicles will even be able to survive in the face of onslaughts from precision-guided missiles, specialised bombs and even artillery projectiles, as well as from increasingly 'smart' mines. The same question, although couched in rather different terms, has been posed by military strategists since 1916, and the answer is still a matter for speculation and debate.